BASIC RADIO

AND

ELECTRONIC CALCULATIONS

USING THE CASIO SCIENTIFIC CALCULATOR

R.E.G.PETRI. G0OAT

For Radio Amateur Examination and trade examination courses
Basic calculator and maths operations explained with examples
Fully worked answers using the Casio Scientific Calculator
Fully worked answers using the formulae
Progressive examples for each topic
Introductory text for each topic

Containing material suitable for the following courses
C &G Radio Amateurs' Examination (RAE)
C & G Electronics Servicing Examination
BTEC Electrical & Electronic Principles N
and general interest

Published by R.E.G.Petri
'Tarnwood' Denesway,
Meopham, Kent DA13 0EA

ISBN 0 9509335 5 4

By the same author -
    The Radio Amateurs' Question & Answer Reference Manual.
    Fifth Edition ISBN 0 9509335 4 6

Printed in Great Britain by
Whitstable Litho Printers Ltd
Whitstable Kent

Contents

Contents

PREFACE

Calculators are now an essential tool for secondary, higher and technical education, allowing for quick and simple manipulation of numbers. They are also used extensively by professional engineers, scientists, business people, bank clerks and housewives. Casio have been at the forefront of calculator development for over 20 years, being one of the first companies to introduce hand held scientific calculators in the 1970s. Our commitment to development has resulted in the introduction of many new features, including the VPAM operating system, which helps to make the use of calculators clearer and simpler, for both this book and mathematics in general.

Casio would like to thank the author for the opportunity to contribute the preface to this book, and wish him every success with the project.

Casio Electronics Co. Ltd.

INTRODUCTION

This book is primarily intended to assist students on basic radio, electronic and electrical courses to master the scientific calculator and some of the most frequently used formulae and mathematical equations that crop up during their training. It is intended to provide supplementary material to span several types of course or be used simply on an interest or refresher basis.

This book contains material suitable for the City and Guilds of London Institute (C&G) Radio Amateurs' Examination and the Electronics Servicing Examination. Also the Business and Technician Education Council (BTEC) Electrical and Electronic Principles N syllabus. Course lecturers will be able to advise on which material should be studied. Always refer to the current examination syllabus.

It is likely that the new student to this branch of engineering will not be familiar with the use and manipulation of formulae and equations. He may be using the scientific calculator for the first time and not realise its full potential. This book has been written such that the majority of it can be used without the need for a scientific calculator, although this was not the primary aim.

The book is divided into 11 chapters. Chapter 1 introduces calculator basics and explores some of the most commonly used function keys with mathematical examples and notes. Please read pages 1-25 to 1-31 of chapter 1 regarding operating modes before proceeding. All other chapters can be studied independently, and consist of a technical introduction followed by a number of practical examples. The examples are worked through in two ways, 1, - by substituting the values directly into the formula; and 2, - by using the scientific calculator. Either method, or a combination of both, may be used to obtain the final result. I would normally make a grab for the calculator.

Much consideration has been given to the choice of calculator used for this book. There are many on the market to choose from. However, after studying the needs of my own classes, and discussion with the manufacturers, I finally chose the Casio hand held scientific calculator as offering excellent value for money and for being readily available in most stationery shops. The models currently (at the time of writing) suitable for use with this book are those using the Casio VPAM system (Visually Perfect Algebraic Method). These include the Fx 115s, Fx 570s, Fx 991s and Fx 992s. It should be noted that when using other calculators the keying sequence (see Appendix B) and displayed result may be different from that given in these examples. In such cases always refer to the manufacturer's operating manual.

The readers who struggled with the subject matter of this book many years ago when the electronic calculator was unheard of, will appreciate just how easy their life could have been had they have had the latest scientific calculator instead of one of the various types of slide rule (guessing stick) used in conjunction with a set of logarithmic and trigonometric tables.

For historical interest, and since this book is about calculations, I have included some illustrations of various types of slide rule, including cylindrical and circular types that a student may have used into the 1970s, when they were finally displaced by the electronic calculator. As a further point of interest, in the late 1960s a simple hand-held electronic calculator would have cost between £40 and £70, and a basic slide rule £2 to £6. Currently, the latest hand-held scientific calculators cost from £7 to £15 and typically offer over 200 functions.

I must now record my thanks to the people who have helped to check and pass constructive comment on the material contained in this book. John Black, John Crump, Brian Phillips, Eddie Bromilow, Shaun Petri and Daniel Petri. Also Casio Electronics Co. Ltd. for supplying up to date information prior to going to press and Chartwell, H.W.Peel and Company for supplying the background chart for the front cover.

This book has taken over two and a half years to prepare and this is the first edition. Much effort has been made to ensure that it is correct. However; should any error be found, please bring it to my attention, with any constructive suggestions for improvement, all will be gratefully received and considered for future editions.

R.E.G.Petri.
1996

Photographs on Pages VIII & IX

Pages VIII and IX overleaf, show a few of the various calculators and slide rules in use up to the early 1970s. They have been included for interest only, since this book is about the electronic calculator and calculations. They will make the modern student aware that calculations were not always achieved by pressing a few buttons on the latest electronic scientific calculator. A set of logarithmic and trigonometric tables would normally be used in conjunction with these instruments, and considerable examination time could be taken up calculating answers.

Photographs on Page VIII show a standard 10 inch slide rule by Blundell (left), and a standard 5 inch slide rule by Unique (centre). Both of these instruments would have been used in secondary and higher education, by engineering students, mechanical and electrical engineers and scientists up to the early 1970s, when they were finally displaced by the electronic calculator. Electronic calculators were in use earlier than this, but they were mainly fairly large desktop models.

The picture on the right of page VIII is the Fuller Calculator. Invented by Professor G.Fuller in the late 1800s and manufactured by W.F.Stanley, probably from about 1910 and up to about 1955. This instrument has a diameter of 3 inches and a scale length of 500 inches (41 feet 8 inches, or 1270cm). The overall height of the instrument, excluding the handle, is 12 inches. Its fundamental principle is the same as the ordinary slide rule and is based on logarithmic scales. To quote the handbook 'The Fuller Calculator will perform all calculations involving :- Multiplication, Division, Proportion, Percentages, and combined multiplication and division.' This calculator is a desk top instrument and would hardly fit into a schoolboy's pocket or an engineer's briefcase.

Page IX. Top left. Fowler's Universal Calculator. This is a circular slide rule. It looks like a pocket watch having a diameter of approximately 3.5 inches. With a logarithmic scale length of 19.5 inches it is claimed to permit calculations being made to 3 or sometimes 4 significant figures. Probably manufactured over the same period as the Fuller calculator. Good eyesight was essential.

Page IX Right. Otis King's Calculator. This is a cylindrical slide rule and has a logarithmic scale length of 66 inches.

Page IX Bottom Left. The Casio Fx570s, just one of the latest hand held scientific calculators brings this nostalgic trip up to date. This is a 10+2 digit machine, having 284 functions, 32 preprogrammed scientific constants and 7 memories. Whereas the slide rule could only give an approximate answer - dare I say it - the electronic calculator gives an answer to a higher degree of accuracy than most students are ever likely to require. It is easy to operate, convenient for the pocket and the engineer's brief case. It has a large easy to read display. A slide rule would need to be many miles in length to approach the accuracy of the electronic calculator.

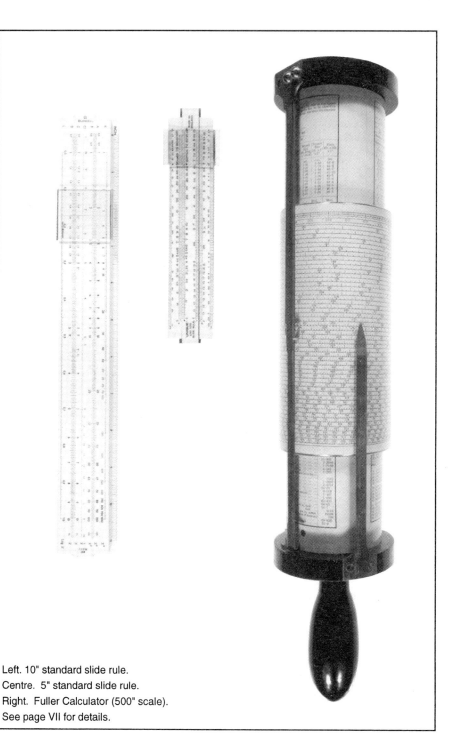

Left. 10" standard slide rule.
Centre. 5" standard slide rule.
Right. Fuller Calculator (500" scale).
See page VII for details.

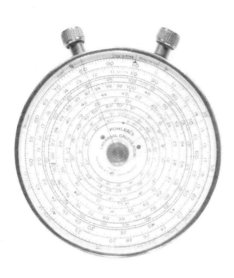

Top Left. Fowler's Universal Calculator.   Right. Otis King's Calculator.
Bottom Left. The Casio Fx570s Digital Scientific Calculator. See page VII for details.

Basic Operations

Chapter 1

Contents

In this section you will :-
a) look at the basic calculator display and operating modes.
b) use some of the calculators basic functions, and work relevant examples.
c) review some basic maths and be introduced to the transposition of formulae.
d) use the memory.
e) use the trigonometric keys.

Calculator Basics

The examples in this book have been worked through on a Casio hand-held scientific calculator, and apply directly to the type of calculators employing Casio's VPAM (Visually Perfect Algebraic Method) operating system. This system allows a formula to be entered as it is written, and pressing the equals key to obtain the result. The execution of arithmetic operations, functions, and expressions within parentheses (brackets) are automatically performed in the correct priority sequence.

At the time of writing the following models use the VPAM system - the 10 + 2 digit Fx115s, Fx570s and Fx991s, and the 12 + 2 digit Fx992s.
I shall be using the 10 + 2 digit Fx115s and the Fx570s. The 12 + 2 digit calculator will in some cases display 2 extra digits in the result, this should not prove a problem.

Casio hand-held scientific calculators prior to these models, and other manufacturers' scientific calculators may have a slightly different keying-in sequence for some of the functions etc. Should you be using one of these calculators always refer to the manufacturers instruction manual. It is strongly recommended that you obtain one of the models, or similar, listed above.

The display

Below is shown the display area of a typical 10 + 2 digit Casio calculator.
The top of the display contains the mode indicators, while the main part of the display shows the input data, intermediate results, and answers to calculations.
I have not shown the statistical or advanced modes on the display since they are beyond the scope of this book.

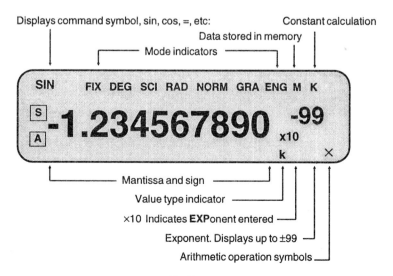

Displays command symbol, sin, cos, =, etc: Constant calculation

Data stored in memory

Mode indicators

SIN   FIX DEG SCI RAD NORM GRA ENG M K

$$S \quad A \quad -1.234567890 \times 10^{-99}$$

k   ×

Mantissa and sign

Value type indicator

×10 Indicates **EXP**onent entered

Exponent. Displays up to ±99

Arithmetic operation symbols

Key Labelling

To reduce the number of keys, and hence the keyboard size, most keys are assigned two or more functions, the primary function of the key being activated by pressing the key, and the alternative function - coloured orange or brown - by first pressing the shift key. A small S will appear on the display when the shift key is pressed. Other key functions may only be active in BASE-N, SD, LR or COMPLEX modes.

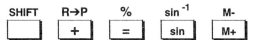

SHIFT   R→P   %   sin⁻¹   M-

Diagram shows some keys with two functions. The SHIFT key is normally located on the top left of the keyboard.
For the functions labelled above the keys, press SHIFT first.
For the functions labelled on the keys simply press the key.

Operating Modes

Before beginning calculations it is essential to ensure that the calculator is in a suitable operating mode for the type of calculation. If it is not, then the result of the calculation may be difficult to interpret, and at the worst, completely wrong.
For most general calculation, the calculator may be used in 'Normal Mode'. However, this is likely to display many decimal places, often unnecessary.
For the examples in this book I have chosen a suitable operating mode, this is my choice, you may decide on another when you gain experience, or you may simply leave the machine in 'Normal' and 'Degree' mode for most of the time.

The operating modes are set by pressing the MODE key a number of times to select the mode menu required, and pressing a number to select the required mode, some modes may prompt you in the top left of the display, to enter further information, such as the number of decimal places or the number of significant figures to be displayed. The selected operating modes will be retained when the calculator is next switched on.

For the calculations in the first chapter of this book I will ensure that the calculator is in COMP MODE, DEGREE MODE, and NORMAL MODE 2.

Key the following :-

| AC | All Clear switches machine on. |
| MODE | The first menu appears. ⇒ |

```
COMP  SD   LR  CMPLX
 1    2    3    4
```

| 1 | Press 1 to select **COMP** mode for general calculations. |

```
DEG  RAD  GRA
 1    2    3
```

| MODE MODE | The second menu appears. ⇒ |
| 1 | Press 1 to select **DEG**ree mode. |

| MODE | MODE | MODE | The third menu   ⟹

FIX SCI NORM
1   2   3

| 3 | Press 3 select **NORM**al mode.

The message 1 ~ 2 appears to ask you   ⟹
which normal mode you require.

1 ~ 2   NORM
                            1

| 2 | Press 2.

NORMal mode **1** displays values less than 10^{-2} (0.01) and greater than 10^{10} in exponential format.

NORMal mode **2** displays values less than 10^{-9} (0.000000001) and greater than 10^{10} in exponential format.

Specifying an Angle Unit Mode

Press the mode key twice, followed by the number indicated :-

| MODE | MODE | 1 | **DEG** is displayed. Angular measurement in Degrees. This unit is used for most calculations.

| MODE | MODE | 2 | **RAD** is displayed. Angular measurement in Radians. This unit is often used in electrical a.c. calculations.

| MODE | MODE | 3 | **GRA** is displayed Angular measurement in Gradients. This unit is not normally encountered.

Specifying The Display Mode

Press the mode key three times, followed by the number indicated :-

| MODE | MODE | MODE | 1 | **FIX Mode. FIX** is displayed. Entering a number, 0 - 9, displays that number of decimal digits.

| MODE | MODE | MODE | 2 | **SCIENTIFIC Mode. SCI** is displayed. Entering a number, 0 - 9, will specify the number of significant digits. 0 will display ten, and 1 displays 1 digit.

| MODE | MODE | MODE | 3 | **NORMAL Mode. NORM** is displayed. See top of this page.

Specifying The Engineering Mode

| MODE | MODE | MODE | MODE | 1 | **ENG** is displayed. Use for engineering symbol calculations. This will be explained later.

For detailed information on FIX SCI NORM and ENG see pages 1-25 to 1-31.

All Clear AC

Clears all the current calculation. It does not clear the constant memory or the independent memory. It does not affect the selected operating modes.

Clear C

Clears the last entry, not the entire calculation. E.g. If you are entering the values for a calculation, and enter an incorrect value, press C before pressing the next arithmetic operation key. This clears the incorrectly entered value, allowing you to re-enter the correct value without altering the previous input data.

Suppose you want to calculate $2 \times 3 \times 10$; but you enter a 4 instead of the 10. Before you press the equals key, press the C key, and then enter the 10. The example below will demonstrate this, and also the method of entry used in this book.

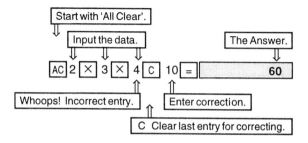

Backspace ▶

Suppose you enter a number, e,g, 12385, but you realise - before pressing the next arithmetic operation key - that 12345 should have been entered; well don't worry, you've spotted it in time, you have the option above, of pressing C and retyping the entire number, or pressing the ▶ key to backspace through the number until the incorrect figure has been deleted, then re-entering only the last part of the number.

AC 12385	12385
▶▶	123
45	12345

Keys and Functions used in this book

The following keys and functions are described or used in the examples given in this book. They have been chosen because they are those most likely to be encountered in basic radio, electronic and electrical calculations. They are also essential to basic mathematics.

Please note. When the required function of a key is the alternative function, and is activated by pressing the SHIFT key, e.g. $\boxed{\text{SHIFT}}$ $\boxed{\text{Min}}$, the shift key operation may not be shown in some of the worked examples, particularly where it is obvious that the second function is required. For the above example I will simply show $\boxed{\text{Min}}$, the SHIFT should be obvious.

Keys	Function
$\boxed{\text{AC}}$ $\boxed{\text{C}}$	All clear/on and Clear
$\boxed{+}$ $\boxed{-}$ $\boxed{=}$	Basic calculations
$\boxed{\times}$ $\boxed{\div}$	Basic calculations
$\boxed{1/x}$	Reciprocal
$\boxed{+/-}$	Change sign
$\boxed{x^2}$ $\boxed{\sqrt{}}$ $\boxed{\sqrt[3]{}}$	Square, square root and cube root
$\boxed{x^y}$ $\boxed{\sqrt[x]{}}$	Power and root
$\boxed{\sin}$ $\boxed{\cos}$ $\boxed{\tan}$	Trigonometric functions. Sine, Cosine, Tangent
$\boxed{\sin^{-1}}$ $\boxed{\cos^{-1}}$ $\boxed{\tan^{-1}}$	Arc sine, Arc cosine, Arc tangent
$\boxed{\log}$ $\boxed{10^x}$	Common logarithm (base 10) and Common antilogarithm
$\boxed{\text{Min}}$ $\boxed{\text{MR}}$	Independent memory. Input and Recall
$\boxed{\text{M+}}$ $\boxed{\text{M-}}$	Add display to memory. Subtract display from memory
$\boxed{\text{STO}}$ $\boxed{\text{RCL}}$	Variable memories. Store and Recall
$\boxed{\text{Mcl}}$	Memory clear. Clears all memory.
$\boxed{x \leftrightarrow y}$	Register exchange
$\boxed{\text{EXP}}$	Enter exponent. A small x10 may be displayed
$\boxed{\text{ENG}}$ $\boxed{\overleftarrow{\text{ENG}}}$	Engineering
$\boxed{\text{R} \rightarrow \text{P}}$ $\boxed{\text{P} \rightarrow \text{R}}$	Rectangular to Polar and Polar to Rectangular conversion
$\boxed{[(\text{---}}$ $\boxed{\text{---})]}$	Parentheses (Brackets)
$\boxed{\blacktriangleright}$	Backspace
$\boxed{\pi}$	Pi = 3.141592654

Maths Review

We will now review some basic maths and work through a few examples to demonstrate the modes and function keys of the calculator.

For the following examples set the MODES as shown below -

| MODE | 1 | COMP - for general calculations.

| MODE | MODE | 1 | DEGREE - for general and trigonometric calculation.

| MODE | MODE | MODE | 3 | 2 | NORMAL 2 - for general calculation.

Addition | + |

The addition of two or more numbers gives the sum of those numbers.

E.g. $3 + 2 = 5$ . . . . ." Three plus two equals five."

          $3 + 4 + 5 = 12$ " Three plus four plus five equals twelve."

Well so far the operation was fairly obvious and did not need much thinking about, now evaluate $128 + 246 + 325 + 1250$

$$
\begin{array}{r}
128 \\
246 \\
325 \\
+ \quad \underline{1250} \\
\text{Answer} \quad \underline{1949}
\end{array}
$$

O.k. That wasn't too bad, but perhaps you forgot to carry over a ten here or there, well don't worry, the scientific calculator will solve the problem for you. Follow the keying sequence below :-

| AC |128 | + | 246 | + | 325 | + | 1250 | = | **1949**

Try the following examples, first mentally, then with pencil and paper, and then using your calculator.

Evaluate $127.23 + 192.3 + 299.9 + 7.02$

| AC |127.23 | + | 192.3 | + | 299.9 | + |7.02 | = | **626.45**

Evaluate $124.77 + 0.34 + 0.8 + 3.99$

| AC | 124.77 | + | .34 | + | .8 | + | 3.99 | = | **129.9**

Subtraction $\boxed{-}$

When one number is subtracted from another, the result is called the difference.

E.g. $10 - 3 = 7$ ......"Ten minus three equals seven."

$12 - 6 = 6$ ......"Twelve minus six equals six."

$120 - 90 = 30$

As with addition, when small or whole numbers are used the basic mathematical operations are fairly easy and evaluation can be carried out in ones head. Now look at the following example :-

Evaluate $11,155,000 - 455,000$

We could subtract the numbers mentally or by the traditional method :-

$$\begin{array}{r} 11,155,000 \\ - \quad 455,000 \\ \hline \end{array}$$
Answer $\underline{10,700,000}$

Did you get the answer, or did you borrow a ten from somewhere and forget to pay it back? Let's do it the easy way and use the calculator.
Follow the keying sequence below :-

$\boxed{AC}$ 11155000 $\boxed{-}$ 455000 $\boxed{=}$ | 10700000 |

Using the calculator evaluate the following examples :-

$1234 - 246 =$

$\boxed{AC}$ 1234 $\boxed{-}$ 246 $\boxed{=}$ | 988 |

$987 - 88.5 - 12.9 =$

$\boxed{AC}$ 987 $\boxed{-}$ 88.5 $\boxed{-}$ 12.9 $\boxed{=}$ | 885.6 |

$5699.4 - 100.96 - 14.73 =$

$\boxed{AC}$ 5699.4 $\boxed{-}$ 100.96 $\boxed{-}$ 14.73 $\boxed{=}$ | 5583.71 |

$812 - 682 - 22.7 - 9.99 =$

$\boxed{AC}$ 812 $\boxed{-}$ 682 $\boxed{-}$ 22.7 $\boxed{-}$ 9.99 $\boxed{=}$ | 97.31 |

Multiplication $\boxed{\times}$

When two or more numbers are multiplied the result is referred to as the product of those numbers. The three main parts of a multiplication problem are the multiplicand, Multiplier and the Product.

E.g. 4 x 2 = 8   "Four times two equals eight."

Where 4 is the multiplicand, 2 is the multiplier and 8 is the product.

4 x 2 means Four, two times, or Two lots of four, i.e. 4 + 4.

Similarly 12 x 3 means 12 + 12 + 12 = 36 (3 lots of 12).

Swapping the multiplicand and the multiplier gives the same result :-

3 x 12 = 3 + 3 + 3 + 3 + 3 + 3 + 3 + 3 + 3 + 3 + 3 + 3 = 36 (12 lots of 3).

Here are some easy examples, you may not need the calculator :-

> 3 x 2 = 6
>
> 23 x 2 = 46
>
> 56 x 10 = 560
>
> 35 x 100 = 3500
>
> 98 x 1000 = 98000

Multiplying small whole numbers or multiplying by 10 or 100 is easy, but larger numbers require more effort. Try the following examples :-

	a) 128 x 325		b) 1024 x 64
	128		1024
	x 325		x 64
	640		4096
	2560		61440
	38400	Answer	65536
Answer	41600		

Did you remember how to work them out? How long did it take? Now use the calculator to make life easier. Follow the keying sequence below :-

a)

$\boxed{AC}$ 128 $\boxed{\times}$ 325 $\boxed{=}$ | 41600 |

b)

$\boxed{AC}$ 1024 $\boxed{\times}$ 64 $\boxed{=}$ | 65536 |

Division ÷

Division is the process of finding how many times one number is contained in another. The three main parts of a division problem are the Dividend, Divisor and Quotient.

E.g.   12 ÷ 4 = 3 . . . ."Twelve divided by four equals three."

In this above example 12 is the dividend, 4 the divisor and 3 the quotient.

The above example is likely to be seen written in various ways :-

12/4 This gets it all on one line and is convenient for typing,

$\frac{12}{4}$ "Twelve over four,"   or $4\overline{)\,12}$ " Four into twelve."

All the above expressions mean the same thing, i.e. How many lots of four are contained in twelve.

For the above example just imagine that you've got 12 toy soldiers and have split them into groups of 4, you will get 3 groups of 4 soldiers.

Evaluate the following, use any method.

300 ÷ 15,   270 ÷ 9,   480 ÷ 4.

I picked fairly easy numbers, but you probably reached for the calculator to save time. You should have keyed in :-

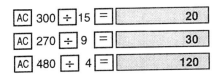

Now try the following :-

128.3 ÷ 29.7, $\frac{74800}{25}$,   999/11.

Using the calculator :-

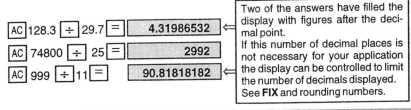

Two of the answers have filled the display with figures after the decimal point.
If this number of decimal places is not necessary for your application the display can be controlled to limit the number of decimals displayed. See **FIX** and rounding numbers.

Priority of Calculation & Brackets.

Operations are performed according to the accepted rules of algebraic hierarchy in the following order of precedence:-

1)   Functions where the value is entered first and then the function key pressed.

2)   Powers, roots, co-ordinate conversions.

3)   Functions where the function key is pressed and then the value entered.

4)   Multiplication and division (including constant calculation)

5)   Addition and subtraction (including constant calculation)

Refer to the instruction manual for more detailed information.

Operations within brackets are carried out first. When there are sets of brackets within brackets, (nested parentheses), the innermost brackets are operated on first.

Example. Suppose we are required to evaluate $14 - 4 + 2 \times 2$, working from left to right with the calculator will give 14. Let us try that:-

$$\boxed{AC}\, 14 \,\boxed{-}\, 4 \,\boxed{+}\, 2 \,\boxed{\times}\, 2 \,\boxed{=}\, \boxed{14}$$

The calculator has worked the example using the order of precedence given above. However, it would have been more clear if the above expression had been written as $14 - 4 + (2 \times 2)$ in the first instance. A change in the position of the brackets in this example will change the result.

Brackets (Parentheses) $\boxed{[(\cdots}\boxed{\cdots)]}$

The use of brackets around certain numbers and operations in a formula or expression indicates the priority and sequence in which the operations are required to be carried out. Brackets can be used to break a formula down into smaller and more manageable packets to operate on, and also save us storing intermediate results in memory.

Note. *Brackets should always be used if there is any doubt as to how the calculator will handle a particular problem.*

$(14 - (4 + 2)) \times 2 = 16$ $\Leftarrow$ | Work the innermost brackets first. |

$(14 - 4 + 2) \times 2 = 24$

$14 - (4 + (2 \times 2)) = 6$ | See keying sequence on next page for using brackets. | $\Rightarrow$

Examples

1. Evaluate $(14 - (4 + 2)) \times 2$

$(14 - (4 + 2)) \times 2 = (14 - 6) \times 2 = 8 \times 2 = 16$

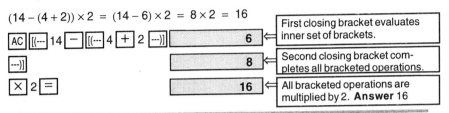

First closing bracket evaluates inner set of brackets.

Second closing bracket completes all bracketed operations.

All bracketed operations are multiplied by 2. **Answer** 16

---

2. Evaluate $(14 - 4 + 2) \times 2 = 24$

$(14 - 4 + 2) \times 2 = 12 \times 2 = 24$

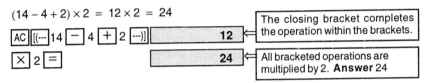

The closing bracket completes the operation within the brackets.

All bracketed operations are multiplied by 2. **Answer** 24

Instead of using brackets for the above example, use could have been made of the equals key, enabling the equation to be broken down without keying in the brackets.

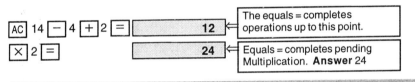

The equals = completes operations up to this point.

Equals = completes pending Multiplication. **Answer** 24

---

3. Evaluate $\dfrac{12 + 6 + 2}{7 + 2 + 1}$

To evaluate this example, the result of the top line must be divided by the result of the bottom line. To ensure this is carried out properly, enclose both top and bottom lines in brackets.

$$\frac{(12 + 6 + 2)}{(7 + 2 + 1)} = \frac{20}{10} = 2$$

Using the calculator :-

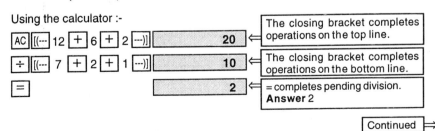

The closing bracket completes operations on the top line.

The closing bracket completes operations on the bottom line.

= completes pending division. **Answer** 2

Continued ⇒

For the current example we need not have enclosed the top line in brackets, It would have been sufficient to have evaluated the top line using the = key. We will still need to enclose the bottom line in brackets.

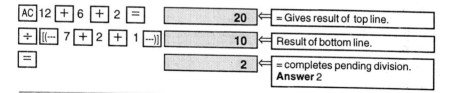

20	← = Gives result of top line.
10	← Result of bottom line.
2	← = completes pending division. **Answer** 2

4. Evaluate $\dfrac{8 \times (4+2)}{(5 \times 2)+2}$

Evaluation of this example is carried out below. Using additional brackets will ensure that the entire top line is divided by the entire bottom line.

$$\frac{(8 \times (4+2))}{((5 \times 2)+2)} = \frac{(8 \times 6)}{(10+2)} = \frac{48}{12} = 4$$

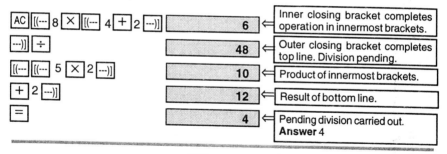

6	← Inner closing bracket completes operation in innermost brackets.
48	← Outer closing bracket completes top line. Division pending.
10	← Product of innermost brackets.
12	← Result of bottom line.
4	← Pending division carried out. **Answer** 4

5. Evaluate $(4 \times 2)(9+3)$

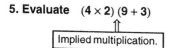

Implied multiplication.

Note. Absence of a sign between the two parts implies multiplication. The calculator will not carry out implied multiplication. A multiplication sign must be used.

$(4 \times 2)(9+3) = (4 \times 2) \times (9+3) = 8 \times 12 = 96$

8	← First multiplication complete. Second Multiplication pending.
12	← Addition complete. Multiplication still pending.
96	← Pending multiplication complete. **Answer** 96

Squares of numbers $\boxed{\chi^2}$

This calculates the square of the displayed number, its action is immediate on the displayed number. To obtain the square of a number, multiply the number by itself. We say that we have squared a number when we have raised it to the power of two.

E.g. $3 \times 3 = 9$.   Instead of writing 3×3,   we write 3^2.

Examples.

1. Evaluate 4^2

$\boxed{AC}$ 4 $\boxed{\chi^2}$ [16   ] ⇐ Result is immediate on pressing χ^2

2. Evaluate 17.2^2

$\boxed{AC}$ 17.2 $\boxed{\chi^2}$ [295.84   ]

3. Calculate the sum of $20^2 + 2^2 + 6^2$

$\boxed{AC}$ 20 $\boxed{\chi^2}$ $\boxed{+}$ 2 $\boxed{\chi^2}$ $\boxed{+}$ 6 $\boxed{\chi^2}$ $\boxed{=}$ [440   ]

4. Find the value of -7.5^2   ⇐ This is a negative number.

$\boxed{AC}$ 7.5 $\boxed{+/-}$ $\boxed{\chi^2}$ [56.25   ] ⇐ Squaring a negative number gives a positive number.

5. Find the value of 0.5^2

$\boxed{AC}$ .5 $\boxed{\chi^2}$ [0.25   ] ⇐ Numbers less than 1 get smaller when they are squared.

6. Evaluate $\left(\dfrac{6}{2}\right)^2$ ⇐ We can solve this problem either using the brackets as it is written, or, without using brackets.

$$\left(\frac{6}{2}\right)^2 = 3^2 = 9$$

$\boxed{AC}$ $\boxed{[(---}$ 6 $\boxed{\div}$ 2 $\boxed{---)]}$ $\boxed{\chi^2}$ [9   ] ⇐ Closing bracket completes divide operation within the brackets. χ^2 takes immediate effect.

An alternative method not using brackets :-

$\boxed{AC}$ 6 $\boxed{\div}$ 2 $\boxed{=}$ $\boxed{\chi^2}$ [9   ] ⇐ The = completes the divide operation, the result of which is squared.

An incorrect method for above :-

$\boxed{AC}$ 6 $\boxed{\div}$ 2 $\boxed{\chi^2}$ $\boxed{=}$ [1.5   ] ✗ ⇐ The 2 was squared before the divide operation took place. You have actually calculated :- $6 \div 2^2$ and not $(6 \div 2)^2$.

Reciprocal $\boxed{1/\chi}$

The reciprocal of a number χ, is $1/\chi$. That is 'one divided by χ.'
The reciprocal key operates immediately on the displayed number.

E.g.   The reciprocal of $4 = \dfrac{1}{4} = 0.25$

         The reciprocal of $10 = \dfrac{1}{10} = 0.1$

         The reciprocal of $0.25 = \dfrac{1}{0.25} = 4$

Examples.

1. What is the reciprocal of 5?

$\boxed{AC}$ 5 $\boxed{1/\chi}$ **0.2**   ⇐ Reciprocal key takes immediate effect.

---

2. What is the reciprocal of 125?

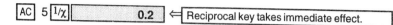

$\boxed{AC}$ 125 $\boxed{1/\chi}$ **0.008** ⇐ | If the answer is 8^{-03} you may be using NORMAL MODE 1. Change to NORMAL MODE 2. Refer to your operating manual.

---

3. Evaluate $3 \times \dfrac{1}{4^2}$

$\boxed{AC}$ 3 $\boxed{\times}$ 4 $\boxed{\chi^2}$ **16**   ⇐ Result of 4^2. Multiplication pending.

$\boxed{1/\chi}$ **0.0625** ⇐ Reciprocal of 4^2. Multiplication still pending.

$\boxed{=}$ **0.1875** ⇐ = Completes the pending multiplication.

---

4. Evaluate $\dfrac{1}{\dfrac{1}{8}+\dfrac{1}{4}}$

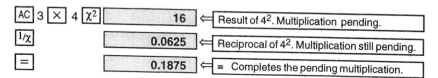

$\boxed{AC}$ 8 $\boxed{1/\chi}$ **0.125** ⇐ Result of 1/8

$\boxed{+}$ 4 $\boxed{1/\chi}$ **0.25** ⇐ Result of 1/4

$\boxed{=}$ **0.375** ⇐ Sum of 1/8 + 1/4

$\boxed{1/\chi}$ **2.666666667** ⇐ Answer

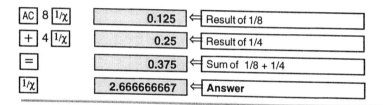

Using The Scientific Calculator

Square root $\boxed{\sqrt{}}$

This key calculates the square root of a number. The square root key should be pressed before the value is entered (see e.g. 6 & 7 below for alternative method). *Other types of calculator may require the value to be entered before the function key is pressed.*

The square root of a given number is the number whose square is equal to the given number. From the above definition it can be seen that the square root of 9 is 3, because the square of 3, (3^2), is 9.

Examples.

1. Find the square root of 16

$\boxed{AC}$ $\boxed{\sqrt{}}$ 16 $\boxed{=}$ $\boxed{\qquad\qquad 4}$

> An operator key must be pressed after the value is entered before the square root takes effect.

2. Evaluate $\sqrt{2} \times \sqrt{2}$

$\boxed{AC}$ $\boxed{\sqrt{}}$ 2 $\boxed{\times}$ $\boxed{\sqrt{}}$ 2 $\boxed{=}$ $\boxed{\qquad\qquad 2}$

3. Calculate the square root of 1.01

$\boxed{AC}$ $\boxed{\sqrt{}}$ 1.01 $\boxed{=}$ $\boxed{1.004987562}$

> The square root of a number greater than 1 (>1) is always greater than 1.

4. What is the square root of 1?

$\boxed{AC}$ $\boxed{\sqrt{}}$ 1 $\boxed{=}$ $\boxed{\qquad\qquad 1}$

5. What is the square root of 0.9604?

$\boxed{AC}$ $\boxed{\sqrt{}}$ .9604 $\boxed{=}$ $\boxed{\qquad 0.98}$

> The square root of a number less than 1 (<1) is always less than 1.

Alternative keying-in method for obtaining the square root.

6. Evaluate $\sqrt{100 \times 6.25}$

$\boxed{AC}$ 100 $\boxed{\times}$ 6.25 $\boxed{=}$ $\boxed{\sqrt{}}$ $\boxed{=}$ $\boxed{\qquad 25}$

> This keying method can be useful and avoid the use of brackets. Use with caution!!

7. Evaluate $\sqrt{200 + 56}$

$\boxed{AC}$ 200 $\boxed{+}$ 56 $\boxed{=}$ $\boxed{\sqrt{}}$ $\boxed{=}$ $\boxed{\qquad 16}$

> This keying method can be useful and avoid the use of brackets. Use with caution!!

Powers $\boxed{\chi^y}$

This key will raise a number, called the base, 'χ', to any power 'y'.

χ^y is the yth power of χ.   Where 'χ' is the Base and 'y' is the power or index.

E.g. $\chi^3 = \chi \times \chi \times \chi$ Read as χ to the power 3

$\chi^4 = \chi \times \chi \times \chi \times \chi$ Read as χ to the power 4

$4^3 = 4 \times 4 \times 4 = 64$ Read as 4 to the power 3

$3^4 = 3 \times 3 \times 3 \times 3 = 81$ Read as 3 to the power 4

Examples.

1. What is the value of 5^3 ?

$\boxed{AC}$ 5 $\boxed{\chi^y}$ 3 $\boxed{=}$ | 125 |

2. What is the value of 3^7 ?

$\boxed{AC}$ 3 $\boxed{\chi^y}$ 7 $\boxed{=}$ | 2187 |

3. What is the value of 0.05^3 ?

$\boxed{AC}$ .05 $\boxed{\chi^y}$ 3 $\boxed{=}$ | 0.000125 |

Multiplying powers of the same base.

Note:- When multiplying powers of the same base, **add the indices.**

$$\chi^2 \times \chi^3 = \chi^{2+3} = \chi^5$$

| Same base || Add Indices |

Example.

4. Evaluate $\chi^2 \times \chi^3$.   Let $\chi = 4$.

Using the calculator prove that $4^2 \times 4^3$ gives the same result as 4^5.

$$4^2 \times 4^3 = 4^{2+3} = 4^5 = 1024$$

$\boxed{AC}$ 4 $\boxed{\chi^2}$ $\boxed{\times}$ 4 $\boxed{\chi^y}$ 3 $\boxed{=}$ | 1024 | ⇐ Result of $4^2 \times 4^3$

$\boxed{AC}$ 4 $\boxed{\chi^y}$ 5 $\boxed{=}$ | 1024 | ⇐ Result of 4^5 is same as $4^2 \times 4^3$

Division of powers

Note:- When dividing powers of the same base, **subtract the indices.**

$$\chi^5 \div \chi^2 = \chi^{5-2} = \chi^3 \qquad \text{or generally } \chi^a \div \chi^b = \chi^{a-b}$$

| Same base | Subtract Indices |

Similarly :-

A negative index

$$\chi^3 \div \chi^5 = \chi^{3-5} = \chi^{-2} \quad \Leftarrow \quad \chi^{-2} \text{ can be written } \frac{1}{\chi^2}$$

Also :-

$$\chi^{-3} = \frac{1}{\chi^3}, \quad \chi^{-5} = \frac{1}{\chi^5}, \quad \text{and} \quad \chi^7 = \frac{1}{\chi^{-7}}, \quad \chi^4 = \frac{1}{\chi^{-4}} \quad etc.$$

Examples.

1. Evaluate $\quad \chi^5 \div \chi^2$ Let $\chi = 5$

Using the calculator show that $\quad 5^5 \div 5^2$ gives the same result as 5^3.

$$5^5 \div 5^2 = 5^{5-2} = 5^3 = 125$$

| AC | 5 | χ^y | 5 | $\div$ | 5 | χ^2 | = | **125** | $\Leftarrow$ Result of $5^5 \div 5^2$ |

| AC | 5 | χ^y | 3 | = | **125** | $\Leftarrow$ Result of 5^3 |

2. Using the calculator check that the result of 5^{-3} is the same as $\dfrac{1}{5^3}$.

| AC | 5 | χ^y | 3 | +/− | = | **0.008** | $\Leftarrow$ The +/− key changes the sign of the index from 3 to −3 |

Now calculate the value of $\quad \dfrac{1}{5^3}$

| AC | 5 | χ^y | 3 | = | 1/χ | **0.008** | $\Leftarrow$ 1/χ Gives the reciprocal 5^3 |

3. Evaluate $2^4 \div 2^6$.

| AC | 2 | χ^y | 4 | $\div$ | 2 | χ^y | 6 | = | **0.25** |

4. What is the value of 25^{-2}.

| AC | 25 | χ^y | 2 | +/− | = | **0.0016** |

Powers of Powers

Look at the following example:-

$$(4^3)^2 = 4^3 \times 4^3 = 4^{3+3} = 4^6$$

It will be seen that we could have obtained the same result if we had multiplied the indices.

$$(4^3)^2 = 4^{3 \times 2} = 4^6 \qquad \text{or generally} \quad (\chi^a)^b = \chi^{a \times b}$$

⇑ ⇑

| Multiply indices |

When raising a power to a further power, **multiply the indices.**
It is necessary to observe the signs of the indices, see next example.

$$(5^2)^{-3} = 5^{2 \times -3} = 5^{-6}$$

Examples.

1. Use the calculator to show that $(5^2)^{-3} = 5^{-6}$

| AC | 5 | χ^2 | χ^y | 3 | +/– | = | 0.000064 | ⇐ | Result of $(5^2)^{-3}$ |

| AC | 5 | χ^y | 6 | +/– | = | 0.000064 | ⇐ | Result of 5^{-6}. Same as above. |

> A display of 6.4^{-05} is also correct, moving decimal point 5 places left gives 0.000064. Changing to NORMAL mode 2 will change this. Refer to your operating manual.

Roots of numbers $\sqrt[3]{}$ $\sqrt[x]{}$

$\sqrt[x]{}$ Extracts the root of a number. $\sqrt[3]{}$ Extracts the cube root of a number.
From previous examples of multiplying powers of the same base, it can be seen that :-

$$\chi^{1/2} \times \chi^{1/2} = \chi^{1/2 + 1/2} = \chi^1 = \chi$$

$$\therefore \chi^{1/2} = \sqrt{\chi} \quad \text{Similarly:-} \ \chi^{1/3} = \sqrt[3]{\chi} \ \text{ and } \ \chi^{1/4} = \sqrt[4]{\chi} \quad \text{etc.}$$

Examples.

2. Calculate the cube root of 15625 ($\sqrt[3]{15625}$)

| AC | SHIFT | $\sqrt[3]{}$ | 15625 | = | 25 |

---

3. Calculate the fourth root of 2401 ($\sqrt[4]{2401}$)

| AC | 4 | SHIFT | $\sqrt[x]{}$ | 2401 | = | 7 |

1 - 19

Common Logarithms Log and Antilogarithms 10ˣ (Base 10)

Prior to the general availability of the scientific calculator in the early 1970s, complicated calculations were performed by looking up numbers in *Log* and *Antilog* tables. The process was laborious and time consuming. Such computations are no longer necessary, although logs are still required in some engineering formulae. See section on decibels.

I will give a few examples of using logs for multiplication, division, and powers. You will see from previous examples that the scientific calculator could have carried out these operations directly.

Examples.

1. Using logarithms, multiply 4.051 by 7.912.

$$4.051 \times 7.912 = 32.052 \text{ (rounded)} \quad \Longleftarrow \boxed{\text{Conventional multiplication.}}$$

When **multiplying** numbers, **add** their logarithms. Then take the antilog.

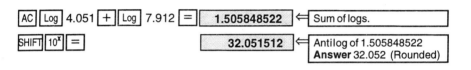

2. Using logarithms, divide 9.333 by 3.111.

$$\frac{9.333}{3.111} = 3 \quad \Longleftarrow \boxed{\text{Conventional division.}}$$

When **dividing** numbers, **subtract** their logarithms. Then take the antilog.

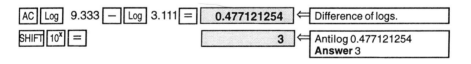

3. Using logarithms, evaluate 25³.

For a number raised to a power, we **multiply** the log of that number by the **power** of that number. Taking the antilog will give the result.

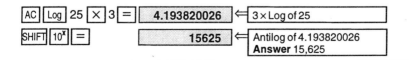

The Independent Memory

SHIFT Min   Stores the displayed number.

MR   Recalls the stored number.

M+   Adds the displayed number to the number in memory.

SHIFT M-   Subtracts the displayed number from the number in memory.

Entering a displayed number into the independent memory will replace any previously stored number. A small **M** will appear at the top of the display when a number is stored.

The memory will retain its contents when the calculator is powered off.
The memory can be cleared by entering a zero. Press 0 and then SHIFT Min
Any number recalled from the memory to the display can be operated on as if it had just been entered from the keyboard. The independent memory can be very useful for storing intermediate results when working through an equation.

> **NOTE. For the following examples set the calculator to MODES - COMP, DEGREES, and NORMAL 2. See P1-3.**

Examples.

1. Store the number 20, recall it, and add 2.

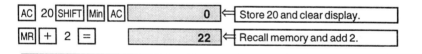

AC 20 SHIFT Min AC	0	Store 20 and clear display.
MR + 2 =	22	Recall memory and add 2.

2. A motorist fills up three times on a journey, with 56.5, 52 and 48.5 litres of petrol. Using the memory, calculate the total petrol used on the journey.

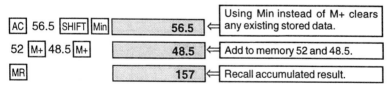

AC 56.5 SHIFT Min	56.5	Using Min instead of M+ clears any existing stored data.
52 M+ 48.5 M+	48.5	Add to memory 52 and 48.5.
MR	157	Recall accumulated result.

3. Make use of the memory to evaluate $(12.5 + 7.5) \times 150$.

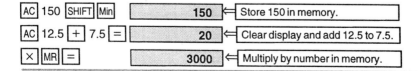

AC 150 SHIFT Min	150	Store 150 in memory.
AC 12.5 + 7.5 =	20	Clear display and add 12.5 to 7.5.
× MR =	3000	Multiply by number in memory.

The Variable Memory (Sometimes referred to as 'Constant' memory)

STO Followed by the memory location A to F and M enters the displayed number into the 'variable' memory

SHIFT May be need to be pressed before STO on some calculators.

RCL Followed by A to F and M retrieves the number in that location.

SHIFT Mcl Clears contents of all memory locations. Individual memories are cleared by entering a zero or overwriting.

There are seven 'variable' memory locations, imagine them as pigeon holes, where you can store numbers and retrieve them to use at any time.
The contents of the memories are not affected when the calculator is switched off.
There is no display indicator to show if memory locations A -F are loaded.

Create your own constants and store long numbers and conversion factors that are frequently required. Store results of long computations that are likely to be required for future calculations.

Examples.
1. Store as a constant, in memory location A, the approximate velocity of radio waves in free space. 300,000,000m/s. (3×10^8)m/s.

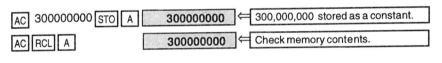

2. The wavelength (λ) in metres, of a radio transmission is given by the

formula:- $\lambda = \dfrac{velocity\ of\ radio\ waves}{frequency\ (Hz)} = \dfrac{Constant\ memory\ A}{frequency\ (Hz)}$

From Example 1. Use the constant previously stored in memory location A to calculate the wavelength of a transmission at a frequency of 5,000,000Hz (5MHz).

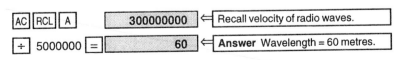

Constant Calculation

There is a special constant memory for storing a number and an operator, $+ - \times +$ for repetitive calculation. A small **K** appears in the display when a number is set as a constant.

Constant addition. n ⊞ ⊞ Adds n to each entry.

Example. Add the following:- 12 + 6,   18 + 6,   12.5 + 6 and 124 + 6.

AC 6 ⊞ ⊞		6
12	=	18
18	=	24
12.5	=	18.5
124	=	130

Constant subtraction. n ⊟ ⊟ Subtracts n from each entry.

Example. Subtract 55 from 100, 450, 55.5 and 22 respectively.

AC 55 ⊟ ⊟		55
100	=	45
450	=	395
55.5	=	0.5
22	=	-33

Constant multiplication. n ⊠ ⊠ Multiplies each entry by n.

Example. Multiply the following numbers by 2.5.   1.5, 2, 20 and –5.

AC 2.5 ⊠ ⊠		2
1.5	=	3.75
2	=	5
20	=	50
5 +/_	=	-12.5

Constant division. n $\boxed{\div}$ $\boxed{\div}$ Divides each entry by n.

Example. Divide 6, -50, 800, and 7200 by 100.

$\boxed{AC}$ 100 $\boxed{\div}$ $\boxed{\div}$	100
6 $\boxed{=}$	0.06
50 $\boxed{+/-}$ $\boxed{=}$	-0.5
800 $\boxed{=}$	8
7200 $\boxed{=}$	72

The Pi key $\boxed{\pi}$ Holds the value of π as a constant and displays 3.141592654 for 10 digit calculators and 3.14159265359 for 12 digit calculators.
Its value cannot be changed by the user.

Example. Calculate the area of a circle of radius 12.5cm.
The formula for the area of a circle is πr^2.

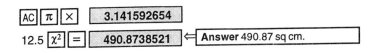

$\boxed{AC}$ $\boxed{\pi}$ $\boxed{\times}$ 3.141592654

12.5 $\boxed{x^2}$ $\boxed{=}$ 490.8738521 $\Leftarrow$ Answer 490.87 sq cm.

Scientific Constant Memory

In addition to the ability to store commonly used constants, some Casio calculators have a large number of preprogrammed scientific constants permanently stored in read only memory. You cannot delete or change these constants. However, the advanced nature of the majority of the preprogrammed scientific constants makes their use beyond the scope of this book.

Answer Memory $\boxed{Ans}$

The Answer Memory stores the result of the previous calculation. Whenever a number is entered followed by the equals key, or the result of a calculation is obtained by pressing the equals key, the number or the result is stored until the equals key is pressed again, and the new result stored.

Example. To prove operation of Answer Memory :-

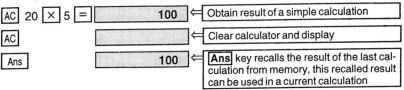

$\boxed{AC}$ 20 $\boxed{\times}$ 5 $\boxed{=}$	100	$\Leftarrow$ Obtain result of a simple calculation
$\boxed{AC}$		$\Leftarrow$ Clear calculator and display
$\boxed{Ans}$	100	$\Leftarrow$ $\boxed{Ans}$ key recalls the result of the last calculation from memory, this recalled result can be used in a current calculation

Operating Modes | MODE | | NORM | | FIX | | SCI | | ENG |

The selected mode of operation affects the way in which intermediate and final results are displayed. Experience and familiarity with the calculator will enable you to choose which mode is best suited to the type of calculation being carried out.

Normal Mode

Normal mode is probably the most common operating mode. Keying | MODE | | MODE | | MODE | and | 3 | enters NORMAL Mode. You must then choose NORMAL Mode 1 or 2 by keying | 1 | or | 2 | to set the lower limit value at which the calculator switches to exponential display. This value is 0.01 for NORMAL 1 and 0.000000001 for NORMAL 2. The upper limit is the same for both NORMAL 1 and 2, displaying up to 9,999,999,999 (for 10 digit calculators) before switching to exponential notation. See instruction manual.

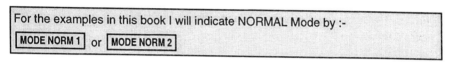

For the examples in this book I will indicate NORMAL Mode by :-
| MODE NORM 1 | or | MODE NORM 2 |

There is no display indicator to show which Normal Mode you are using. To check this, perform the following calculation :-

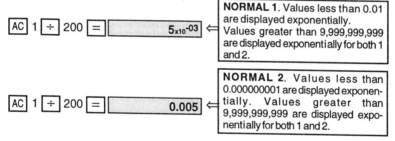

| AC | 1 | ÷ | 200 | = | $5_{x10}{}^{-03}$ | ← | **NORMAL 1.** Values less than 0.01 are displayed exponentially. Values greater than 9,999,999,999 are displayed exponentially for both 1 and 2.

| AC | 1 | ÷ | 200 | = | 0.005 | ← | **NORMAL 2.** Values less than 0.000000001 are displayed exponentially. Values greater than 9,999,999,999 are displayed exponentially for both 1 and 2.

The largest intermediate value or final result to be displayed, in either Normal 1 or Normal 2 Mode is 9,999,999,999 for 10 digit calculators. Values above this will switch to exponential display.

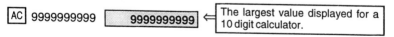

| AC | 9999999999 | 9999999999 | ← | The largest value displayed for a 10 digit calculator.

It will be seen that by increasing the displayed number by one (10 digit calculators), the result will be displayed exponentially.

| AC | 9999999999 | + | 1 | = | $1_{x10}{}^{10}$ | ← | Result is automatically displayed exponentially.

FIX Mode

Fixes the number of digits displayed after the decimal point.
Rounding the displayed number is automatic and does not affect the accuracy of the number inside the calculator. (*See Rule for rounding, below*).

FIX mode is activated by pressing | MODE || MODE || MODE | and | 1 | followed by a number representing the number of decimal places to be displayed, 0 to 9 for 10 digit calculators. A small FIX appears in the display when FIX Mode is active.
FIX Mode is released by returning to NORMAL or SCIENTIFIC Mode.

For the examples in this book I will indicate FIX Mode by :-

| MODE FIX 2 || MODE FIX 4 | Where 2 and 4 etc. represent the number of decimal digits.

Example. **Divide 999 by 11 and display the result in NORMAL Mode, and in FIX Mode to 3, 2, and 0 decimal places respectively.**
Note. The mode can be changed without re-entering the whole calculation.

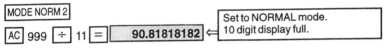

| MODE NORM 2 |

| AC | 999 | ÷ | 11 | = || **90.81818182** | ⇐ Set to NORMAL mode. 10 digit display full.

Now **FIX** to limit the number of decimal places displayed.

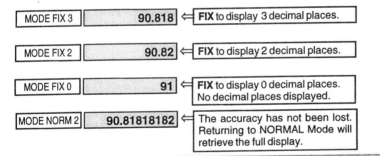

| MODE FIX 3 || **90.818** | ⇐ FIX to display 3 decimal places.

| MODE FIX 2 || **90.82** | ⇐ FIX to display 2 decimal places.

| MODE FIX 0 || **91** | ⇐ FIX to display 0 decimal places. No decimal places displayed.

| MODE NORM 2 || **90.81818182** | ⇐ The accuracy has not been lost. Returning to NORMAL Mode will retrieve the full display.

Problems may arise when using **FIX**ed decimal places.
E.g. Divide 60 by 3100. The result in normal mode will be 0.019354838.
Try it again, in **FIX 3**. Result = 0.019.
Try in **FIX 2**. Result = 0.02.
Try once more in **FIX 1**. Result = 0. Is this what you expected?
Caution! FIX to suit your application.

Rule for rounding.
If the first figure or digit to be dropped is 5 or greater, add 1 to the preceding digit.
If the first figure or digit to be dropped is less than 5, the preceding digit is not changed.

Powers of 10

$1000 = 10 \times 10 \times 10 = 10^3$

$100 = 10 \times 10 = 10^2$

$10 = 1 \times 10 = 10^1$

$\dfrac{1}{100} = \dfrac{1}{10 \times 10} = \dfrac{1}{10^2} = 10^{-2}$

$\dfrac{1}{1000} = \dfrac{1}{10 \times 10 \times 10} = \dfrac{1}{10^3} = 10^{-3}$

> Before moving to standard form and scientific notation, first look at these numbers, they are all expressed as powers of 10

Scientific Notation (Standard Form)

Scientific notation is a convenient form of shorthand for expressing both very small and very large numbers so that they can be easily handled.

When numbers are expressed in scientific notation the decimal point is placed to the right of the first significant figure, with the value and sign of the exponent indicating the position of the decimal point when the number is written in its ordinary form. If the exponent is -3, the decimal point is moved 3 places to the left. *A negative exponent moves the decimal point left.* If the exponent is 2, the decimal point is moved 2 places to the right. *A positive exponent moves the decimal point right.*

The following examples show numbers in Scientific Notation :-

3200 equals 3.2×1000, and can be written 3.2×10^3

280 equals 2.8×100, and can be written 2.8×10^2

0.045 equals $\dfrac{4.5}{100}$, and can be written 4.5×10^{-2}

0.0053 equals $\dfrac{5.3}{1000}$, and can be written 5.3×10^{-3}

> These numbers are expressed in Scientific Notation. The decimal point is always to the right of the first significant figure.

EXPONENT -3

Entering an EXPONENT [EXP]

When entering a number with an exponent (e.g. 1.2789×10^{-6}), the ten is implied when the EXP key is pressed. x10 will appear in the display of some calculators.

Example. To enter 1.2789×10^{-6} key the following :-

[AC] 1.2789 [EXP] 6 [+/-]   **1.2789x10⁻⁰⁶**

> Note :- Number is in Standard Form or Scientific Notation. The decimal is to the right of the first significant figure.

Example. To enter 300×10^6 key the following :-

[AC] 300 [EXP] 6   **300x10⁰⁶**

> Note :- Number is not in Standard form or Scientific Notation.

Scientific Mode

In this mode the user is able to specify the number of significant digits or figures. A small **SCI** appears in the display when this mode is set.

Press MODE MODE MODE 2 and you will be prompted to enter a number 0 ~ 9 to specify the number of significant figures or digits to be displayed. 0 displays 10 significant digits, and 1 displays 1 significant digit.

> For the examples in this book I will indicate SCIENTIFIC Mode by :-
> MODE SCI 2   MODE SCI 4   Where 2 and 4 etc. represent the number of significant figures or digits displayed.

Example. Enter and display the following numbers in scientific notation:-
0.0246, 0.246, 2.46, 24.6 and 246. Display to four significant figures.

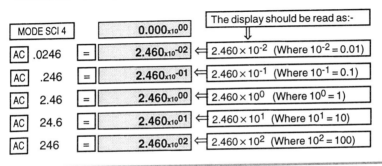

		The display should be read as:-
MODE SCI 4	0.000ₓ₁₀⁰⁰	⇓
AC .0246 =	2.460ₓ₁₀⁻⁰²	2.460×10^{-2} (Where $10^{-2} = 0.01$)
AC .246 =	2.460ₓ₁₀⁻⁰¹	2.460×10^{-1} (Where $10^{-1} = 0.1$)
AC 2.46 =	2.460ₓ₁₀⁰⁰	2.460×10^{0} (Where $10^{0} = 1$)
AC 24.6 =	2.460ₓ₁₀⁰¹	2.460×10^{1} (Where $10^{1} = 10$)
AC 246 =	2.460ₓ₁₀⁰²	2.460×10^{2} (Where $10^{2} = 100$)

Engineering Key ENG

The ENG key changes the displayed number to Engineering Notation. This is similar to Scientific Notation except that numbers are expressed in the range 1 to 1000 times 10 raised to a power that is a multiple of 3 (e.g. 10^{-9}, 10^{-6}, 10^{-3}, 10^{3}, and 10^{6} etc.). This is more convenient and less confusing when handling metric and engineering units such as :- Mega = 10^{6}, kilo = 10^{3}, milli = 10^{-3}, micro = 10^{-6} etc.

Values displayed in **NORM**al, **FIX**, and **SCI**entific notation can be converted to **ENG**ineering notation by pressing the ENG key.

Example. Converting the display to ENG Notation

With the calculator in Scientific Mode (set to 4 significant figures). Input the number 21,000 and convert display to Engineering Notation.

MODE SCI 4	0.000ₓ₁₀⁰⁰	Set to 4 significant figures
AC 21000 =	2.100ₓ₁₀⁰⁴	2.100×10^{4} (Where $10^{4} = 10000$)
ENG	21ₓ₁₀⁰³	21×10^{3} (Where $10^{3} = 1000$)

**Example. A current of 4 amps flows in a 550 ohm resistor.
What is the potential difference (V volts), developed across the resistor?**
Use the formula $V = I \times R$ = Current $\times$ Resistance = 4×550.

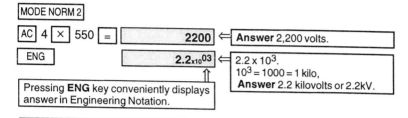

MODE NORM 2

AC 4 × 550 = 2200   ← Answer 2,200 volts.

ENG   2.2×10^03   ← 2.2 x 10³.
                          10³ = 1000 = 1 kilo,
Pressing **ENG** key conveniently displays   **Answer** 2.2 kilovolts or 2.2kV.
answer in Engineering Notation.

Engineering Symbol Mode

From the above example it can be seen that $\times 10^3$ could have been replaced by the symbol **k** to indicate kilo. Well, Casio have included such a feature on some of their scientific calculators. This mode should not be confused with the | ENG | key.

Keying | MODE || MODE || MODE || MODE || 1 | will put the calculator into a mode that displays and allows data to be input using engineering symbols, i.e. 10^3 becomes **k** (kilo), and 10^{-3} becomes **m** (milli) etc. A small **ENG** is displayed when this mode is active. Cancel Engineering Mode by pressing | MODE || MODE || MODE || MODE || 1 | again.

Symbols are entered from the data entry keypad by keying | SHIFT | and a number 1 to 9. See manual for calculator. Below shows the data entry keys with the unit symbol next to the key number, the unit value is also shown.

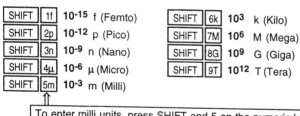

| SHIFT || 1f | 10^{-15} f (Femto) | SHIFT || 6k | 10^3 k (Kilo)
| SHIFT || 2p | 10^{-12} p (Pico) | SHIFT || 7M | 10^6 M (Mega)
| SHIFT || 3n | 10^{-9} n (Nano) | SHIFT || 8G | 10^9 G (Giga)
| SHIFT || 4µ | 10^{-6} µ (Micro) | SHIFT || 9T | 10^{12} T (Tera)
| SHIFT || 5m | 10^{-3} m (Milli)

To enter milli units, press SHIFT and 5 on the numeric keypad.
The symbol m (for milli) is not printed on the key of the calculator.
On some machines it may be printed beside the key.

For the examples in this book, I will show Engineering Symbol Mode as - MODE ENG
For entering the engineering unit type, I shall use | SHIFT || 6k | etc. (k for kilo units).

The following examples will be worked on the calculator using EXPONENT entry and also in Engineering Symbol Mode.

Example. A current of 400 milliamps flows in a 5000 ohm resistor.
What is the potential difference (V volts), developed across the resistor?
Use the formula $V = I \times R$ = Current $\times$ Resistance.

The values substituted into the formula must be in basic units. I.e. Current in amps (not milliamps or microamps). Voltage in volts (not millivolts or kilovolts). Resistance in Ohms (not milliohms or Megohms). In this case we are given a current of 400mA, it must be converted to the basic unit of the ampere (amp). Now 400mA is 400 thousandth of an amp, $400/1000A = 0.4A$. This is expressed in exponential form as 400×10^{-3} A.

$$V = I \times R = \underline{400 \times 10^{-3}} \times 5000 = 0.4 \times 5000 = 2000V\,(2kV)$$

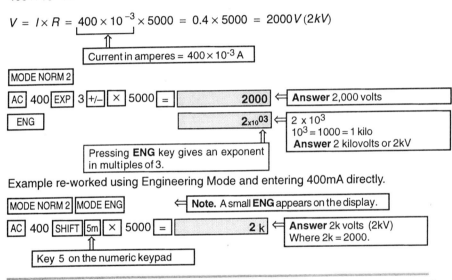

Current in amperes = 400×10^{-3} A

MODE NORM 2

AC 400 EXP 3 +/– × 5000 =   **2000** ⇐ Answer 2,000 volts

ENG   **2$_{x10}$03** ⇐ 2 x 10³
$10^3 = 1000 = 1$ kilo
Answer 2 kilovolts or 2kV

Pressing **ENG** key gives an exponent in multiples of 3.

Example re-worked using Engineering Mode and entering 400mA directly.

MODE NORM 2 ‖ MODE ENG   ⇐ Note. A small **ENG** appears on the display.

AC 400 SHIFT 5m × 5000 =   **2 k** ⇐ **Answer** 2k volts (2kV)
Where 2k = 2000.

Key 5 on the numeric keypad

Example. Multiply 6.8mH (millihenrys) by 12. Evaluate first in normal mode using the EXP key, and then in Engineering Symbol mode.
($6.8mH = 6.8 \times 10^{-3}$ henrys).

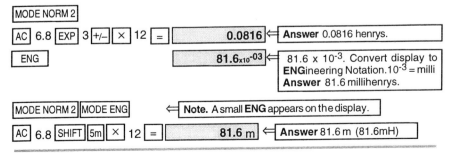

MODE NORM 2

AC 6.8 EXP 3 +/– × 12 =   **0.0816** ⇐ **Answer** 0.0816 henrys.

ENG   **81.6$_{x10}$-03** ⇐ 81.6 x 10⁻³. Convert display to
ENGineering Notation. 10^{-3} = milli
Answer 81.6 millihenrys.

MODE NORM 2 ‖ MODE ENG   ⇐ Note. A small **ENG** appears on the display.

AC 6.8 SHIFT 5m × 12 =   **81.6 m** ⇐ **Answer** 81.6 m (81.6mH)

Engineering Units and Symbols

Table 1 shows the values and symbols assigned to powers of 10 in Engineering Notation. Typical usage is shown. The two right hand columns show the method of data input in both exponential form and in symbol form, see handbook. Some scientific calculators do not have symbols.

TABLE 1

VALUE		SYMBOL & NAME	TYPICAL USAGE	EXPONENT ENTRY				ENTRY USING ENG SYMBOLS		
0.000000000000001	10^{-15}	f (Femto)	$3fF = 3 \times 10^{-15}F$	3	EXP	15	+/-	3	SHIFT	1f
0.000000000001	10^{-12}	p (Pico)	$4pW = 4 \times 10^{-12}W$	4	EXP	12	+/-	4	SHIFT	2p
0.000000001	10^{-9}	n (Nano)	$6nF = 6 \times 10^{-9}F$	6	EXP	9	+/-	6	SHIFT	3n
0.000001	10^{-6}	μ (Micro)	$4\mu H = 4 \times 10^{-6}H$	4	EXP	6	+/-	4	SHIFT	4μ
0.001	10^{-3}	m (Milli)	$25mV = 25 \times 10^{-3}V$	25	EXP	3	+/-	25	SHIFT	5m
1.0	10^{0}	Basic units.	Volts, Amps, Hertz, Seconds, Metres, etc:							
1000	10^{3}	k (Kilo)	$8kV = 8 \times 10^{3}V$	8	EXP	3		8	SHIFT	6k
1000000	10^{6}	M (Mega)	$2MV = 2 \times 10^{6}V$	2	EXP	6		2	SHIFT	7M
1000000000	10^{9}	G (Giga)	$4GHz = 4 \times 10^{9}Hz$	4	EXP	9		4	SHIFT	8G
1000000000000	10^{12}	T (Tera)	$2THz = 2 \times 10^{12}Hz$	2	EXP	12		2	SHIFT	9T

Table 2 compares numbers in normal entry format with the same numbers converted to :-
a) FIX to 1 decimal place. b) FIX to 3 decimal places. c) Scientific Notation - 4 significant figures. d) Engineering units by pressing the ENG key.

TABLE 2

NORMAL ENTRY	MODE FIX 1	MODE FIX 3	MODE SCI 4	ENG key
0.000256	0.0	0.000	2.560×10^{-4}	256×10^{-6}
0.0535	0.1	0.054	5.350×10^{-2}	53.5×10^{-3}
0.7555	0.8	0.756	7.555×10^{-1}	755.5×10^{-3}
2.37	2.4	2.370	2.370×10^{0}	2.37×10^{0}
94.5	94.5	94.500	9.450×10^{1}	94.5×10^{0}
39560	39560.0	39560.000	3.956×10^{4}	39.56×10^{3}

⇑   ⇑

FIX - Result can be misleading.   ⇑   **ENG** - Exponent in multiples of 3.

SCI - Decimal point behind the first non-zero figure.

Typical algebraic operations

Before we look at formulae and transposition, we will take a look at some typical algebraic operations. In each case we will substitute known values.

For the following examples let a = 5 and b = 2.

$$a + b = 5 + 2 = 7$$

$$ab = a \times b = 5 \times 2 = 10$$

> The multiplication sign is omitted from algebraic expressions, it is not really necessary and it might get confused for an X.

$$\frac{a}{b} = \frac{5}{2} = 2.5$$

> $\frac{a}{b}$ means a ÷ b or a divided by b, sometimes written a/b so that we can get it all on one line when printing.

$$a + b^2 = 5 + 2^2 = 5 + 4 = 9$$

$$a^2 + b = 5^2 + 2 = 25 + 2 = 27$$

$$(a + b)^2 = (5 + 2)^2 = 7^2 = 49$$

$$2a + b = (2 \times a) + b = (2 \times 5) + 2 = 10 + 2 = 12$$

$$5(a + b) = 5 \times (a + b) = 5 \times (5 + 2) = 5 \times 7 = 35$$

$$3(ab)^2 = 3 \times (a \times b)^2 = 3 \times (5 \times 2)^2 = 3 \times 10^2 = 3 \times 100 = 300$$

$$2\sqrt{5a} = 2 \times \sqrt{5 \times a} = 2 \times \sqrt{5 \times 5} = 2 \times \sqrt{25} = 2 \times 5 = 10$$

$$2\sqrt{4a^2} = 2 \times \sqrt{4 \times 5^2} = 2 \times \sqrt{4 \times 25} = 2 \times \sqrt{100} = 2 \times 10 = 20$$

$$2\sqrt{(4a)^2} = 2 \times \sqrt{(4 \times 5)^2} = 2 \times \sqrt{20^2} = 2 \times \sqrt{400} = 2 \times 20 = 40$$

$$2\sqrt{4}\,a^2 = 2 \times \sqrt{4} \times 5^2 = 2 \times 2 \times 5^2 = 2 \times 2 \times 25 = 100$$

Formulae

All calculations are based on some sort of formula or other, so before attempting the following sections in this book it may be as well to run over a few basic points concerning formulae and transposition.

A formula is a general and established rule for solving a particular problem, it is expressed in algebraic symbols. A formula can be considered as a tool, and as such it is not necessary to understand how it was originally derived, so long as we know how and when to apply it; in fact some formulas are the result of lengthy scientific experimentation, while others may have been found by reasoning, and used mentally on a daily basis without realising it. In practice, when all quantities except one, are known, and are substituted into the formula, it becomes an equation with one unknown quantity, which is then easily solved to find that quantity.

Transposition of Formulae

A formula is often expressed or remembered in one form only. Look at the following Ohm's Law formula :-

$$I = \frac{V}{R}$$

Where I is the current in amps, V is the potential difference in volts, and R is the resistance in ohms. In this case I is the subject of the formula, therefore if we know the values of V and R - perhaps as the result of an experiment - we can substitute the known values into the formula and solve for I.

Now there are two other forms this formula can take, and as it is a fairly common formula it is possible to remember them; however, if we can remember the one basic formula above, the other two forms can be obtained by *transposition*.

Note. It may require several steps to transpose a formula. Some general rules are shown below, and are based on examples.

1. Multiply both sides by the same quantity.

Transpose $I = \frac{V}{R}$ to make V the subject of the formula.

$I \times R = \dfrac{V \times R}{R}$	⇐ Multiply both sides by R. This is similar to placing a 1kg bag of sugar on each side of the scales. The scales balance.
$I \times R = V$	⇐ The R on the top and bottom of Right Hand side (RHS) cancel and leave the required formula.
$V = I \times R \ \ or \ \ V = IR$	⇐ To follow convention, rearrange the formula and put V on the Left Hand Side (LHS).

2. Divide both sides by the same quantity.

Transpose $I = \frac{V}{R}$ to make R the subject of the formula.

$\dfrac{I}{V} = \dfrac{V}{R\,V}$	⇐ Divide both sides by V. The V on the top and bottom of the RHS cancel eachother.
$\dfrac{I}{V} = \dfrac{1}{R}$	⇐ Here we have the reciprocal of R.
$\dfrac{V}{I} = \dfrac{R}{1}$	⇐ Inverting both sides to get R. R over 1 = R.
$R = \dfrac{V}{I}$	⇐ Rearrange to get R on the LHS.

3. Subtract the same quantity from each side.

Transpose $E = V + v$ to make v the subject of the formula.

$$E - V = V + v - V$$ $\Leftarrow$ | Subtract V from both sides. Both V and $-V$ cancel on RHS.

$$\therefore \ v = E - V$$ $\Leftarrow$ | Rearrange to put v on the LHS.

---

4. Add the same quantity to each side.

Transpose $x = a - b$ to make a the subject of the formula.

$$x + b = a - b + b$$ $\Leftarrow$ | Add b to both sides. Both b and $-b$ cancel on RHS.

$$\therefore \ a = x + b$$ $\Leftarrow$ | Rearrange to put a on the LHS.

---

5. Take the same root of each side.

Transpose $W = \dfrac{V^2}{R}$ to make V the subject of the formula.

$$W \times R = \frac{V^2 \times R}{R}$$ $\Leftarrow$ | Multiply both sides by R. Cancel R on top and bottom of RHS.

$$WR = V^2$$ $\Leftarrow$ | R top and bottom RHS cancelled.

$$\therefore \ V = \sqrt{WR}$$ $\Leftarrow$ | Take the square root of each side and rearrange.

---

6. Take the same power of each side.

Transpose $V = \sqrt{WR}$ to make R the subject of the formula.

$$V^2 = W \times R$$ $\Leftarrow$ | Square both sides, this removes the square root sign from the RHS.

$$\frac{V^2}{W} = \frac{W \times R}{W}$$ $\Leftarrow$ | Divide both sides by W. Cancel W top and bottom on RHS.

$$\therefore \ R = \frac{V^2}{W}$$ $\Leftarrow$ | Rearrange to put R on LHS.

Note. Six general rules have been shown, and providing they are obeyed, there is no set order in which a transposition has to be carried out.
We will continue with a few practical and complicated examples.

7. Transpose $X_L = 2 \pi f L$ to make L the subject of the formula.

$$\frac{X_L}{2 \pi f} = \frac{2 \pi f L}{2 \pi f}$$

Divide both sides by $2 \pi f$. Cancel $2 \pi f$ on RHS, this will leave L on its own on the RHS.

$$\therefore \quad L = \frac{X_L}{2 \pi f}$$

Rearrange formula to put L on the Left Hand Side (LHS).

---

8. Transpose $Z = \sqrt{R^2 + X^2}$ to make X the subject of the formula.

$$Z^2 = R^2 + X^2$$

Square both sides, this gets rid of the root sign on the RHS.

$$Z^2 - R^2 = R^2 + X^2 - R^2$$

Subtract R^2 from both sides. The R^2 and the $-R^2$ on the RHS cancel.

$$Z^2 - R^2 = X^2$$

$$\therefore \quad X = \sqrt{Z^2 - R^2}$$

Take the square root of both sides. Rearrange to put X on the LHS.

---

9. Transpose $f = \dfrac{1}{2 \pi \sqrt{L C}}$ to make L the subject of the formula.

$$f^2 = \frac{1^2}{2^2 \pi^2 L C}$$

Squaring both sides gets rid of root sign on the RHS. 1^2 on top line $= 1$.

$$f^2 L = \frac{1 L}{4 \pi^2 L C}$$

Multiply both sides by L. Cancel L on top and bottom of RHS.

$$\frac{f^2 L}{f^2} = \frac{1}{4 \pi^2 f^2 C}$$

Divide both sides by f^2. Cancel f^2 on top and bottom of LHS.

$$\therefore \quad L = \frac{1}{4 \pi^2 f^2 C}$$

Note. There are several methods by which this formula could have been transposed. Using this method we have squared, multiplied and divided in order to obtain the required transposition.

---

10. Transpose $R = R_0 (1 + \alpha t)$ to make α the subject of the formula.

$$R = R_0 + R_0 \alpha t$$
$\Leftarrow$ | Multiply expression in the brackets by R_0 to get rid of the brackets. |

$$R - R_0 = R_0 \alpha t$$
$\Leftarrow$ | Subtract R_0 from both sides. |

$$\frac{R - R_0}{R_0 t} = \frac{R_0 \alpha t}{R_0 t}$$
$\Leftarrow$ | Divide both sides by $R_0 t$. The $R_0 t$ on the RHS cancel. |

$$\therefore \quad \alpha = \frac{R - R_0}{R_0 t}$$
$\Leftarrow$ | Rearrange to put α on LHS. |

---

11. Transpose $\lambda = \dfrac{3 \times 10^8}{f}$ to make f the subject of the formula.

$$\lambda f = \frac{3 \times 10^8 \times f}{f}$$
$\Leftarrow$ | Multiply both sides by f. Cancel f top and bottom RHS. |

$$\frac{\lambda f}{\lambda} = \frac{3 \times 10^8}{\lambda}$$
$\Leftarrow$ | Divide both sides by λ. Cancel λ top and bottom of LHS. |

$$\therefore \quad f = \frac{3 \times 10^8}{\lambda}$$

---

12. Transpose $Q = \dfrac{\omega L}{R}$ to make L the subject of the formula.

$$\frac{Q}{\omega} = \frac{\omega L}{\omega R}$$
$\Leftarrow$ | Divide both sides by ω. Cancel ω top and bottom RHS. |

$$\frac{QR}{\omega} = \frac{LR}{R}$$
$\Leftarrow$ | Multiply both sides by R. Cancel R top and bottom RHS. |

$$\frac{QR}{\omega} = L$$

$$\therefore \quad L = \frac{QR}{\omega}$$
$\Leftarrow$ | Rearrange to put L on LHS. |

Transpose the following examples for practice, cover up the answers first.

	Transpose	**Transposed**
1.	$B = \dfrac{f_o}{Q}$ for f_o	$f_o = B\,Q$
2.	$f_o = B\,Q$ for Q	$Q = \dfrac{f_o}{B}$
3.	$P = \dfrac{V^2}{(R_1 + R_2)}$ for V	$V = \sqrt{P\,(R_1 + R_2)}$
4.	$Z = \sqrt{R^2 + X^2}$ for R	$R = \sqrt{Z^2 - X^2}$
5.	$Z_o = \sqrt{Z_{o/c}\,Z_{s/c}}$ for $Z_{s/c}$	$Z_{s/c} = \dfrac{Z_o{}^2}{Z_{o/c}}$
6.	$K = \sqrt{\dfrac{Z_1}{Z_2}}$ for Z_1	$Z_1 = K^2\,Z_2$
7.	$R_x = \dfrac{R_2\,R_3}{R_1}$ for R_3	$R_3 = \dfrac{R_x\,R_1}{R_2}$
8.	$X_c = \dfrac{1}{\omega\,C}$ for C	$C = \dfrac{1}{\omega\,X_c}$
9.	$I = V\,\omega\,C$ for V	$V = \dfrac{I}{\omega\,C}$
10.	$I = \dfrac{V}{\omega\,L}$ for L	$L = \dfrac{V}{\omega\,I}$
11.	$e = \dfrac{7.02\,\sqrt{erp}}{d}$ for erp	$erp = \left(\dfrac{e\,d}{7.02}\right)^2$
12.	$e = \dfrac{7.02\,\sqrt{erp}}{d}$ for d	$d = \dfrac{7.02\,\sqrt{erp}}{e}$

The Trigonometric Keys | sin | | cos | | tan |

The trigonometric keys shown above calculate the sine, cosine and tangent of an angle. On the calculators used for these examples the function keys must be pressed before the value is entered, other calculators may require the value entered first. The unit of measure must be selected, i.e. **DEG**rees, **RAD**ians or **GRA**dients.

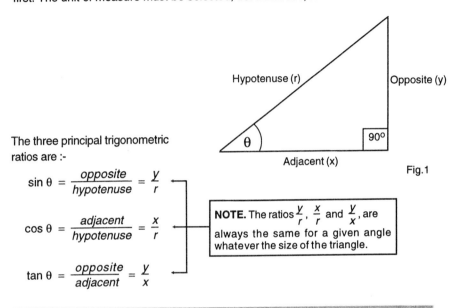

The three principal trigonometric ratios are :-

$$\sin \theta = \frac{opposite}{hypotenuse} = \frac{y}{r}$$

$$\cos \theta = \frac{adjacent}{hypotenuse} = \frac{x}{r}$$

$$\tan \theta = \frac{opposite}{adjacent} = \frac{y}{x}$$

NOTE. The ratios $\frac{y}{r}$, $\frac{x}{r}$ and $\frac{y}{x}$, are always the same for a given angle whatever the size of the triangle.

Fig.1

The Inverse Trigonometric Functions | sin⁻¹ | | cos⁻¹ | | tan⁻¹ |

The keys, $\sin^{-1}$ (arc sine), $\cos^{-1}$ (arc cosine), and $\tan^{-1}$ (arc tangent), calculate the angle in degrees when the ratios - sine, cosine and tangent are known. Since these are normally second functions of the key, the **SHIFT** key must be pressed first.

$\theta = \sin^{-1} \frac{y}{r}$ *Read as " Theta is the angle whose sine is $\frac{y}{r}$ "*

$\theta = \cos^{-1} \frac{x}{r}$ *Read as " Theta is the angle whose cosine is $\frac{x}{r}$ "*

$\theta = \tan^{-1} \frac{y}{x}$ *Read as " Theta is the angle whose tangent is $\frac{y}{x}$ "*

From the above :- If two sides of a right angled triangle are known, or one side and one angle, the unknown sides and angles may be found.

Solving Right-Angled Triangles

The solution of right-angled triangles (finding the unknown sides or angles), in one form or another, is often required when working with alternating currents and vector quantities.

Two methods used for solving right-angled triangles are :-

a) by application of Pythagoras' Theorem.
Pythagoras' Theorem states that the square on the hypotenuse of a right-angled triangle is equal to the sum of the squares on the other two sides.
Expressed as a formula, and referring to fig.2, this is :-

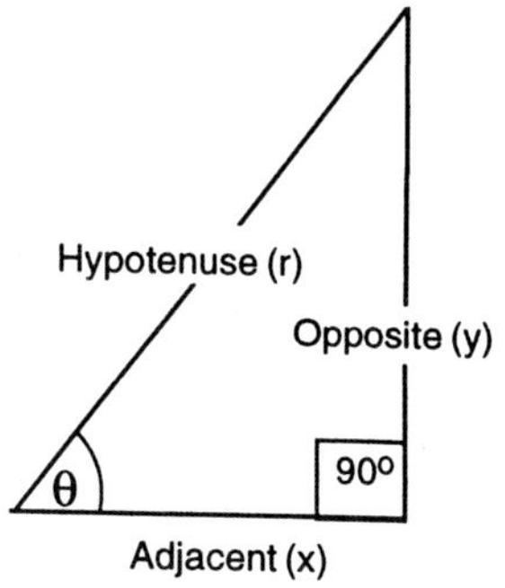

Hypotenuse (r)
Opposite (y)
90°
Adjacent (x)
θ

Fig.2

$$r^2 = x^2 + y^2$$

Taking the square root of both sides :-

$$r = \sqrt{x^2 + y^2}$$

Transposing for side y :-

$$y = \sqrt{r^2 - x^2}$$

Transposing for side x :-

$$x = \sqrt{r^2 - y^2}$$

b) by calculation based on the appropriate trigonometric ratios.
When solving right angled triangles using the trigonometric ratios, the three common ratios can be rearranged :-

$$\sin \theta = \frac{y}{r}, \quad y = r\sin \theta \quad \text{and} \quad r = \frac{y}{\sin \theta}$$

$$\cos \theta = \frac{x}{r}, \quad x = r\cos \theta \quad \text{and} \quad r = \frac{x}{\cos \theta}$$

$$\tan \theta = \frac{y}{x}, \quad y = x\tan \theta \quad \text{and} \quad x = \frac{y}{\tan \theta}$$

Examples.

1. Referring to fig.3. x = 3, y = 4 and r = 5.
Calculate the values of :-
a) sin θ
b) cos θ
c) tan θ.
Answers to 4 decimal places.

Note. *Since we are working in degrees the
calculator must be in* **DEG***ree mode.*

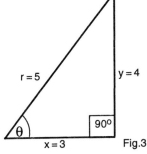

r = 5   y = 4   90°   θ   x = 3   Fig.3

a) **Calculate sin θ**

$$\sin \theta = \frac{Opposite}{Hypotenuse} = \frac{y}{r} = \frac{4}{5} = 0.8000$$

| MODE DEG | MODE FIX 4 |
⇐ **FIX** 4 decimal places. **DEG** and **FIX** appear.

| AC | 4 | ÷ | 5 | = | **0.8000**   ⇐ Sine of angle θ.

b) **Calculate cos θ**

$$\cos \theta = \frac{Adjacent}{Hypotenuse} = \frac{x}{r} = \frac{3}{5} = 0.6000$$

| AC | 3 | ÷ | 5 | = | **0.6000**   ⇐ Cosine of angle θ.

c) **Calculate tan θ**

$$\tan \theta = \frac{Opposite}{Adjacent} = \frac{y}{x} = \frac{4}{3} = 1.3333$$

| AC | 4 | ÷ | 3 | = | **1.3333**   ⇐ Tangent of angle θ.

---

2. What is the angle θ° in fig.3? Use results obtained in Question 1.

From Q1, sin θ = 0.8

$$\therefore \; \theta^{o} = \sin^{-1} 0.8 = 53.1301^{o} \; or \; 53^{o} 7' 48.37''$$

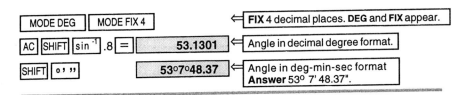

| MODE DEG | MODE FIX 4 |
⇐ **FIX** 4 decimal places. **DEG** and **FIX** appear.

| AC | SHIFT | sin⁻¹ | .8 | = | **53.1301**   ⇐ Angle in decimal degree format.

| SHIFT | ° ' '' | **53°7°48.37**   ⇐ Angle in deg-min-sec format
Answer 53° 7' 48.37".

Examples.
3. Referring to fig.4. Calculate the :-
a) length of the hypotenuse (r).
b) angle θ.

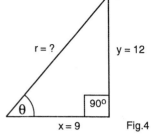

a) Using Pythagoras to find r :-

$$r = \sqrt{x^2 + y^2} = \sqrt{9^2 + 12^2}$$

$$= \sqrt{81 + 144} = \sqrt{225} = 15 \ (\textit{Length of r})$$

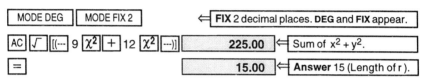

b) Find the angle θ. Since all three sides are now known, any of the three inverse functions may be used to calculate the angle θ. We will use :-

$$\theta^o = \sin^{-1} \frac{y}{r} = \sin^{-1} \frac{12}{15} = \sin^{-1} 0.8 = 53.1301^o$$

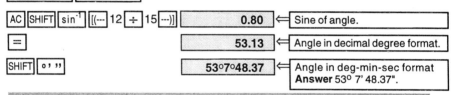

4. Calculate angle θ, fig.5.

We must find the angle whose tangent is $\frac{y}{x}$

$$\theta^o = \tan^{-1} \frac{y}{x} = \tan^{-1} \frac{20}{20} = \tan^{-1} 1 = 45^o$$

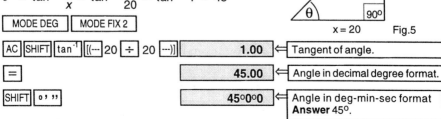

5. Referring to fig.6. Calculate the :-
a) side (y) opposite to the angle θ.
b) side (x) adjacent to the angle θ.

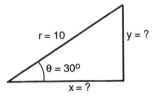

We have been given the known quantities in polar form, r ∠θ. In this example 10∠30°. Where r is the radius or hypotenuse and ∠θ is the angle. We will deal with Polar to Rectangular conversion later.

Fig.6

a) Calculate the vertical side (y) opposite angle θ :-

$$\sin \theta = \frac{y}{r} \quad \therefore \quad y = r \sin \theta = 10 \sin 30 = 10 \times 0.5 = 5 \ (\textit{Length of y})$$

| MODE DEG | MODE FIX 2 |

AC 10 × sin 30 =   **5.00** ⇐ Length of side y.

b) Calculate the horizontal side (x) adjacent to angle θ.

$$\cos \theta = \frac{x}{r} \quad \therefore \quad x = r \cos \theta = 10 \cos 30 = 10 \times 0.8660 = 8.66 \ (\textit{Length of x})$$

| MODE DEG | MODE FIX 2 |

AC 10 × cos 30 =   **8.66** ⇐ Length of side x.

Fig.7 shows the right-angled triangle of fig.6 with its sides calculated and the appropriate formula.
The polar coordinates r∠θ (10∠30°) have been converted to give the rectangular coordinates (x,y) in this case (8.66,5)

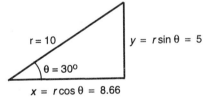

$$y = r \sin \theta = 5$$
$$x = r \cos \theta = 8.66$$

Fig.7

Note. As a cross check on the answer, substitute the x (adjacent) and y (opposite) values previously calculated into the Pythagoras formula. The result, if all is correct, should be the r (hypotenuse) value, in this case 10.

Use Pythagoras to find r :-

$$r = \sqrt{x^2 + y^2} = \sqrt{8.66^2 + 5^2} = \sqrt{75 + 25} = \sqrt{100} = 10 \ (\textit{hypotenuse})$$

| MODE DEG | MODE FIX 2 |

AC √ [(--- 8.66 x^2 + 5 x^2 ---)]   **100.00** ⇐ Sum of x² + y².

=   **10.00** ⇐ **Answer** 10 (Length of r).

Polar to Rectangular Conversion $\boxed{P \rightarrow R}$

Rectangular to Polar Conversion $\boxed{R \rightarrow P}$

The *polar coordinate* system describes point **P** in terms of a line or vector drawn from the origin **O**, to point **P**, fig.8.
The length of the line (**r**), and the angle θ of the line from the horizontal, is given in the form r∠θ, read as "r angle theta", in this case 10∠36.87°.

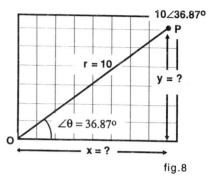

fig.8

Formulae for converting from polar to rectangular, i.e. finding values of x and y :-

$$x = r\cos\theta \quad \text{and} \quad y = r\sin\theta$$

In the *rectangular coordinate* system, point **P** can be described by its position on a grid, (**x,y**) in this case (8,6).Fig.9.

Formulae for converting from rectangular to polar, i.e. finding values of r∠θ :-

$$r = \sqrt{x^2 + y^2} \quad \text{and} \quad \theta° = \tan^{-1}\frac{y}{x}$$

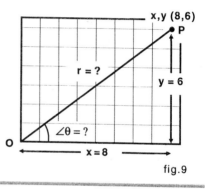

fig.9

Examples.

1. **To convert the polar coordinates 10∠36.87° in fig.8, to the rectangular coordinates (x,y) of fig.9.**

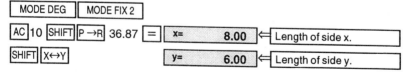

To convert the rectangular coordinates (8,6) in fig.9, to the polar coordinates (r∠θ) of fig.8.

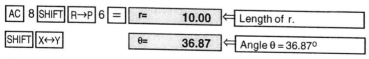

1 - 43

2. For the impedance triangle shown in fig.10, calculate the impedance Z, and phase angle θ in the form Z∠θ.
Where -
Reactance X = 500 ohms.
Resistance R = 200 ohms.

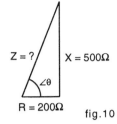

The (x,y) values are (200,500) and side r is now Z.
The value of R (200) must be entered first.

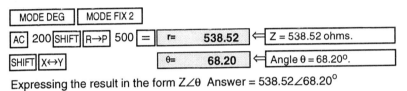

Expressing the result in the form Z∠θ Answer = 538.52∠68.20°

---

3. The stay wires on an antenna mast fig.11 are to be replaced. The mast height is 800 feet and the stay wire anchoring points are 460 feet from the base of the mast.
Calculate the length of the stay wires from the top of the mast to the ground, and the angle θ° they make to the ground.

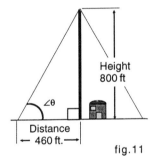

Using the rectangular to polar functions of the calculator we can convert the distance and height (x,y) (460,800) directly into polar coordinates to obtain the length of the stay wires and the angle. Don't forget that in a real life situation you will need to add an extra length for making-off.

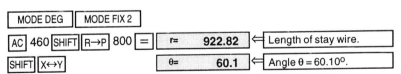

The length of the stay wires will be 922.82ft at an angle θ of 60.10°.

Polar to Rectangular Conversion

4. A ladder 25 feet long is placed against a wall and makes an angle θ 70° to the ground. See fig.12.
What is the distance from the foot of the ladder to the wall, and to what height on the wall will the ladder reach?

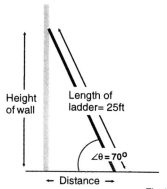

Height of wall   Length of ladder= 25ft

$\angle\theta = 70^\circ$

← Distance →

Fig.12

Since we have been given the length and the angle we can say that $r\angle\theta = 25\angle70^\circ$.
We can now use the calculator to convert to rectangular coordinates.

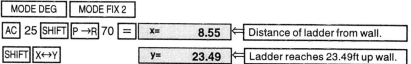

| MODE DEG | MODE FIX 2 |

| AC | 25 | SHIFT | P →R | 70 | = | x= | 8.55 | ⇐ Distance of ladder from wall. |

| SHIFT | X↔Y | | y= | 23.49 | ⇐ Ladder reaches 23.49ft up wall. |

Note. In a practical situation always secure the ladder correctly before working from it, otherwise the angle the ladder makes to the ground may rapidly become zero (0°), and the distance from the foot of the ladder to the base of the wall will probably become 25ft. i.e. 25∠0° in polar form, and in rectangular form (x,y) (25,0).

5. The boy flying the kite in fig.13 has 200 metres of line let out.
The angle of the line to the ground is 40°. Ignoring the height of the children, calculate the height of the kite above ground level (agl), and the distance between the boy and the girl. Answer to one decimal place.

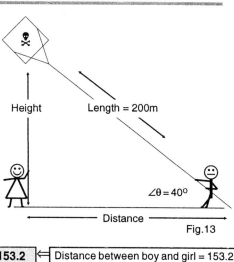

Height   Length = 200m

$\angle\theta = 40^\circ$

← Distance →   Fig.13

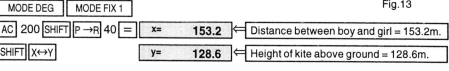

| MODE DEG | MODE FIX 1 |

| AC | 200 | SHIFT | P →R | 40 | = | x= | 153.2 | ⇐ Distance between boy and girl = 153.2m. |

| SHIFT | X↔Y | | y= | 128.6 | ⇐ Height of kite above ground = 128.6m. |

Notes

D.C.Calculations

Chapter 2

Contents

In this section you will:-
a) calculate current, voltage and resistance in a simple d.c. circuit.
b) calculate the effective resistance of series and parallel circuits, and also calculate the current and voltage in various parts of those circuits.
c) calculate the effects of internal resistance in a power source.
d) calculate power dissipated in the simple circuit.
e) calculate values of the multiplier and shunt resistors required to extend the d.c. range of the basic moving coil meter movement.

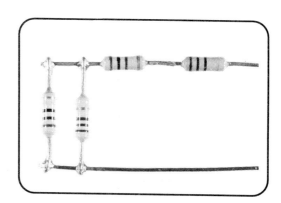

Picture showing resistors connected in Series-Parallel.

Ohm's Law

Current (*I*) amperes, Potential difference - p.d, (*V*) volts, and Resistance (*R*) ohms, are related by Ohm's Law. Many d.c. electrical problems and some a.c. problems are solved by the application of Ohm's Law.

Ohm's Law may be quoted as:-

1. The current flowing in a circuit is directly proportional to the applied p.d :-

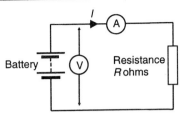

Fig.1 The basic d.c. circuit. With ammeter A, for measuring the current *I* amps, and voltmeter *V*, for measuring the applied p.d. (potential difference) in volts.

I α *V*   I.e. Doubling *V* will double *I*. Halving *V* will halve *I*. (*R* to remain unchanged.)

2. The current flowing in a circuit is inversely proportional to the resistance :-

$I \alpha \dfrac{1}{R}$ I.e. Doubling *R* will halve *I*. Halving *R* will double *I*. (P.d. to remain unchanged.)

From the above statements we get three dependent forms of Ohm's Law:-

$$I = \frac{V}{R}$$

$$V = I \times R$$

$$R = \frac{V}{I}$$

Where the units are :-
I = Current in **AMPS**
V = Potential difference in **VOLTS**
R = Resistance in **OHMS** (symbol Ω)

The three forms are easily remembered by using the Ohm's Law Triangle of fig.2. Simply cover the unit required with the finger and the formula remains.
E.g. If *V* is your unknown, cover *V*, and *I R*, meaning *I* times *R* remains.
If *I* is unknown, cover *I*, and *V/R* (*V* over *R*) remains.
If *R* is unknown, cover *R, and V/I (V* over *I)* remains.

The VOLT may be defined as that e.m.f. or p.d. which when applied across a resistance of 1 ohm causes a current of 1 amp to flow.

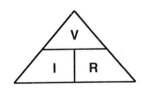

Fig.2 The Ohm's Law Triangle.

Examples.

The following three examples demonstrate that *the current flowing in a circuit is directly proportional to the applied p.d.* (Resistance fixed at 10Ω).

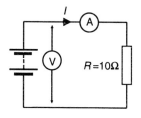

Fig.3

1. For the circuit shown in fig.3, calculate the current flowing when the p.d. across the resistor is 5 volts.

Use the formula :-

$$I = \frac{V}{R} = \frac{5}{10} = \frac{1}{2} \, amp \; or \; 0.5 \, amp$$

MODE NORM 2

AC 5 ÷ 10 =   0.5 ⇐ Answer 0.5A

---

2. Referring to fig.3. Calculate the current flowing when the p.d. across the resistor is 10 volts.

$$I = \frac{V}{R} = \frac{10}{10} = 1 \, amp$$

MODE NORM 2

AC 10 ÷ 10 =   1 ⇐ Answer 1A

---

3. Calculate the current flowing when the circuit shown in fig.3 is connected to a 20 volt supply.

$$I = \frac{V}{R} = \frac{20}{10} = 2 \, amps$$

MODE NORM 2

AC 20 ÷ 10 =   2 ⇐ Answer 2A

It can be seen from examples 1, 2 and 3, that for a fixed value of resistance, the current flowing in the circuit increases in direct proportion to the voltage.

The following three examples demonstrate that *the current flowing in a circuit is inversely proportional to the resistance.* (Potential difference remaining at 10 volts.)

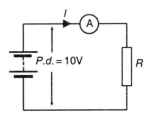

Fig.4

4. Referring to fig.4. The resistor R has a value of 5Ω. What is the current flowing through it when the applied p.d. is 10 volts?

Use the formula :-

$$I = \frac{V}{R} = \frac{10}{5} = 2 \; amps$$

| MODE NORM 2 |

| AC 10 ÷ 5 = | 2 ⇐ | Answer 2A |

---

5. What is the value of the current flowing in the circuit shown in fig.4 when the resistor R has a value of 10Ω?

$$I = \frac{V}{R} = \frac{10}{10} = 1 \; amp$$

| MODE NORM 2 |

| AC 10 ÷ 10 = | 1 ⇐ | Answer 1A |

---

6. What current would you expect to read on ammeter A, fig.4, when the resistance R is 20Ω?

$$I = \frac{V}{R} = \frac{10}{20} = \frac{1}{2} \; or \; 0.5 \; amp$$

| MODE NORM 2 |

| AC 10 ÷ 20 = | 0.5 ⇐ | Answer 0.5A |

It can be seen from examples 4, 5 and 6, that for a fixed voltage or potential difference across R, the current decreases as the resistance increases.

7. In fig.5, 100V is applied across a 50Ω resistor.
What is the current flowing in the circuit?

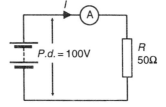

$P.d. = 100V$

R
$50Ω$

Fig.5

$$I = \frac{V}{R} = \frac{100}{50} = 2 \; amps$$

MODE NORM 2

AC 100 ÷ 50 =	2	⇐	Answer 2A

---

8. A 75Ω resistive load has a p.d. of 300 volts across its terminals.
What is the current flowing in the load?

$$I = \frac{V}{R} = \frac{300}{75} = 4 \; amps$$

MODE NORM 2

AC 300 ÷ 75 =	4	⇐	Answer 4A

---

9. A 100 volt supply is connected across a 2000Ω (2kΩ or 2×10^3Ω) resistor. What is the value of the current flowing in the resistor?

$$I = \frac{V}{R} = \frac{100}{2000} = 0.05 \; amps \; or \; 50 \; milliamps$$

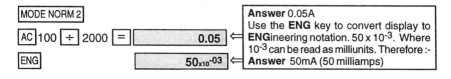

MODE NORM 2

AC 100 ÷ 2000 =   0.05 ⇐

ENG $50_{x10}{}^{-03}$ ⇐

Answer 0.05A
Use the **ENG** key to convert display to **ENG**ineering notation. 50×10^{-3}. Where 10^{-3} can be read as milliunits. Therefore :-
Answer 50mA (50 milliamps)

---

10. You measure a p.d. of 60 volts across a 3000Ω (3kΩ or 3×10^3Ω) resistor.
What is the value of the current flowing in the resistor?

$$I = \frac{V}{R} = \frac{60}{3000} = 0.02 \; amps \; or \; 20 \; milliamps$$

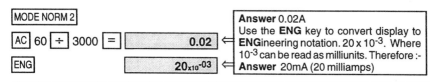

MODE NORM 2

AC 60 ÷ 3000 =   0.02 ⇐

ENG $20_{x10}{}^{-03}$ ⇐

Answer 0.02A
Use the **ENG** key to convert display to **ENG**ineering notation. 20×10^{-3}. Where 10^{-3} can be read as milliunits. Therefore :-
Answer 20mA (20 milliamps)

---

11. A 500,000Ω (500kΩ or 500 × 10³Ω) resistor is connected across a 250 volt supply.
What is the supply current?

$$I = \frac{V}{R} = \frac{250}{500,000} = 0.0005 \text{ } amps \text{ } or \text{ } 500 \text{ } microamps$$

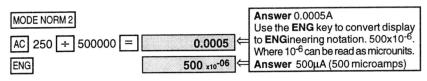

MODE NORM 2

AC 250 ÷ 500000 =   0.0005

ENG   500 ₓ₁₀⁻⁰⁶

Answer 0.0005A
Use the **ENG** key to convert display to **ENG**ineering notation. 500x10⁻⁶. Where 10⁻⁶ can be read as microunits.
Answer 500μA (500 microamps)

---

12. The element of an electric heater has a resistance of 20Ω and is connected to a 240 volt supply. What is the heater current?

$$I = \frac{V}{R} = \frac{240}{20} = 12 \text{ } amps$$

MODE NORM 2

AC 240 ÷ 20 =   12   **Answer** 12A

---

13. A potential difference of 1800 volts is measured across the terminals of a 3MΩ (3 × 10⁶Ω) resistor.
What is the current flowing in the resistor?

$$I = \frac{V}{R} = \frac{1800}{3 \times 10^6} = 0.0006 \text{ } amps \text{ } or \text{ } 600 \text{ } microamps$$

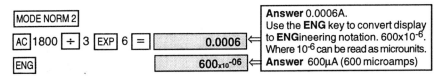

MODE NORM 2

AC 1800 ÷ 3 EXP 6 =   0.0006

ENG   600ₓ₁₀⁻⁰⁶

Answer 0.0006A.
Use the **ENG** key to convert display to **ENG**ineering notation. 600x10⁻⁶. Where 10⁻⁶ can be read as microunits.
Answer 600μA (600 microamps)

---

14. What is the current flowing in a 4000Ω resistor when the p.d. across its terminals is 6000V?

$$I = \frac{V}{R} = \frac{6000}{4000} = 1.5 \text{ } amps$$

Note. Both 4000 and 6000 could have been entered as 4 **EXP** 3 and 6 **EXP** 3, but it is just as easy to enter the whole numbers.

MODE NORM 2

AC 6000 ÷ 4000 =   1.5   **Answer** 1.5A

15. When a 24 volt supply is connected across an unknown resistor *R*, fig.6, the ammeter reads a current of 1.2 amps. What is the resistance of *R*?

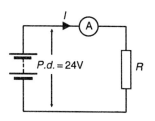

$$R = \frac{V}{I} = \frac{24}{1.2} = 20 \; ohms$$

Fig.6

| MODE NORM 2 |

| AC | 24 | ÷ | 1.2 | = | 20 | ⇐ | Answer 20Ω |

---

16. What is the value of a resistor that passes a current of 2.5 amps when connected to a 500 V supply?

$$R = \frac{V}{I} = \frac{500}{2.5} = 200 \; ohms$$

| MODE NORM 2 |

| AC | 500 | ÷ | 2.5 | = | 200 | ⇐ | Answer 200Ω |

---

17. A resistor has a p.d. across its terminals of 90 volts and a current flowing through it of 7.5 amps. What is the value of the resistor?

$$R = \frac{V}{I} = \frac{90}{7.5} = 12 \; ohms$$

| MODE NORM 2 |

| AC | 90 | ÷ | 7.5 | = | 12 | ⇐ | Answer 12Ω |

---

18. A resistive load, connected to a 120V supply passes a current of 300mA (300×10^{-3}A). What is the resistance of the load?

$$R = \frac{V}{I} = \frac{120}{300 \times 10^{-3}} = 400 \; ohms$$

| MODE NORM 2 |

| AC | 120 | ÷ | 300 | EXP | 3 | +/− | = | 400 | ⇐ | Answer 400Ω |

19. Referring to fig.7. The p.d. across the resistor R is 9V and the current flowing is 100mA (100×10^{-3}A).
What is the value of the resistor?

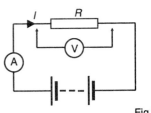

Fig.7

$$R = \frac{V}{I} = \frac{9}{100 \times 10^{-3}} = 90 \; ohms$$

MODE NORM 2

AC 9 ÷ 100 EXP 3 +/– =   90 ⇐ Answer 90Ω

---

20. Measurements are taken on the circuit shown in fig.7. The voltmeter reads 12.8V and the ammeter reads 6.4mA (6.4×10^{-3}A).
What is the value of the resistor?

$$R = \frac{V}{I} = \frac{12.8}{6.4 \times 10^{-3}} = 2000 \; ohms \; or \; 2 \; kilohms \; (2k\Omega)$$

MODE NORM 2

AC 12.8 ÷ 6.4 EXP 3 +/– =   2000 ⇐ Answer 2000Ω

---

21. The p.d. between the terminals of the resistor shown in fig.7 is 242V, and the current flowing in it is 1.1mA (1.1×10^{-3}A).
What is the value of the resistor?

$$R = \frac{V}{I} = \frac{242}{1.1 \times 10^{-3}} = 220,000 \; ohms \; or \; 220 \; kilohms \; (220k\Omega)$$

MODE NORM 2

AC 242 ÷ 1.1 EXP 3 +/– =   220000 ⇐ Answer 220,000Ω

---

22. A p.d. of 6.8V and a current of 10mA (10×10^{-3}A) are measured in the circuit shown in fig.7. What is the value of the resistor?

$$R = \frac{V}{I} = \frac{6.8}{10 \times 10^{-3}} = 680 \; ohms$$

MODE NORM 2

AC 6.8 ÷ 10 EXP 3 +/– =   680 ⇐ Answer 680Ω

**23. Referring to fig.8. The resistor *R* has a resistance of 20Ω, and the current flowing through it is 5 amps.
What is the p.d. (*V* volts) developed across the resistor?**

Use the formula $V = I \times R$

$V = I \times R = 5 \times 20 = 100 \ volts$

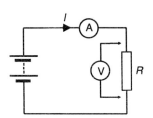

Fig.8

| MODE NORM 2 |

| AC | 5 | × | 20 | = | | 100 | ⇐ | Answer 100V |

**24. The current flowing in a circuit consisting only of a 470Ω resistor is 200mA (200 × 10⁻³A).
What is the voltage across the resistor terminals?**

$V = I \times R = 200 \times 10^{-3} \times 470 = 94 \ volts$

| MODE NORM 2 |

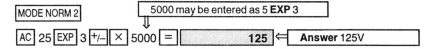

---

25. What is the voltage developed across a 5000Ω (5kΩ or 5 × 10³Ω) resistor when it is passing a current of 25mA (25 × 10⁻³A)?

$V = I \times R = 25 \times 10^{-3} \times 5000 = 125 \ volts$

| MODE NORM 2 | | 5000 may be entered as 5 **EXP** 3 |
                          ⇓

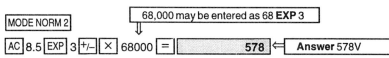

---

26. What supply voltage, when connected across a 68,000Ω (68kΩ or 68 × 10³Ω) resistor, will cause a current of 8.5mA (8.5 × 10⁻³A) to flow?

$V = I \times R = 8.5 \times 10^{-3} \times 68000 = 578 \ volts$

| MODE NORM 2 | | 68,000 may be entered as 68 **EXP** 3 |
                          ⇓

| AC | 8.5 | EXP | 3 | +/– | × | 68000 | = | | 578 | ⇐ | Answer 578V |

Resistors in Series

The two resistors shown in fig.9 are said to be connected in series.
There is only one path in which the current can flow.

The total or effective resistance R_T of a series circuit is simply the sum of the individual resistances in the circuit:-

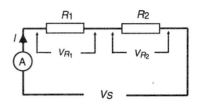

Fig.9 Typical series circuit. The current I is the same in each resistor. The p.d. across each resistor may not be the same.

$$R_T = R_1 + R_2 + R_3 + \cdots + R_N \quad \text{(Where } R_N \text{ is the } N^{th} \text{ series resistor).}$$

Points to note.
1. The total resistance is the sum of the individual resistances in the circuit.
2. Adding series resistance increases the total resistance R_T.
3. The total resistance will always be higher than the highest single resistance in the circuit.
4. The same current flows in each resistor and in every part of the circuit.
5. An ammeter inserted at any point in the circuit will read the same current.
6. The p.d. across the individual resistors may not be the same.
7. The sum of the p.d.s across the individual resistances in the circuit, equals the supply voltage. $V_S = V_{R_1} + V_{R_2} + V_{R_3} + \cdots + V_{R_N}$
8. The p.d. across any resistor in the circuit is given by *the current in that resistor (in amps) times the value of that resistor (in ohms).*
9. Ohm's Law formulae apply.
10. The total resistance of a practical circuit will include the resistance of all the connecting wires etc:

Examples.
27. Two resistors are connected in series as shown in fig.9.
$R_1 = 510\Omega$ and $R_2 = 680\Omega$.
What is the total resistance R_T of the circuit?

$$R_T = R_1 + R_2 = 510 + 680 = 1190 \, ohms$$

| MODE NORM 2 |

| AC | 510 | + | 680 | = | 1190 | ⇐ | Answer 1190Ω |

28. Three resistors are connected in series. $R_1 = 470\Omega$, $R_2 = 1200\Omega$ and $R_3 = 30\Omega$. They are to be replaced by a single resistor of an equivalent value. What is the value of the equivalent resistor?

$$R_T = R_1 + R_2 + R_3 = 470 + 1200 + 30 = 1700\,ohms \ or \ 1.7 \ kilohms$$

MODE NORM 2

AC 470 [+] 1200 [+] 30 [=] ▨ 1700 ▨ ⟸ Answer 1700Ω

---

29. Fig.10 shows a typical series circuit. Calculate the :-
a) total resistance R_T.
b) current flowing in the circuit.
c) p.d. (V_{R_1}) across R_1.
d) p.d. (V_{R_2}) across R_2.

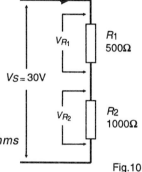

$V_S = 30V$

a) The total resistance :-

$$R_T = R_1 + R_2 = 500 + 1000 = 1500 \ ohms \ or \ 1.5 \ kilohms$$

MODE NORM 2   Fig.10

AC 500 [+] 1000 [=] ▨ 1500 ▨ ⟸ Answer 1500Ω

b) The current can be calculated using the formula $I = \dfrac{V_S}{R_T}$

$$I = \frac{V_S}{R_T} = \frac{30}{1500} = 0.02 \ amp = 20 \ milliamps$$

MODE NORM 2	**Answer** 0.02A. Use the **ENG** key
AC 30 [÷] 1500 [=] ▨ 0.02 ▨	to display answer in **ENG**ineering notation. Read as 20×10^{-3}. $10^{-3} = $ milli.
ENG ▨ $20_{x10}{-03}$ ▨	**Answer** 20mA

c) Calculate the p.d. across R_1. Use the formula $V_{R_1} = I \times R_1$

$$V_{R_1} = I \times R_1 = 0.02 \times 500 = 10 \ volts$$

MODE NORM 2

AC .02 [×] 500 [=] ▨ 10 ▨ ⟸ Answer 10V

Continued ⟹

29. Continued.

d) Calculate the p.d. across R_2. Use the formula $V_{R_2} = I \times R_2$

$V_{R_2} = I \times R_2 = 0.02 \times 1000 = 20$ *volts*

MODE NORM 2				
AC .02 ⊠ 1000 =	20	⇐	**Answer** 20V	

The sum of V_{R_1} and V_{R_2} equal the supply voltage, i.e. 30V.

---

30. Using information given in fig.11, calculate the following :-
a) Total resistance R_T.
b) The applied p.d. (V_S).
c) The p.d. (V_{R_1}) across R_1.
d) The p.d. (V_{R_2}) across R_2.

$I = 1.5$ A

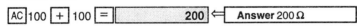

R_1
100Ω

V_{R_1}

V_S

V_{R_2}

R_2
100Ω

Fig.11

a) Calculate the total resistance :-

$R_T = R_1 + R_2 = 100 + 100 = 200$ *ohms*

MODE NORM 2				
AC 100 + 100 =	200	⇐	**Answer** 200 Ω	

b) Calculate the applied p.d. Use the formula $V_S = I \times R_T$

$V_S = I \times R_T = 1.5 \times 200 = 300$ *volts*

MODE NORM 2				
AC 1.5 ⊠ 200 =	300	⇐	**Answer** 300V	

c) Calculate the p.d. across R_1. Use the formula $V_{R_1} = I \times R_1$

$V_{R_1} = I \times R_1 = 1.5 \times 100 = 150$ *volts*

MODE NORM 2				
AC 1.5 ⊠ 100 =	150	⇐	**Answer** 150V	

d) Since R_1 and R_2 are equal, with the same current in each, the p.d. across R_2 is the same as the p.d. across R_1. **Answer** 150 volts.

---

31. A 1000V (1kV) supply is connected to the circuit shown in fig.12.
Calculate the :-
a) effective resistance R_T.
b) current flowing.
c) p.d. (V_{R_1}) across R_1.
d) p.d. (V_{R_2}) across R_2.
e) p.d. (V_{R_3}) across R_3.

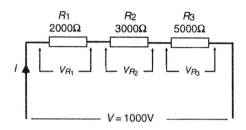

Fig.12

a) The total resistance :-

$R_T = R_1 + R_2 + R_3 = 2000 + 3000 + 5000 = 10000$ *ohms or* 10 *kilohms*

| MODE NORM 2 |

| AC | 2000 | + | 3000 | + | 5000 | = | 10000 ⇐ Answer 10000Ω |

b) The current can be calculated using the formula $I = \dfrac{V}{R_T}$

$I = \dfrac{V}{R_T} = \dfrac{1000}{10000} = 0.1$ *amp or* 100 *milliamps*

| MODE NORM 2 |

| AC | 1000 | ÷ | 10000 | = | 0.1 |
| ENG | 100×10⁻³ |

Answer 0.1A. Use the ENG key to display answer in ENGineering notation. Read as 100 x 10⁻³.
10⁻³ = milli.
Answer 100mA

c) Calculate the p.d. across R_1. Use the formula $V_{R_1} = I \times R_1$
$V_{R_1} = I \times R_1 = 0.1 \times 2000 = 200$ *volts*

| MODE NORM 2 |

| AC | .1 | × | 2000 | = | 200 ⇐ Answer 200V |

d) Calculate the p.d. across R_2. Use the formula $V_{R_2} = I \times R_2$
$V_{R_2} = I \times R_2 = 0.1 \times 3000 = 300$ *volts*

| MODE NORM 2 |

| AC | .1 | × | 3000 | = | 300 ⇐ Answer 300V |

Continued ⇒

2 - 13

31. Continued.

e) Calculate the p.d. across R_3. Use the formula $V_{R3} = I \times R_3$

$V_{R3} = I \times R_3 = 0.1 \times 5000 = 500$ *volts*

MODE NORM 2

| AC | .1 | × | 5000 | = | | 500 | ⇐ | **Answer 500V** |

To check that the p.d. across each resistor has been calculated correctly, add the individual p.d.s, they should equal the applied p.d.

$V = V_{R1} + V_{R2} + V_{R3} = 200 + 300 + 500 = 1000$ *volts or* 1 *kilovolt*

---

32. The circuit shown in fig.13 is a series circuit. There is only one path for the current to flow.
The applied p.d. is 400 volts.
Calculate the :-
a) total circuit resistance R_T.
b) supply current.
c) p.d. (V_{R2}) across R_2.
d) p.d. (V_{R3}) across R_3.
e) p.d. (V_{R4}) across R_4.

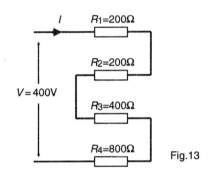

Fig.13

a) Calculate the total resistance :-

$R_T = R_1 + R_2 + R_3 + R_4 = 200 + 200 + 400 + 800 = 1600$ *ohms or* 1.6 *kilohms*

MODE NORM 2

| AC | 200 | + | 200 | + | 400 | + | 800 | = | | 1600 | ⇐ | **Answer 1600Ω** |

b) Calculate the supply current. Use the formula $I = \dfrac{V}{R_T}$

$I = \dfrac{V}{R_T} = \dfrac{400}{1600} = 0.25$ *amp* $= 250$ *milliamps*

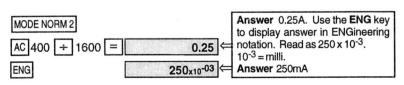

Answer 0.25A. Use the **ENG** key to display answer in ENGineering notation. Read as 250 x 10^{-3}. $10^{-3} =$ milli.

Answer 250mA

Continued ⇨

32. Continued.

c) Calculate the p.d. across R_2. Use the formula $V_{R2} = I \times R_2$

$V_{R2} = I \times R_2 = 0.25 \times 200 = 50\ volts$

MODE NORM 2

| AC | .25 | × | 200 | = | 50 | ⇐ | **Answer** 50V |

d) Calculate the p.d. across R_3. Use the formula $V_{R3} = I \times R_3$

$V_{R3} = I \times R_3 = 0.25 \times 400 = 100\ volts$

MODE NORM 2

| AC | .25 | × | 400 | = | 100 | ⇐ | **Answer** 100V |

e) Calculate the p.d. across R_4. Use the formula $V_{R4} = I \times R_4$

$V_{R4} = I \times R_4 = 0.25 \times 800 = 200\ volts$

MODE NORM 2

| AC | .25 | × | 800 | = | 200 | ⇐ | **Answer** 200V |

Note. The following example will be worked using the Engineering Symbol Mode. Some calculators do not have this facility.

33. Calculate the effective resistance of three series connected resistors whose values are 10,000Ω (10kΩ), 18,000Ω (18kΩ) and 27,000Ω (27kΩ).

Calculate the total resistance :-

$R_T = R_1 + R_2 + R_3 = 10,000 + 18,000 + 27,000 = 55,000\ ohms\ or\ 55\ kilohms$

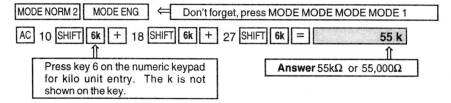

| MODE NORM 2 | MODE ENG | ⇐ Don't forget, press MODE MODE MODE MODE 1 |

| AC | 10 | SHIFT | 6k | + | 18 | SHIFT | 6k | + | 27 | SHIFT | 6k | = | 55 k |

Press key 6 on the numeric keypad for kilo unit entry. The k is not shown on the key.

Answer 55kΩ or 55,000Ω

To exit | MODE ENG | press MODE MODE MODE MODE 1 again.

2-15

Resistors in Parallel

The three resistors shown in fig.14 are said to be connected in parallel.
The applied p.d. is the same across each resistor but the individual branch currents can be different. Any number of resistors can be added in parallel, resulting in a decrease in effective resistance and an increase in supply current I_T.

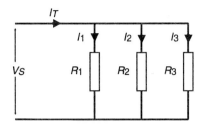

Fig.14 A basic parallel circuit containing three resistors. The p.d. is the same across each. The supply current, or total current I_T is the sum of the branch currents.

The effective or total resistance R_T of a parallel circuit containing *any number of resistors* is given by :-

$$\frac{1}{R_T} = \frac{1}{R_1} + \frac{1}{R_2} + \frac{1}{R_3} + \cdots + \frac{1}{R_N}$$ (Where R_N is the Nth parallel resistor.)

When there are *only two resistors* connected in parallel the following formula can be used to calculate the total resistance :-

$$R_T = \frac{R_1 \times R_2}{R_1 + R_2}$$
⇐
This is a very useful and convenient formula. It is derived from the general formula above. Don't forget;- *It is for two resistors only.*

The total current I_T in the parallel circuit is given by :-

$$I_T = I_1 + I_2 + I_3 + \cdots + I_N$$

Points to note.

1. The applied p.d. is the same across all the parallel branches.
2. A voltmeter connected across any branch will read the supply voltage.
3. The supply current I_T splits among the parallel branches.
4. The current is not necessarily the same in all the branches .
5. Adding extra parallel paths reduces the effective resistance of the circuit.
6. Any number of resistors or branches can be connected in parallel.
7. Adding extra parallel paths causes an increase in supply current.
8. The effective resistance of a parallel circuit is always lower than the lowest value of parallel connected resistor.
9. Ohm's Law formulae apply.

Examples.

34. Fig.15 shows two resistors connected in parallel. Calculate the :-
a) effective resistance R_T.
b) current I_1 flowing in R_1.
c) current I_2 flowing in R_2.
d) total current I_T.

Fig.15

a) Calculate R_T.

Use the general formula :- $\dfrac{1}{R_T} = \dfrac{1}{R_1} + \dfrac{1}{R_2}$ or the formula for two resistors only

in parallel :- $R_T = \dfrac{R_1 \times R_2}{R_1 + R_2}$

Using the first formula :-

$$\dfrac{1}{R_T} = \dfrac{1}{R_1} + \dfrac{1}{R_2} = \dfrac{1}{100} + \dfrac{1}{100} = \dfrac{2}{100} = \dfrac{1}{50} = 0.02 \;\; \Leftarrow \boxed{\text{Reciprocal of } R_T. \text{ (Not } R_T)}$$

since $\dfrac{1}{R_T} = 0.02 \;\cdots\cdots\; R_T = \dfrac{1}{0.02} = 50\ ohms$

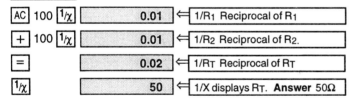

The alternative formula $R_T = \dfrac{R_1 \times R_2}{R_1 + R_2}$ will give the same result.

$$R_T = \dfrac{R_1 \times R_2}{R_1 + R_2} = \dfrac{100 \times 100}{100 + 100} = \dfrac{10000}{200} = 50\ ohms$$

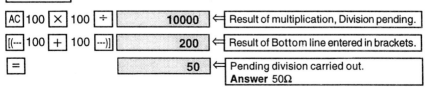

$\boxed{\text{Continued}} \Rightarrow$

34. Continued.

b) Calculate the current I_1 flowing in R_1.

$$I_1 = \frac{V_S}{R_1} = \frac{100}{100} = 1 \; amp$$

MODE NORM 2

AC 100 ÷ 100 =   1 ⟸ **Answer** 1A

c) Calculate the current I_2 flowing in R_2.

$$I_2 = \frac{V_S}{R_2} = \frac{100}{100} = 1 \; amp$$

MODE NORM 2

AC 100 ÷ 100 =   1 ⟸ **Answer** 1A

d) Calculate the total current I_T flowing in the circuit.

In this case $I_T = I_1 + I_2 = 1 + 1 = 2 \; amps$

Note. Since R_1 and R_2 are equal in value and have the same p.d. across their terminals the same current flows in each.

The effective resistance of a number of equal value, parallel connected resistors is the value of an individual resistor divided by the number of resistors connected in parallel.

---

35. A 200Ω and a 50Ω resistor are connected in parallel. What is their effective resistance?

Use the formula for two resistors only in parallel:- $R_T = \dfrac{R_1 \times R_2}{R_1 + R_2}$

$$R_T = \frac{R_1 \times R_2}{R_1 + R_2} = \frac{200 \times 50}{200 + 50} = \frac{10000}{250} = 40 \; ohms$$

MODE NORM 2

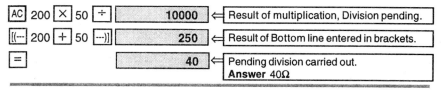

AC 200 × 50 ÷   **10000** ⟸ Result of multiplication, Division pending.

[(⋯ 200 + 50 ⋯)]   **250** ⟸ Result of Bottom line entered in brackets.

=   **40** ⟸ Pending division carried out.
    Answer 40Ω

36. Fig.16 shows three resistors
connected in parallel.
It has been decided to replace
them with a single resistor.
Calculate the :-
a) resistance of the
replacement.
b) current I_1 in R_1.
c) current I_2 in R_2.
d) current I_3 in R_3.
e) total current I_T by two
different methods.

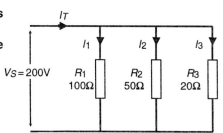

Fig.16

a) Replace the three resistors with an equivalent resistor equal to R_T.

$$\frac{1}{R_T} = \frac{1}{R_1} + \frac{1}{R_2} + \frac{1}{R_3} = \frac{1}{100} + \frac{1}{50} + \frac{1}{20} = \frac{8}{100} = 0.08$$

now since $\dfrac{1}{R_T} = 0.08 \cdots\cdots R_T = \dfrac{1}{0.08} = 12.5\ ohms$

| MODE NORM 2 |

| AC | 100 | 1/x | + | 50 | 1/x |

| + | 20 | 1/x | = | 0.08   ⟸ 1/R_T Sum of reciprocals.

| 1/x | 12.5   ⟸ Answer 12.5Ω

b) Calculate the current I_1 flowing in R_1.

$$I_1 = \frac{V_S}{R_1} = \frac{200}{100} = 2\ amps$$

| MODE NORM 2 |

| AC | 200 | ÷ | 100 | = | 2   ⟸ Answer 2A

c) Calculate the current I_2 flowing in R_2.

$$I_2 = \frac{V_S}{R_2} = \frac{200}{50} = 4\ amps$$

| MODE NORM 2 |

| AC | 200 | ÷ | 50 | = | 4   ⟸ Answer 4A

Continued ⇒

2 - 19

36. Continued.

d) Calculate the current I_3 flowing in R_3.

$$I_3 = \frac{V_S}{R_3} = \frac{200}{20} = 10 \; amps$$

| MODE NORM 2 |

AC 200 ÷ 20 = | 10 | ⇐ Answer 10A

e) The first method of calculating the total current I_T is to add the branch currents :-
$$I_T = I_1 + I_2 + I_3 = 2 + 4 + 10 = 16 \; amps$$

| MODE NORM 2 |

AC 2 + 4 + 10 = | 16 | ⇐ Answer 16A

The second method of calculating the total current I_T is to use Ohm's Law :-

$$I_T = \frac{V_S}{R_T} = \frac{200}{12.5} = 16 \; amps$$

| MODE NORM 2 |

AC 200 ÷ 12.5 = | 16 | ⇐ Answer 16A

---

37. A 50 ohm resistor is required for an experiment. But there is only a big box of 1000 ohm resistors available. How many will you need to connect in parallel to make up the required resistance?

Note. For any number of resistors of equal value connected in parallel, the effective resistance R_T equals the value of one of the resistors divided by the number of resistors :-

$$R_T = \frac{Value \; of \; one \; resistor}{Number \; of \; resistors}$$

$$\therefore \; Number \; of \; resistors = \frac{Value \; of \; one \; resistor}{R_T} = \frac{1000}{50} = 20$$

| MODE NORM 2 |

AC 1000 ÷ 50 = | 20 | ⇐ Answer 20

Twenty 1000Ω parallel connected resistors will be required to make 50Ω.

38. What is the value of the resistor R_2 in fig.17, that when connected in parallel with R_1 will produce an effective resistance R_T of 20Ω?

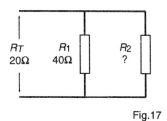

Fig.17

Rearrange $\dfrac{1}{R_T} = \dfrac{1}{R_1} + \dfrac{1}{R_2}$

to give $\dfrac{1}{R_2} = \dfrac{1}{R_T} - \dfrac{1}{R_1}$

Substituting the known values :-

$$\frac{1}{R_2} = \frac{1}{R_T} - \frac{1}{R_1} = \frac{1}{20} - \frac{1}{40} = \frac{2-1}{40} = \frac{1}{40} = 0.025 \quad \Longleftarrow \boxed{\text{Reciprocal of R}_2.\ (\text{Not R}_2)}$$

now since $\dfrac{1}{R_2} = 0.025 \cdots\cdots R_2 = \dfrac{1}{0.025} = 40\ ohms$

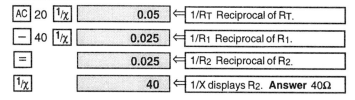

MODE NORM 2

AC 20 1/χ	0.05	⇐ 1/R_T Reciprocal of R_T.
− 40 1/χ	0.025	⇐ 1/R_1 Reciprocal of R_1.
=	0.025	⇐ 1/R_2 Reciprocal of R_2.
1/χ	40	⇐ 1/X displays R_2. **Answer** 40Ω

---

39. A circuit contains two resistors R_1 and R_2 connected in parallel. Their effective resistance R_T is 20Ω. The resistance of R_1 is 100Ω. What is the value of R_2?

$$\frac{1}{R_2} = \frac{1}{R_T} - \frac{1}{R_1} = \frac{1}{20} - \frac{1}{100} = \frac{5-1}{100} = \frac{4}{100} = 0.04 \quad \Longleftarrow \boxed{\text{Reciprocal of R}_2.\ (\text{Not R}_2)}$$

now since $\dfrac{1}{R_2} = 0.04 \cdots\cdots R_2 = \dfrac{1}{0.04} = 25\ ohms$

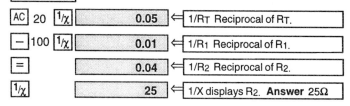

MODE NORM 2

AC 20 1/χ	0.05	⇐ 1/R_T Reciprocal of R_T.
− 100 1/χ	0.01	⇐ 1/R_1 Reciprocal of R_1.
=	0.04	⇐ 1/R_2 Reciprocal of R_2.
1/χ	25	⇐ 1/X displays R_2. **Answer** 25Ω

The Series-Parallel Circuit

Some circuit configurations encountered in everyday life may contain combinations of both series and parallel resistance.

It is essential to recognise the individual configurations within the circuit, and by applying previously learnt methods calculate the voltages and currents in any part of that circuit.

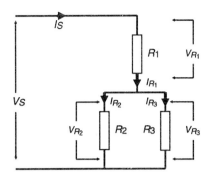

Fig.18 A basic series-parallel circuit. R_1 is connected in series with the parallel circuit R_2 and R_3

The first step in calculating the total, effective, or equivalent resistance R_T of fig.18 will be to calculate the effective resistance of the parallel circuit (R_2 and R_3). The effective resistance, $R_{2,3}$, is then treated as a single resistance connected in series with R_1.

To calculate the resistance of the parallel part of the circuit use the following formula :-

$$R_{2,3} = \frac{R_2 \times R_3}{R_2 + R_3}$$

The effective resistance of the complete circuit is then simply :-

$$R_T = R_1 + \left(\frac{R_2 \times R_3}{R_2 + R_3} \right)$$

The supply current $I_S = \dfrac{V_S}{R_T}$

P.d across R_1, $\quad V_{R_1} = I_S \times R_1$

Current in R_1, $\quad I_{R_1} = I_S$

P.d. across $R_{2,3}$, $\quad V_{R_{2,3}} = I_S \times \left(\dfrac{R_2 \times R_3}{R_2 + R_3} \right)$

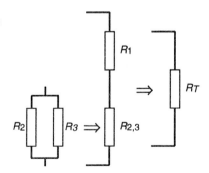

Fig.19 Showing how the circuit in fig.18 is broken down to its equivalent resistance R_T.

$$I_{R_2} = \frac{p.d.\ across\ R_2\ (V_{R_2})}{R_2} \quad \text{and} \quad I_{R_3} = \frac{p.d.\ across\ R_3\ (V_{R_3})}{R_3}$$

Examples.

40. Fig.20 shows a simple series-parallel circuit.

Calculate the :-

a) effective resistance R_T.

b) supply current I_S.

c) current in R_1.

d) p.d. across R_1.

e) p.d. across $R_{2,3}$.

f) current flowing in R_2.

g) current flowing in R_3.

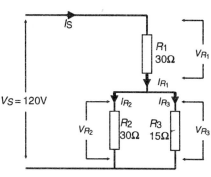

Fig.20

a) Calculate the effective resistance R_T of the circuit.

First calculate the parallel combination, then add the series resistor R_1.

$$R_T = R_1 + \left(\frac{R_2 \times R_3}{R_2 + R_3} \right) = 30 + \left(\frac{30 \times 15}{30 + 15} \right) = 30 + \left(\frac{450}{45} \right) = 30 + 10 = 40 \ ohms$$

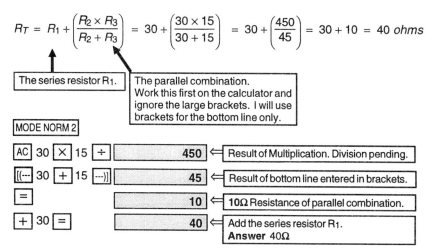

b) Calculate the supply current I_S.

$$I_S = \frac{V_S}{R_T} = \frac{120}{40} = 3 \ amps$$

MODE NORM 2

| AC | 120 | ÷ | 40 | = | | 3 | ⇐ **Answer** 3A |

c) The current in R_1 is the same as the supply current. There is no path for I_S to flow other than R_1 in this part of the circuit. **Answer** 3A.

Continued ⇒

2 - 23

d) Calculate the p.d. across R_1. By applying Ohm's Law $V = I \times R$ we get :-

$$V_{R_1} = I_S \times R_1 = 3 \times 30 = 90 \ volts$$

MODE NORM 2

$\boxed{AC}$ 3 $\boxed{\times}$ 30 $\boxed{=}$ | **90** $\Leftarrow$ **Answer** 90V (P.d. across R1)

e) Calculate the p.d. across $R_{2,3}$. Because they are in parallel the p.d. developed across R_2 and R_3 is the same. From answer a) we can see that the effective or equivalent resistance of the combination $R_{2,3}$ is 10 ohms. In answer b) we found I_S to be 3 amps, this current flows into the $R_{2,3}$ combination.
By applying Ohm's Law, $V = I \times R$, we get :-

$$V_{R_{2,3}} = I_S \times R_{2,3} = 3 \times 10 = 30 \ volts$$

MODE NORM 2

$\boxed{AC}$ 3 $\boxed{\times}$ 10 $\boxed{=}$ | **30** $\Leftarrow$ **Answer** 30V (P.d. across R2,3)

f) Calculate the current in R_2. In e) above we calculated the p.d. across $R_{2,3}$, 30 volts. We know that $R_2 = 30$ ohms. Now apply Ohm's Law.

$$I_{R_2} = \frac{V_{R_2}}{R_2} = \frac{30}{30} = 1 \ amp$$

MODE NORM 2

$\boxed{AC}$ 30 $\boxed{\div}$ 30 $\boxed{=}$ | **1** $\Leftarrow$ **Answer** 1A (Current flowing in R2)

g) Calculate the current in R_3. Applying Ohm's Law as in f) above :-

$$I_{R_3} = \frac{V_{R_3}}{R_3} = \frac{30}{15} = 2 \ amps$$

MODE NORM 2

$\boxed{AC}$ 30 $\boxed{\div}$ 15 $\boxed{=}$ | **2** $\Leftarrow$ **Answer** 2A (Current flowing in R3)

Note. The sum of the currents in R_2 and R_3 will equal the supply current, i.e.
$$I_S = I_{R_2} + I_{R_3}$$

41. The circuit shown in fig.21 is a series-parallel circuit.

Calculate the :-
a) R_T.
b) I_S.
c) p.d. across R_1.
d) p.d. across R_2.   e) p.d. across $R_{3,4}$.
f) current I_{R3}.   g) current I_{R4}.

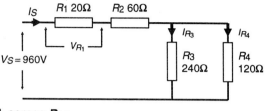

Fig.21

a) Calculate R_T. First calculate the equivalent resistance of R_3 and R_4 in parallel, and add this value to R_1 and R_2 as for a series circuit.

$$R_T = R_1 + R_2 + \left(\frac{R_3 \times R_4}{R_3 + R_4}\right) = 20 + 60 + \left(\frac{240 \times 120}{240 + 120}\right) = 20 + 60 + 80 = 160 \ ohms$$

The series resistors R₁,R₂.

The parallel combination.
Work this first on the calculator and ignore the large brackets. I will use brackets for the bottom line only.

MODE NORM 2

| AC | 240 | × | 120 | ÷ | | **28800** | Result of Multiplication. Division pending. |

| [(--- | 240 | + | 120 | ---)] | | **360** | Result of bottom line entered in brackets. |

| = | | **80** | 80Ω Resistance of parallel combination. |

| + | 20 | + | 60 | = | | **160** | Add the series resistors R₁ and R₂. **Answer** 160Ω |

b) Calculate the supply current I_S.

$$I_S = \frac{V_S}{R_T} = \frac{960}{160} = 6 \ amps$$

MODE NORM 2

| AC | 960 | ÷ | 160 | = | | **6** | **Answer** 6A (Total supply current) |

Note. The supply current, or total current is 6 amps. This current will flow in both R_1 and R_2 but will divide between R_3 and R_4.

Continued ⇒

2 - 25

c) Calculate the p.d. across R_1. Apply Ohm's Law :- $V = I \times R$.

$V_{R_1} = I_S \times R_1 = 6 \times 20 = 120 \text{ volts}$

MODE NORM 2

AC 6 ☒ 20 = | 120 ⇐ **Answer** 120V (P.d. across R1)

d) Calculate the p.d. across R_2.

$V_{R_2} = I_S \times R_2 = 6 \times 60 = 360 \text{ volts}$

MODE NORM 2

AC 6 ☒ 60 = | 360 ⇐ **Answer** 360V (P.d. across R2)

e) Calculate the p.d. across the parallel combination $R_{3,4}$.
Since we know that the sum of the voltage drops around a series circuit is equal to the applied p.d; i.e. $V_S = V_{R_1} + V_{R_2} + V_{R_{3,4}}$, and we also know the value of V_{R_1} and V_{R_2}, we can say that :- $V_{R_{3,4}} = V_S - (V_{R_1} + V_{R_2})$

$\therefore V_{R_{3,4}} = V_S - (V_{R_1} + V_{R_2}) = 960 - (120 + 360) = 960 - 480 = 480 \text{ volts}$

MODE NORM 2

AC 960 ☐−☐

[(--- 120 ☐+☐ 360 ---)] = | 480 ⇐ **Answer** 480V (P.d. across R3,4)

f) Calculate the current in R_3. Applying Ohm's Law :-

$I_{R_3} = \dfrac{V_{R_3}}{R_3} = \dfrac{480}{240} = 2 \text{ amps}$

MODE NORM 2

AC 480 ☐÷☐ 240 = | 2 ⇐ **Answer** 2A (Current flowing in R3)

g) Calculate the current in R_4. With an I_T of 6 amps, and 2 amps flowing in R_3, there must be 4 amps flowing in R_4. **Answer** 4 amps.

2 - 26

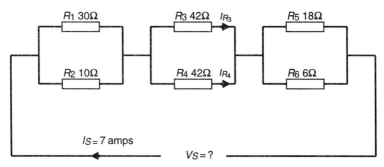

Fig.22

42. The series-parallel circuit above consists of 3 parallel pairs of resistors connected in series. What is the :-
a) effective resistance R_T?
b) applied p.d. when the supply current is 7 amps?
c) current flowing in R_3?
d) p.d. developed across $R_{5,6}$?
e) current flowing in R_6?
f) current flowing in R_5?

a) Calculate the effective resistance R_T?   First reduce each parallel pair to its equivalent resistance, then, since the equivalent resistances are connected in series, add them.

$$R_T = \left(\frac{R_1 \times R_2}{R_1 + R_2}\right) + \left(\frac{R_3 \times R_4}{R_3 + R_4}\right) + \left(\frac{R_5 \times R_6}{R_5 + R_6}\right)$$

⇐ | This rather large and complicated looking formula is simply the sum of the three parallel pairs of resistors.

⇓   ⇓   ⇓

$$R_T = \left(\frac{30 \times 10}{30 + 10}\right) + \left(\frac{42 \times 42}{42 + 42}\right) + \left(\frac{18 \times 6}{18 + 6}\right)$$

The total or effective resistance of the whole circuit, R_T.

⇓   ⇓   ⇓   ⇓

$$R_T = \quad 7.5 \quad + \quad 21 \quad + \quad 4.5 \quad = \quad 33 \text{ } ohms$$

There is more than one method that we could employ when solving this problem using the calculator. You can probably see that it may require liberal use of brackets. However, keeping track of the brackets, for the inexperienced user, can be a problem. I am going to make use of the *Constant Memory* of the calculator.

 Continued ⇒

2 - 27

The result of $R_{1,2}$ will be stored in A, the result of $R_{3,4}$ will be stored in B, and the result of $R_{5,6}$ will be stored in C. Finally the individual results will be added as they are recalled from the constant memories.

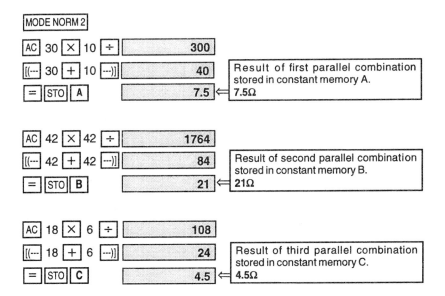

The effective resistances of the parallel combinations are safely stored in the constant memory locations, it only remains to recall and add them to find the R_T of the circuit.

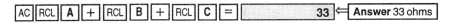

Note. The effective or equivalent resistance of fig.22 is 33 ohms. This means that the six resistors can be replaced by a single resistor of 33 ohms and the measuring instrument would not be aware of the change.

b) What is the applied p.d. when the supply current is 7 amps.
Applying Ohm's Law :-

$$V_S = I_S \times R_T = 7 \times 33 = 231 \; volts$$

MODE NORM 2

| AC | 7 | × | 33 | = | | 231 | ⇐ **Answer** 231V (P.d. across circuit) |

Continued ⇨

42. Continued.
c) What is the current flowing in R_3?
No need for calculation this time. A look at the diagram fig.22 shows that R_3 and R_4 have the same value of resistance, therefore the current will divide equally between them, and since the supply current is 7 amps, 3.5 amps will flow in each.
Answer 3.5A.

d) What is the p.d. developed across $R_{5,6}$?
Consider $R_{5,6}$ as an equivalent single resistance of 4.5 ohms, passing the full supply current of 7 amps. The p.d. developed across $R_{5,6}$ is then found by application of Ohm's Law.

$$V_{R_{5,6}} = I_S \times R_{5,6} = 7 \times 4.5 = 31.5 \ volts$$

MODE NORM 2

| AC | 7 | $\times$ | 4.5 | $=$ | 31.5 | $\Leftarrow$ **Answer** 31.5V (P.d. across R5,6) |

e) What is the current flowing in R_6?
We have calculated the p.d. across R_6 and know that it has a resistance of 6 ohms. Therefore we can apply Ohm's Law.

$$I_{R_6} = \frac{V_{R_6}}{R_6} = \frac{31.5}{6} = 5.25 \ amps$$

MODE NORM 2

| AC | 31.5 | $\div$ | 6 | $=$ | 5.25 | $\Leftarrow$ **Answer** 5.25A (Current flowing in R6) |

f) What is the current flowing in R_5?

$$I_{R_5} = \frac{V_{R_5}}{R_5} = \frac{31.5}{18} = 1.75 \ amps$$

MODE NORM 2

| AC | 31.5 | $\div$ | 18 | $=$ | 1.75 | $\Leftarrow$ **Answer** 1.75A (Current flowing in R5) |

Note. The sum of the currents flowing in R_5 and R_6 should equal the supply current of 7amps.

43. Referring to fig.23.

Calculate :-

a) I_1.
b) I_2.
c) I_T.
d) p.d. across R_2.
e) p.d. across R_3.
f) R_T.

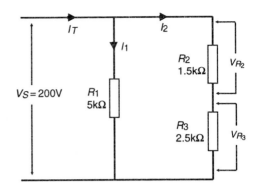

Fig.23

a) Calculate I_1.

Use Ohm's Law :-

$$I_1 = \frac{V}{R_1} = \frac{200}{5000} = 0.04 \ amp \ or \ 40 \ milliamps$$

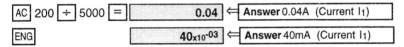

MODE NORM 2		
AC 200 ÷ 5000 =	0.04	⇐ Answer 0.04A (Current I_1)
ENG	40x10⁻03	⇐ Answer 40mA (Current I_1)

b) Calculate the current I_2 in the series R_2, R_3 branch of the circuit.

$$I_2 = \frac{V}{R_2 + R_3} = \frac{200}{1500 + 2500} = \frac{200}{4000} = 0.05 \ amp \ or \ 50 \ milliamps$$

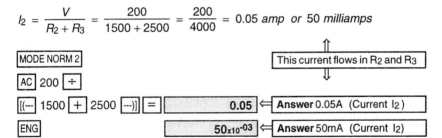

⇑

MODE NORM 2		This current flows in R₂ and R₃
AC 200 ÷		⇓
[(--- 1500 + 2500 ---)] =	0.05	⇐ Answer 0.05A (Current I_2)
ENG	50x10⁻03	⇐ Answer 50mA (Current I_2)

c) The total current in the circuit will be the sum of the branch currents I_1 and I_2.

$$I_T = I_1 + I_2 = 0.04 + 0.05 = 0.09 \ amp \ or \ 90 \ milliamps$$

MODE NORM 2		
AC .04 + .05 =	0.09	⇐ Answer 0.09A (Current I_T)
ENG	90x10⁻03	⇐ Answer 90mA (Current I_T)

Continued ⇒

d) Calculate the p.d. across R_2. Use Ohm's Law.

$V_{R2} = I_2 \times R_2 = 0.05 \times 1500 = 75$ *volts*

| MODE NORM 2 |

| AC | .05 | × | 1500 | = | | 75 | ⇐ | **Answer** 75V (P.d. across R2) |

e) Calculate the p.d. across R_3. Use Ohm's Law.

$V_{R3} = I_2 \times R_3 = 0.05 \times 2500 = 125$ *volts*

| MODE NORM 2 |

| AC | .05 | × | 2500 | = | | 125 | ⇐ | **Answer** 125V (P.d. across R3) |

f) Calculate the total or equivalent resistance R_T of the circuit. There are two methods we can use to calculate R_T.

Method 1. Since we know, by calculation, that the total current is 0.09A, and the applied p.d. is 200V, we can apply Ohm's Law.

$$R_T = \frac{V}{I_T} = \frac{200}{0.09} = 2222.2 \text{ ohms}$$

| MODE NORM 2 |

| AC | 200 | ÷ | .09 | = | 2222.222222 | ⇐ | Rounding by inspection to one decimal place. **Answer** $R_T = 2222.2\Omega$ |

Method 2. We can employ the formula for two parallel resistors.

| Sum of series branch R2 and R3 |
⇓

$$R_T = \frac{R_1 \times (R_2 + R_3)}{R_1 + (R_2 + R_3)} = \frac{5000 \times (1500 + 2500)}{5000 + (1500 + 2500)} = \frac{20000000}{9000} = 2222.2 \text{ ohms}$$

| MODE NORM 2 |

| AC | 5000 | × | [(--- | 1500 | + | 2500 | ---)] | ÷ |

| [(--- | 5000 | + | 1500 | + | 2500 | ---)] | = | 2222.222222 | ⇐ | **Answer** 2222.2Ω Rounded to one decimal place. |

Internal Resistance

Fig.24 represents a single cell which produces an electromotive force (e.m.f.) E volts, capable of driving a current through the internal resistance r of the cell and an external load resistance.

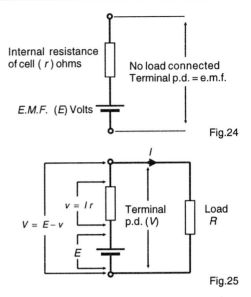

Internal resistance of cell (r) ohms

No load connected
Terminal p.d. = e.m.f.

E.M.F. (E) Volts

Fig.24

With no external load connected there can be no current flow and hence no voltage drop across the internal resistance r, the e.m.f. appearing as the p.d. V volts across the cell terminals.

$v = I r$

$V = E - v$

Terminal p.d. (V)

Load R

When a load R is connected, fig.25, a current will flow in both the load R and the internal resistance r. The current flowing in r

E

Fig.25

causes a voltage drop within the cell. This voltage drop is subtracted from the e.m.f. and the p.d. across the cell terminals is less than the e.m.f. of the cell.

Voltage drop within the cell :- $v = I r$

The terminal p.d. $V = E - v = E - I r$

E.m.f. of cell :- $E = v + V = I r + I R = I(r + R)$

Current supplied to circuit :- $I = \dfrac{E}{R + r}$

Where :-
E = E.M.F. of cell (Volts).
V = Terminal p.d. of cell (Volts).
v = Voltage drop within cell.
r = Internal resistance (Ohms).
R = Load resistance (Ohms).
I = Current in circuit (Amps).

Internal resistance :- $r = \dfrac{(E - V)}{I}$, but $I = \dfrac{V}{R}$ $\therefore$ $r = \dfrac{(E - V)}{V} R$

Points to note.
1. With no load connected the e.m.f. = p.d. across the cell terminals.
2. When a load is connected the p.d. V, will be less then the e.m.f. E.
3. For accurate measurement of e.m.f., the test meter must not consume power from the source. In practice a high resistance voltmeter will usually give a sufficiently accurate e.m.f. reading for most purposes.
4. Internal resistance r increases as the cell becomes exhausted.
5. Testing the voltage of exhausted cells or batteries, when removed from a circuit can give misleading results. Test them under load.
6. The internal resistance r is due to the materials with which the cell is constructed.
7. The value of r will vary from one type of cell to another.

8. Under short-circuit conditions, current flow will be limited by *r*. This current could be very high, particularly in the case of car batteries, nickel cadmium cells and batteries, and other high power cells and batteries, and cause overheating, fire, damage to the battery, and possible vaporisation of the shorting wire.
9. All electrical conductors have resistance, including cells and batteries.
10. When cells are connected in series to form a battery and provide increased voltage, the internal resistances of the individual cells act in series, and the total internal resistance of the battery is the sum of the individual cell resistances.
11. When cells are connected in parallel to form a battery capable of supplying higher current, the internal resistances are in parallel. If the internal resistance of each cell is identical, the internal resistance of the battery equals $\frac{resistance\ of\ one\ cell}{Number\ of\ cells}$

Examples.
44. A battery has an internal resistance of 4Ω, and an e.m.f. of 12V. It is connected to a 20Ω load.
a) What current flows in the circuit?
b) What is the terminal p.d. when the load is connected?

a) The current flowing in the circuit can be found using Ohm's Law.

$$I = \frac{E}{R+r} = \frac{12}{20+4} = \frac{12}{24} = 0.5\ amp$$

MODE NORM 2
AC 12 ÷
[(--- 20 + 4 ---)] = **0.5** ⇐ Answer 0.5A (Current flowing in circuit)

b) Calculate the terminal p.d. when the load is connected. Using Ohm's Law calculate *v* and subtract it from *E*.

The internal voltage drop $v = I \times r = 0.5 \times 4 = 2\ volts$

AC .5 × 4 = **2** ⇐ Answer 2V (Internal voltage drop of cell)

The terminal p.d. $V = E - v = 12 - 2 = 10\ volts$

AC 12 − 2 = **10** ⇐ Answer 10V (Terminal p.d. of cell)

45. Refer to fig.26. 4 dry cells are connected in series to form a battery. The
off load voltage *E* of each cell is 1.5V, and
the internal resistance of each cell is 1Ω.
A load resistance R_L of 6 ohms is connected across the cells.
What is the :-
a) current flowing in the circuit?
b) p.d. across the load?
c) voltage drop within the battery?

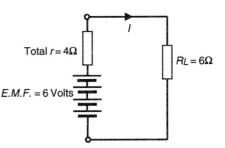

Total $r = 4Ω$

E.M.F. = 6 Volts

$R_L = 6Ω$

Fig.26

a) What is the total current flowing in the circuit?
First gather a few facts :-
For 4, 1.5V cells connected in series the total e.m.f. is 4×1.5 *volts* = 6 *volts*
and the total internal resistance is 4×1 *ohm* = 4 *ohms*

From Ohm's Law, $I = \dfrac{E}{(R_L + r)} = \dfrac{6}{6+4} = \dfrac{6}{10} = 0.6$ *amp*

MODE NORM 2

AC 6 ÷

[(--- 6 + 4 ---)] =   **0.6** ⇐ **Answer** 0.6A (Current flowing in circuit)

b) Calculate the p.d. V_L across the load resistance R_L

From Ohm's Law. $V_L = I \times R_L = 0.6 \times 6 = 3.6$ *volts*

AC .6 × 6 =   **3.6** ⇐ **Answer** 3.6V (p.d. across load)

With the load connected across the battery, the terminal voltage of the battery equals
3.6 volts. The missing volts are lost in the battery.

c) What is the voltage drop within the battery?
Internal voltage drop $v = I \times r = 0.6 \times 4 = 2.4$ *volts*

AC .6 × 4 =   **2.4** ⇐ **Answer** 2.4V (Volt drop within battery)

46. A battery consists of six cells connected in series, each having an e.m.f. of 2 volts. When a 40 ohm load is connected, the terminal voltage of the battery is 8 volts. Calculate :-
a) the total internal resistance of the battery.
b) the internal resistance of each cell.

a) Calculate the total internal resistance of the battery.
First collect a few facts :-
Off load voltage or e.m.f. of the battery, $E = 6 \times 2 = 12$ *volts*
Terminal p.d. under load, $V = 8$ *volts*
Voltage drop within the battery, $v = E - V = 12 - 8 = 4$ *volts*
Applying Ohm's Law calculate the current flowing in R_L, this current will also flow in the internal resistance r.

$$I = \frac{V \text{ across load}}{\text{resistance of load}} = \frac{V_L}{R_L} = \frac{8}{40} = 0.2 \text{ amp or } 200 \text{ milliamps}$$

MODE NORM 2

| AC | 8 | ÷ | 40 | = | **0.2** | ⇐ **Answer 0.2A (Current flowing in circuit)** |

The circuit current of 0.2A produces a p.d. of 4 volts across the internal resistance r of the battery. The value of r can be found by applying Ohm's Law.

$$r = \frac{\text{Volts lost in battery}}{\text{current}} = \frac{E - V}{I} = \frac{v}{I} = \frac{4}{0.2} = 20 \text{ ohms}$$

| AC | 4 | ÷ | .2 | = | **20** | ⇐ **Answer 20Ω (Internal Resistance r)** |

b) Calculate the internal resistance of each cell. Since the total resistance of six cells in series is 20 ohms, the internal resistance of one cell must be one sixth of the total internal resistance of the battery (assuming all cells have equal resistance).

Resistance of one cell $= \dfrac{20}{6} = 3.33$ *ohms* (Rounded to two decimal places.)

| AC | 20 | ÷ | 6 | = | **3.333333333** | ⇐ Round to two decimal places. **Answer** 3.33Ω (Resistance per cell) |

**47. The internal resistance of a cell is 1Ω, and the e.m.f. is 1.5V.
What is the p.d. across the cell terminals when it is delivering a current of 0.25A
to an external load?**

The internal voltage drop $v = I \times r = 0.25 \times 1 = 0.25$ *volt*

MODE NORM 2

| AC | .25 | ☒ | 1 | = | | 0.25 | ⇐ | Answer 0.25V (Internal volt drop) |

The terminal p.d. $V = E - v = 1.5 - 0.25 = 1.25$ *volts*

| AC | 1.5 | ⊟ | .25 | = | | 1.25 | ⇐ | Answer 1.25V (Terminal p.d.) |

**48. The e.m.f. *E*, of a battery is 24 volts. When a load of 1.9 ohms is connected, the
p.d. *V*, across its terminals falls to 22.8 volts.
What is :-
a) the internal resistance *r* of the battery?
b) the current in the load?**

a) Calculate the internal resistance of the battery.

$$r = \frac{(E-V)}{V} \times R_L = \frac{(24 - 22.8)}{22.8} \times 1.9 = \frac{1.2}{22.8} \times 1.9 = 0.1 \ ohm$$

MODE NORM 2

| AC | 24 | ⊟ | 22.8 | = | | 1.2 | ⇐ | E - V = 1.2V (Volts drop in battery) |
| ÷ | 22.8 | ☒ | 1.9 | = | | 0.1 | ⇐ | Answer 0.1Ω (Internal resistance) |

b) Calculate the current supplied by the battery. Use ohm's Law.

$$I = \frac{E}{R+r} = \frac{24}{1.9 + 0.1} = \frac{24}{2} = 12 \ amps$$

| AC | 24 | ÷ |

| [(--- | 1.9 | ⊞ | .1 | ---)] | = | | 12 | ⇐ | Answer 12A (Current flowing in circuit) |

49. A heavy duty power supply unit has an internal resistance r of 0.01 ohm, and an e.m.f. of 50 volts d.c.
What is the the p.d. across its terminals when the load current is 100 amps?

The p.d. $V = E - (I \times r) = 50 - (100 \times 0.01) = 50 - 1 = 49$ *volts*

MODE NORM 2

[AC] 50 [$-$]

[(($\cdots$]100 [$\times$].01 [$\cdots$)]] [$=$]   **49** $\Leftarrow$ **Answer** 49V (Terminal p.d. of p.s.u.)

---

50. A power supply unit has an e.m.f. of 13.8 volts. When connected to a 5 ohm load it has a terminal voltage (or p.d.) of 10 volts.
What is the internal resistance r?

$$r = \frac{(E-V)}{V} \times R_L = \frac{(13.8-10)}{10} \times 5 = \frac{3.8}{10} \times 5 = 1.9 \text{ ohms}$$

MODE NORM 2

[AC] 13.8 [$-$] 10 [$=$]   **3.8** $\Leftarrow$ E - V = 3.8V (Volts drop in battery)

[$\div$] 10 [$\times$] 5 [$=$]   **1.9** $\Leftarrow$ **Answer** 1.9Ω (Internal resistance)

---

51. A power supply unit has an e.m.f. of 100 volts, and supplies a current of 2.5 amps. The internal resistance of the unit is 0.1 ohm. Calculate the p.d. across the load, and the load resistance R_L.

The p.d. $V = E - (I \times r) = 100 - (2.5 \times 0.1) = 100 - 0.25 = 99.75$ *volts*

MODE NORM 2

[AC] 100 [$-$]

[(($\cdots$] 2.5 [$\times$].1 [$\cdots$)]] [$=$]   **99.75** $\Leftarrow$ **Answer** 99.75V (Terminal p.d.)

The load resistance $R_L = \dfrac{V_L}{I} = \dfrac{99.75}{2.5} = 39.9$ *ohms*

MODE NORM 2

[AC] 99.75 [$\div$] 2.5 [$=$]   **39.9** $\Leftarrow$ **Answer** 39.9Ω (Load resistance)

Power

Power (P) is the rate of using or expending energy, and is measured in watts (W). In a resistor or heating element electrical energy is converted into heat. It is normally the physical size and construction that determines the power rating, i.e. how many watts it will dissipate - in heat - into the surrounding atmosphere. In a lamp, electrical energy is converted into light. An electric motor converts electrical energy into mechanical rotation. The power amplifier stage of a radio transmitter converts DC input power into RF output power.

In power engineering the common units are the *kilowatt, kW* (10^3W) and the *Megawatt MW* (10^6W). In communication engineering the power levels are commonly *milliwatts mW* (10^{-3}W) and *microwatts* μW (10^{-6}W). However, in radio engineering power levels can vary from 100kW or more for powerful t.v. and radio transmitters, down to very low power - maybe in the order of *picowatts pW* (10^{-12}W) in the antenna circuit of a sensitive receiver.

Electrical power in the d.c. circuit is given by the formula :-

1) $W = V I$ or $V \times I$

Now from Ohm's Law $I = \dfrac{V}{R}$, by substituting $\dfrac{V}{R}$ in 1) for the current I :-

2) $W = V \times \dfrac{V}{R} = \dfrac{V \times V}{R} = \dfrac{V^2}{R}$ (Note. $V \times V = V^2$)

And since $V = I \times R$, by similar substitution in 1) above we get :-

3) $W = I \times R \times I = I^2 \times R$ or $I^2 R$

The above three power formulae and their transpositions are :-

$W = VI$ $\Rightarrow$ $V = \dfrac{W}{I}$ $\Rightarrow$ $I = \dfrac{W}{V}$

$W = \dfrac{V^2}{R}$ $\Rightarrow$ $V = \sqrt{WR}$ $\Rightarrow$ $R = \dfrac{V^2}{W}$

$W = I^2 R$ $\Rightarrow$ $I = \sqrt{\dfrac{W}{R}}$ $\Rightarrow$ $R = \dfrac{W}{I^2}$

Note. When formulae are written, a *P is often used in place of W*, and *E is often used in place of V*. The above formulae may also be applied to alternating current (a.c.) problems when the load is resistive.

Examples.

52. Fig.27 shows a 2 ohm load connected across a 10 volt supply.
Calculate the power dissipated in the load. Use formulas 1, 2 and 3 on the previous page, this will verify the correct answer.

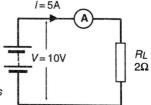

Fig.27

Using formula 1) $W = V \times I = 10 \times 5 = 50\ watts$

| MODE NORM 2 |

| AC | 10 | × | 5 | = | 50 | ⇐ **Answer** 50W (Power dissipated in load) |

Using formula 2) $W = \dfrac{V^2}{R} = \dfrac{10^2}{2} = \dfrac{100}{2} = 50\ watts$

| AC | 10 | x² | ÷ | 2 | = | 50 | ⇐ **Answer** 50W (Power dissipated in load) |

Using formula 3) $W = I^2 R = 5^2 \times 2 = 25 \times 2 = 50\ watts$

| AC | 5 | x² | × | 2 | = | 50 | ⇐ **Answer** 50W (Power dissipated in load) |

---

53. The p.d. across a 25Ω resistive load is 100 volts, and the current flowing is 4 amps. What is the power dissipated in the load?

Any of the three previous formulae could be used to solve this example.

I will use the formula $W = V \times I = 100 \times 4 = 400\ watts$

| MODE NORM 2 |

| AC | 100 | × | 4 | = | 400 | ⇐ **Answer** 400W (Power dissipated in load) |

As a check on the result a different formula can be used :-

$$W = \frac{V^2}{R} = \frac{100^2}{25} = \frac{10000}{25} = 400\ watts$$

| AC | 100 | x² | ÷ | 25 | = | 400 | ⇐ **Answer** 400W (Power dissipated in load) |

54. The current flowing in a 20Ω resistive load is 8A.
Calculate the power in the load.

Use the formula $W = I^2 R = 8^2 \times 20 = 64 \times 20 = 1280$ *watts*

MODE NORM 2

| AC | 8 | χ^2 | $\times$ | 20 | = | | 1280 | ⟸ | **Answer** 1280W (Power dissipated in load) |

---

55. A wire wound 1000Ω resistor is connected across a 240V supply.
What is the power dissipated?

$$W = \frac{V^2}{R} = \frac{240^2}{1000} = \frac{57600}{1000} = 57.6 \ watts$$

MODE NORM 2

| AC | 240 | χ^2 | $\div$ | 1000 | = | | 57.6 | ⟸ | **Answer** 57.6W (Power dissipated in load) |

---

56. A current of 100mA (100×10^{-3}A) flows in a 2.2kΩ (2.2×10^3Ω) resistor.
What power will the resistor dissipate?

Use the formula $W = I^2 R = (100 \times 10^{-3})^2 \times (2.2 \times 10^3) = 22$ *watts*

MODE NORM 2

| AC | 100 | EXP | 3 | +/- | χ^2 |
| $\times$ | 2.2 | EXP | 3 | = | | 22 | ⟸ | **Answer** 22W (power dissipation in R) |

---

57. The power rating of a 1000Ω resistor is 100W.
What is the maximum current that can flow without exceeding its power rating?

$$I = \sqrt{\frac{W}{R}} = \sqrt{\frac{100}{1000}} = 0.316 \ amp$$

MODE NORM 2

| AC | 100 | $\div$ | $\sqrt{\ }$ | 1000 | = | | 0.316227766 | ⟸ | **Answer** 0.316A (Max current in R) |

---

2 - 40

58. The power dissipated in a resistor is 0.5W, and the current flowing in it is 0.125A.
What is the p.d. across its terminals?

$$V = \frac{W}{I} = \frac{0.5}{0.125} = 4 \; volts$$

MODE NORM 2

AC .5 ÷ .125 = | 4 ⇐ Answer 4V (P.d. across terminals)

---

59. A resistor is dissipating 5W. The p.d. across its terminals is 200V.
What is the current flowing?

$$I = \frac{W}{V} = \frac{5}{200} = 0.025 \; amp$$

MODE NORM 2

AC 5 ÷ 200 = | 0.025 ⇐ Answer 0.025A (Current in R)

---

60. A car has a 12 volt electrical system. The brake light bulbs are rated at 18W. When the brakes are applied calculate :-
a) the current in each bulb.
b) the filament resistance of each bulb when operating normally.

a) The current in each bulb :-

$$I = \frac{W}{V} = \frac{18}{12} = 1.5 \; amps$$

MODE NORM 2

AC 18 ÷ 12 = | 1.5 ⇐ Answer 1.5A (Current in bulb)

b) The filament resistance :-

$$R = \frac{V^2}{W} = \frac{12^2}{18} = \frac{144}{18} = 8 \; ohms$$

AC 12 χ^2 ÷ 18 = | 8 ⇐ Answer 8Ω (Filament resistance)

2-41

61. A generator giving an output of 10kW (10×10^3W) is supplying a current of 100A to a resistive load.

What is the :-

a) load resistance R_L?

b) voltage across the load?

a) $R_L = \dfrac{W}{I^2} = \dfrac{10 \times 10^3}{100^2} = \dfrac{10000}{10000} = 1 \; ohm$

MODE NORM 2

AC 10 EXP 3 ÷

100 χ^2 = [1] ⇐ Answer 1Ω (Load resistance RL)

b) Supply voltage across load.

$V = \dfrac{W}{I} = \dfrac{10 \times 10^3}{100} = 100 \; volts$

AC 10 EXP 3 ÷

100 = [100] ⇐ Answer 100V (Voltage across load)

62. A resistive load dissipates 1800W when connected to a 240V supply.

a) What current will the load draw from the supply?

b) What is the resistance of the load?

a) The supply current :-

$I = \dfrac{W}{V} = \dfrac{1800}{240} = 7.5 \; amps$

MODE NORM 2

AC 1800 ÷ 240 = [7.5] ⇐ Answer 7.5A (Load current)

b) The resistance of the load :-

$R = \dfrac{V^2}{W} = \dfrac{240^2}{1800} = \dfrac{57600}{1800} = 32 \; ohms$

AC 240 χ^2 ÷ 1800 = [32] ⇐ Answer 32Ω (Load resistance)

63. A load dissipates 3kW (3000W) when connected to a 240V supply. Calculate the resistance of the load.

The resistance of the load:-

$$R = \frac{V^2}{W} = \frac{240^2}{3000} = \frac{57600}{3000} = 19.2 \ ohms$$

MODE NORM 2

AC 240 $\boxed{\chi^2}$ $\boxed{\div}$ 3000 $\boxed{=}$ | 19.2 ⇐ Answer 19.2Ω (Load resistance) |

---

64. A 500V d.c. generator is delivering a current of 200A to a resistive load. Calculate the power in the load?

Use formula $W = V \times I = 500 \times 200 = 100{,}000 \ watts \ or \ 100 \ kilowatts$

MODE NORM 2

AC 500 $\boxed{\times}$ 200 $\boxed{=}$ | 100000 ⇐ Answer 100000W (Power in load 100kW) |

---

65. The d.c. input power to the power amplifier (p.a.) stage of a transmitter is calculated from measurements of the current supplied to the p.a. and the p.a. supply voltage.
Calculate the d.c. input power to a p.a. stage when the current is 1.5A and the applied voltage is 400V.

Use formula $W = V \times I = 400 \times 1.5 = 600 \ watts$

MODE NORM 2

AC 400 $\boxed{\times}$ 1.5 $\boxed{=}$ | 600 ⇐ Answer 600W (D.c. input power to p.a.) |

---

66. The power dissipated by a 50Ω load is 800W. Calculate the current in the load?

$$I = \sqrt{\frac{W}{R}} = \sqrt{\frac{800}{50}} = 4 \ amps$$

MODE NORM 2

AC $\boxed{\sqrt{\ }}$ [(--- 800 $\boxed{\div}$ 50 ---)] $\boxed{=}$ | 4 ⇐ Answer 4A (Current in load) |

67. What power (approximately) is dissipated in a 50Ω load when the p.d. developed across it is 70.7V?

$$W = \frac{V^2}{R} = \frac{70.7^2}{50} = \frac{4998.49}{50} = 99.96 \text{ watts } \textit{or by rounding up}\text{:- } 100 \text{ watts}$$

MODE NORM 2

| AC | 70.7 | χ^2 | ÷ | 50 | = | | 99.9698 | ⇐ | **Answer** 100W (Rounded answer) |

---

68. The current flowing in a 100Ω load is 2.8A. Calculate the power dissipated by the load.

$$W = I^2 R = 2.8^2 \times 100 = 784 \text{ watts}$$

MODE NORM 2

| AC | 2.8 | χ^2 | × | 100 | = | | 784 | ⇐ | **Answer** 784W (Power in load) |

---

69. A p.d. of 200mV (200×10^{-3}V) is developed across a 50Ω resistor.
a) Calculate the power dissipated by the resistor.
b) Calculate the current in the load.

a) Power in the load :-

$$W = \frac{V^2}{R} = \frac{(200 \times 10^{-3})^2}{50} = \frac{0.04}{50} = 800 \times 10^{-6} \text{ watts } \textit{or } 800 \text{ microwatts}$$

MODE NORM 2

AC 200 EXP 3 +/− χ^2

÷ 50 =   **0.0008** ⇐ Read as 8 x 10⁻⁴ Convert this result to **ENG**ineering notation. 10⁻⁶ = micro

ENG   **800x10⁻⁰⁶** ⇐ **Answer** 800μW (Power in resistor)

b) Current in the load :-

$$I = \sqrt{\frac{W}{R}} = \sqrt{\frac{800 \times 10^{-6}}{50}} = 4 \times 10^{-3} \text{ amps } \textit{or } 4 \text{ milliamps}$$

AC √ [(··· 800 EXP 6 +/− ÷ 50 ···)]   **0.00016** ⇐ Result of division within brackets. Root pending.

=   **0.004** ⇐ Read as 4 x 10⁻³ 10⁻³ = milli

ENG   **4x10⁻⁰³** ⇐ **Answer** 4mA (Load current)

70. Referring to fig.28. Calculate :-
a) the power in each of the 50Ω resistors.
b) the total power in the circuit?

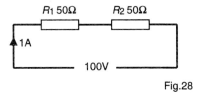

Fig.28

a) Calculate the power in the 50Ω resistors. Since R_1 and R_2 are equal and the same current flows in each, the power in R_1 will be the same as for R_2.

$$\therefore \ W = I^2 R = 1^2 \times 50 = 50 \ watts$$

MODE NORM 2

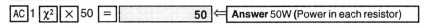

b) The total power P_T is the sum of the individual powers.

$$W_T = W_{R_1} + W_{R_2} = 50 + 50 = 100 \ watts$$

---

71. From fig.29 calculate the :-
a) power in R_1.
b) power in R_2.
c) total power in the circuit.

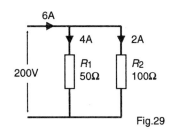

Fig.29

a) Calculate the power in R_1.

$$W = I^2 R_1 = 4^2 \times 50 = 16 \times 50 = 800 \ watts$$

MODE NORM 2

AC 4 x^2 ✕ 50 =   **800** ⇐ **Answer** 800W (Power in R1)

b) Calculate the power in R_2.

$$W = I^2 R_2 = 2^2 \times 100 = 4 \times 100 = 400 \ watts$$

AC 2 x^2 ✕ 100 =   **400** ⇐ **Answer** 400W (Power in R2)

c) The total power P_T is the sum of the individual powers.

$$W_T = W_{R_1} + W_{R_2} = 800 + 400 = 1200 \ watts$$

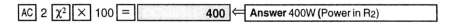

The D.C. Moving Coil Meter

The moving coil meter movement will only measure direct current. The analogue multimeter consists of a basic moving coil meter movement, with additional circuitry added to extend its range and make it capable of measuring alternating voltage and current.

Resistors called *multipliers* are connected in series with the basic movement to extend the d.c. voltage range, and low value resistors called *shunts* are connected in parallel with the movement to extend the d.c. current ranges. A.c. ranges require an instrument rectifier, and when a.c. current is to be measured, a current transformer.

Typical moving coil instruments require a current of between 20μA and 10mA for *full scale deflection* (f.s.d.), and have resistances in the order of 2000Ω to 5Ω. An instrument having an f.s.d. of 20μA is more sensitive, but less robust than the 10mA f.s.d. instrument.
The f.s.d. and meter resistance are usually written on the instrument scale.

The moving coil d.c. voltmeter.

The sensitivity of a voltmeter is expressed in *'ohms per volt'* (Ω/V).
E.g. A 1000Ω/V meter - when switched to the 10 volt range - has a resistance of $10 \times 1000Ω = 10,000Ω$. Knowledge of meter resistance is essential in order to calculate the loading effect on the circuit being measured.

The Ω/V rating for a d.c. voltmeter is given by the formula :-

$$\Omega/V = \frac{1 \ volt}{current \ for \ f.s.d.}$$

Where :-
R_M = Resistance of multiplier.
R_m = Resistance of meter movement.
I_m = Meter current for f.s.d.
V_m = P.d. across the meter for f.s.d.
V = The required voltage for f.s.d.

The multiplier resistance :-

$$R_M = \frac{V}{I_m} - R_m$$

In practice, where the movement resistance R_m is small, and the multiplier resistance R_M is large, it may be possible to neglect R_m and simplify the formula to :-

$$R_M = \frac{V}{I_m}$$

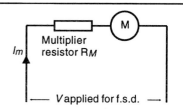

Multiplier
I_m resistor R_M

— V applied for f.s.d. —

Fig.30 shows a basic moving coil meter movement M converted to a d.c. voltmeter. The multiplier resistance R_M is chosen to drop the difference in potential between the maximum voltage to be measured and the small p.d. across the meter movement for f.s.d.

The moving coil d.c. ammeter.

Fig.31 shows a basic meter movement employing a shunt resistance R_s to provide a higher current range.

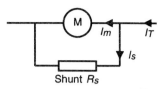

The shunt resistance R_s diverts a known proportion of the external circuit current I_T. The remainder flows in the meter coil.

Shunt R_s

Fig.31

E.g. See fig.32. A meter movement, with an f.s.d. of 1mA, is required to have a 10mA range. In this case, of the 10mA flowing in the external circuit, 1mA will flow in the meter, and 9mA will flow in the shunt.

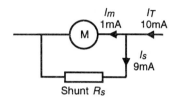

Shunt R_s

The p.d. across the shunt, V_s, is the same as the p.d. V_m across the meter, since both are in parallel :-

$$\therefore \quad V_m = V_s = I_m \times R_m$$

Fig.32 shows a 1mA meter movement shunted to make the instrument indicate 10mA f.s.d.

The current in the shunt :-

$$I_s = I_T - I_m$$

Resistance of shunt, from Ohm's Law :-

$$R_s = \frac{V_m}{I_s} = \frac{I_m \times R_m}{I_T - I_m}$$

Where :-
R_s = Resistance of the shunt.
R_m = Resistance of meter movement.
I_m = Meter current for f.s.d.
I_T = The required range current.
I_s = Current in shunt for f.s.d.
V_m = P.d. across the meter for f.s.d.
V_s = P.d. across the shunt for f.s.d.

Points to note.
1. Ohm's Law may be applied in all calculations.
2. Voltmeters should be connected across the circuit they are measuring.
3. The lower the current for f.s.d. the higher the Ω/V rating.
4. The higher the Ω/V rating, the less will be the loading on the circuit.
5. Meter resistance can affect the circuit under test and cause false readings.
6. A good moving coil voltmeter may have a sensitivity of 20,000 - 50,000Ω/V.
7. When calculating a voltmeter multiplier resistance, the meter resistance can be ignored if it is small compared with the multiplier resistance.
8. Ammeters should have very low resistance to minimise voltage drop.
9. Ammeters should be connected in series with the circuit whose current they are measuring.
10. Damage may result if an ammeter is connected directly across a circuit.
11. The basic meter movement will only measure direct currents.

Examples.

72. Calculate the sensitivity, in Ω/V, of a moving coil meter movement having an f.s.d. of 1mA (1×10^{-3}A).

$$\Omega/V = \frac{1 \ volt}{current \ for \ f.s.d.} = \frac{1}{1 \times 10^{-3}} = \frac{1 \times 10^3}{1} = 1 \times 10^3 = 1000\Omega/V$$

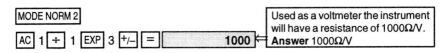

| MODE NORM 2 | | Used as a voltmeter the instrument will have a resistance of $1000\Omega/V$. |
| AC 1 ÷ 1 EXP 3 +/– = ⟵ 1000 | ⟵ | Answer $1000\Omega/V$ |

---

73. What is the sensitivity, in Ω/V, of a basic moving coil meter movement having an f.s.d. of 20µA (20×10^{-6}A)?

$$\Omega/V = \frac{1 \ volt}{current \ for \ f.s.d.} = \frac{1}{20 \times 10^{-6}} = \frac{1 \times 10^6}{20} = 50 \times 10^3 = 50,000\Omega/V$$

| MODE NORM 2 | | Used as a voltmeter the instrument will have a resistance of $50,000\Omega/V$. |
| AC 1 ÷ 20 EXP 6 +/– = ⟵ 50000 | ⟵ | Answer $50,000\Omega/V$ |

---

74. A moving coil meter movement has a resistance of 10Ω and an f.s.d. of 1mA (1×10^{-3}A). It is to be converted to a voltmeter with an f.s.d. of 10V. A series resistor called a multiplier is fitted to limit the meter current to 1mA when 10V is applied. Calculate :-
a) the resistance R_M of the multiplier.
b) the p.d. developed across the multiplier.

a) The multiplier resistance :-

$$R_M = \frac{V}{I_m} - R_m = \frac{10}{1 \times 10^{-3}} - 10 = 10 \times 10^3 - 10 = 9,990 \ ohms$$

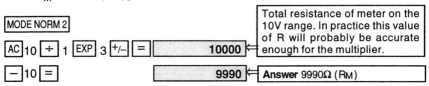

		Total resistance of meter on the 10V range. In practice this value of R will probably be accurate enough for the multiplier.
MODE NORM 2		
AC 10 ÷ 1 EXP 3 +/– = ⟵ 10000	⟵	
– 10 = ⟵ 9990	⟵	Answer 9990Ω (R_M)

b) P.d. across the multiplier = $I_m \times R_M = 1 \times 10^{-3} \times 9,990 = 9.99V$

| AC 1 EXP 3 +/– × 9990 = ⟵ 9.99 | ⟵ | Answer 9.99V (P.d. across R_M) |

75. You have just built a 13.8V power supply unit and require a meter on the front panel having an f.s.d. of 15V. In your junk box is a moving coil meter movement having a resistance of 500Ω and a full scale deflection of 100μA (100×10^{-6}A). What value of resistance R_M should you fit in series with the meter?

The multiplier resistance :-

$$R_M = \frac{V}{I_m} - R_m = \frac{15}{100 \times 10^{-6}} - 500 = 150 \times 10^3 - 500 = 149,500 \ ohms$$

MODE NORM 2	Total resistance of meter on the 15V range. In practice this value of R will probably be accurate
AC 15 ÷ 100 EXP 6 +/– = **150000**	⇐ enough for the multiplier.
– 500 = **149500**	⇐ **Answer** 149,500Ω (R_M)
ENG **149.5**ₓ₁₀**03**	⇐ Engineering Notation. (10^3 = kilo) **Answer** 149.5kΩ (R_M)

76. A meter movement requires 200μA (200×10^{-6}A) for f.s.d. and has a resistance of 1000Ω. What will be the value of the multiplier resistance R_M, if it is to be used as a voltmeter having a full scale deflection of 500V d.c?

$$R_M = \frac{V}{I_m} - R_m = \frac{500}{200 \times 10^{-6}} - 1000 = 2.5 \times 10^6 - 1000 = 2.499 \ Megohms$$

MODE NORM 2	Total resistance of meter on the 500V range. In practice this value of R will probably be
AC 500 ÷ 200 EXP 6 +/– = **2500000**	⇐ accurate enough for the multi-
– 1000 = **2499000**	⇐ **Answer** 2,499,000Ω (R_M)
ENG **2.499**ₓ₁₀**06**	⇐ **Answer** 2.499MΩ (R_M) (10^6=Mega)

77. A d.c. voltmeter has a sensitivity of 20,000Ω/V. What is its resistance, R_v, when switched to the 250V range?

$$R_v = Range \ f.s.d. \times ohms/volt = 250 \times 20,000 = 5,000,000Ω = 5 \ Megohms$$

MODE NORM 2	Total resistance of meter R_v on the 250V range. This is the resistance that loads the circuit under test.
AC 250 × 20000 = **5000000**	⇐ **Answer** 5MΩ
ENG **5**ₓ₁₀**06**	⇐ **Answer** 5MΩ (R_M) (10^6=Mega)

78. A voltmeter V, with a sensitivity of 1000Ω/V is switched to its 10V range and connected across points A-B fig.33.
What voltage will the meter indicate?

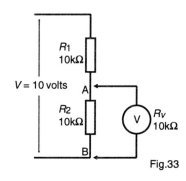

The voltmeter resistance R_v, on the 10V range is 10 × 1000Ω = 10,000Ω (10kΩ).
Without the meter connected the p.d. across each resistor will be half of the supply voltage, 5V, due to the fact that both resistors are of equal value and have the same current in them.

Fig.33

However, the parallel combination of R_v and R_2, which we will call R_{eff} (the effective resistance), will result in a resistance of 5000Ω in series with R_1, see fig.34.
To find R_{eff} use the formula :-

$$R_{eff} = \frac{R_v \times R_2}{R_v + R_2} = \frac{10,000 \times 10,000}{10,000 + 10,000} = 5,000 \ ohms$$

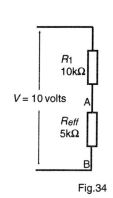

MODE NORM 2

| AC | 10000 | × | 10000 | ÷ | 100000000 |

| [(--- | 10000 | + | 10000 | ---)] | 20000 |

| = | | | | | 5000 |

Effective resistance of R_v and R_1
Answer 5000Ω (5kΩ)

Fig.34

Now use the voltage division formula to calculate the p.d. across the meter and R_2, i.e. the actual p.d. measured between points A - B:-

$$V_{A-B} = \frac{R_{eff}}{R_{eff} + R_1} \times V = \frac{5,000}{5,000 + 10,000} \times 10 = 3.33 \ Volts$$

Using the calculator :-

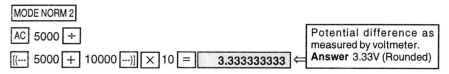

MODE NORM 2

AC 5000 ÷

[(--- 5000 + 10000 ---)] × 10 = 3.333333333

Potential difference as measured by voltmeter.
Answer 3.33V (Rounded)

The resistance of a voltmeter connected in a circuit may result in false readings.

79. The circuit of fig.35 has been designed to produce a p.d. across R_1 of 75V. What p.d. will be measured across R_1 when a moving coil multimeter having a resistance R_v of 40kΩ (40,000Ω) is connected across it?

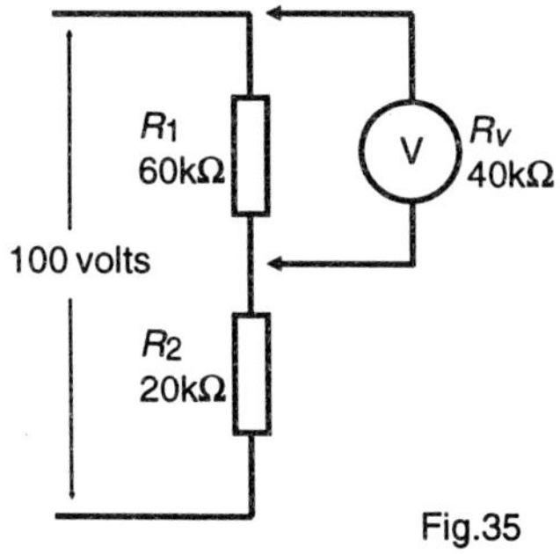

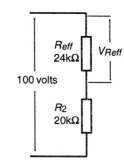

We will solve this problem by the same method as the previous question.

Fig.35

First calculate the effective resistance R_{eff} of R_v and R_1 in parallel.

$$R_{eff} = \frac{R_v \times R_1}{R_v + R_1} = \frac{40,000 \times 60,000}{40,000 + 60,000} = 24,000 \ ohms$$

MODE NORM 2

| AC | 40000 | × | 60000 | ÷ | | 2400000000 |

| [(--- | 40000 | + | 60000 | ---)] | | 100000 |

| = | | | | | | 24000 |

⇑
Effective resistance of R_v and R_1
Answer 24,000Ω (24kΩ)

Fig.36. Equivalent circuit for fig.35. Showing effect of meter resistance R_v in parallel with R_1

Now use the voltage division formula to calculate the p.d. across the effective resistance, R_{eff}, 24,000Ω of the meter and R_1 in parallel.

$$V_{Reff} = \frac{R_{eff}}{R_{eff} + R_1} \times V = \frac{24,000}{24,000 + 20,000} \times 100 = 54.55 \ Volts$$

⇑
Voltage measured across R_1
when meter is connected.

P.d. measured by the meter. This is lower than the design p.d. of 75V due to the loading effect of meter.
Answer 54.55V (Rounded)

MODE NORM 2

| AC | 24000 | ÷ |

| [(--- | 24000 | + | 20000 | ---)] | × | 100 | = | | 54.54545455 |

80. A basic moving coil meter movement has an f.s.d. of 1mA and a resistance of 10Ω. It is to be shunted by a resistor to give it a d.c. range of 10mA f.s.d. What is the resistance of the shunt?

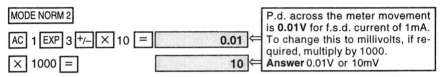

In this example 1mA will flow in the meter and 9mA will be bypassed by the shunt. See fig.37. The voltage across the meter coil for f.s.d. is given by :-

$$V_m = I_m \times R_m = 1 \times 10^{-3} \times 10 = 0.01 \text{ volts}$$

Fig.37

MODE NORM 2				P.d. across the meter movement is **0.01V** for f.s.d. current of 1mA.
AC 1 EXP 3 +/– × 10 =			0.01	To change this to millivolts, if required, multiply by 1000.
× 1000 =			10	**Answer** 0.01V or 10mV

This voltage, 0.01V, is also the voltage across the shunt resistor with 9mA flowing in it. ($V_m = V_s$) Therefore using Ohm's Law :-

$$R_s = \frac{V_m}{I_s} = \frac{0.01}{9 \times 10^{-3}} = \frac{10}{9} = 1.111 \text{ ohms}$$

AC .01 ÷ 9 EXP 3 +/– =	1.111111111	Resistance of shunt. Rounded to 3 decimal places. **Answer** 1.111Ω

---

81. The instrument in Q80 above is to be given a 100mA range. Calculate the resistance R_s of the shunt.

In the previous example we directly applied Ohm's Law, now we will use a formula developed from it especially for calculating the shunt resistance.
The current in the meter I_m = 1mA, and the shunt current I_s = 99mA.
The total current to be measured at f.s.d. I_T = 100mA, and R_m = 10Ω.

$$R_s = \frac{V_m}{I_s} = \frac{I_m \times R_m}{I_T - I_m} = \frac{1 \times 10^{-3} \times 10}{100 \times 10^{-3} - 1 \times 10^{-3}} = \frac{0.01}{99 \times 10^{-3}} = 0.101 \text{ ohm}$$

MODE NORM 2	Resistance of shunt. Rounded to 3 decimal places. **Answer** 0.101Ω
AC 1 EXP 3 +/– × 10 ÷	
[(--- 100 EXP 3 +/– — 1 EXP 3 +/– ---)] =	0.101010101

82. The basic moving coil meter move-ment M, shown in fig.38 indicates f.s.d. when passing 500μA (500 × 10⁻⁶A).
a) What value of shunt resistance R_s is required to extend the range of the instrument to read 1A?
b) What is the power dissipated in the shunt resistor?

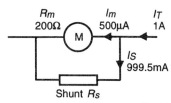

Fig.38

a) Of the total current of 1A (1000mA) flowing in the external circuit, 500μA (0.5 mA) flows in the meter, and 999.5mA flows in the shunt resistor.

$$R_s = \frac{V_m}{I_s} = \frac{I_m \times R_m}{I_T - I_m} = \frac{500 \times 10^{-6} \times 200}{1 - 500 \times 10^{-6}} = \frac{0.1}{0.9995} = 0.10005 \ ohms$$

MODE NORM 2

AC 500 EXP 6 +/− × 200 ÷

[(--- 1 − 500 EXP 6 +/− ---)] =   **0.100050025** ⇐ Shunt resistance
Answer 0.10005Ω

Since I_m (0.5mA) is small compared with I_T (1000mA), the error to be encountered if I_m is ignored in the bottom line of the above equation will be negligible for most practical purposes. Re-working the calculation to ignore I_m in the bottom line :-

$$R_s = \frac{V_m}{I_s} = \frac{I_m \times R_m}{I_T} = \frac{500 \times 10^{-6} \times 200}{1} = \frac{0.1}{1} = 0.1 \ ohms$$

AC 500 EXP 6 +/− ×

200 ÷ 1 =   **0.1** ⇐ Shunt resistance (Approximation)
Answer 0.1Ω

b) The power dissipated by the shunt resistor.
Since I_s = 999.5mA we can round it up to 1000mA (1A) to make life easier.

$$W = I_s^2 R_s = 1^2 \times 0.1 = 0.1 \ watt$$

AC 1 χ² × .1 =   **0.1** ⇐ (Power dissipated by shunt)
Answer 0.1W

83. The voltmeter shown in fig.39 is constructed with a basic moving coil instrument having an f.s.d. of 50μA and a resistance R_m of 1000Ω. Calculate the value of the range multiplying resistors R_1, R_2 and R_3 to provide 1, 3 and 10 volt ranges.

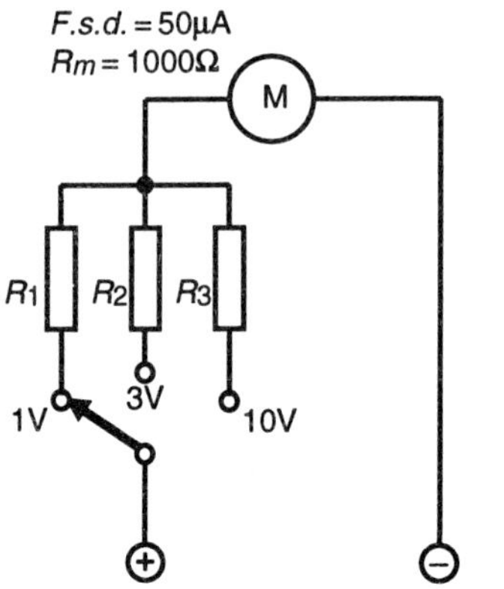

$F.s.d. = 50\mu A$
$R_m = 1000\Omega$

Use the formula :- $R_M = \dfrac{V}{I_m} - R_m$

Where:-
V = range f.s.d.
R_M = multiplier resistance.
I_m = f.s.d. current of meter movement.
R_m = meter resistance.

Fig.39

a) For the 1 volt range.

$$R_M = \frac{V}{I_m} - R_m = \frac{1}{50 \times 10^{-6}} - 1000 = 20 \times 10^3 - 1000 = 19,000 \; ohms$$

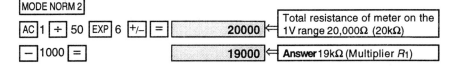

MODE NORM 2

[AC] 1 [÷] 50 [EXP] 6 [+/−] [=]   20000 ⇐ Total resistance of meter on the 1V range 20,000Ω (20kΩ)

[−] 1000 [=]   19000 ⇐ **Answer** 19kΩ (Multiplier R_1)

b) For the 3 volt range.

$$R_M = \frac{V}{I_m} - R_m = \frac{3}{50 \times 10^{-6}} - 1000 = 60 \times 10^3 - 1000 = 59,000 \, ohms$$

[AC] 3 [÷] 50 [EXP] 6 [+/−] [=]   60000 ⇐ Total resistance of meter on the 3V range 60,000Ω (60kΩ)

[−] 1000 [=]   59000 ⇐ **Answer** 59kΩ (Multiplier R_2)

c) For the 10 volt range.

$$R_M = \frac{V}{I_m} - R_m = \frac{10}{50 \times 10^{-6}} - 1000 = 200 \times 10^3 - 1000 = 199,000 \; ohms$$

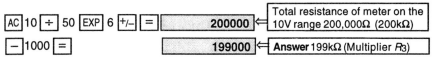

[AC] 10 [÷] 50 [EXP] 6 [+/−] [=]   200000 ⇐ Total resistance of meter on the 10V range 200,000Ω (200kΩ)

[−] 1000 [=]   199000 ⇐ **Answer** 199kΩ (Multiplier R_3)

Alternating Currents

Chapter 3

Contents

In this section you will:-
a)   calculate the frequency and period of a sinusoidal waveform.
b)   calculate peak, and peak-to-peak values of a waveform.
c)   convert between the R.M.S. and maximum value of a sinusoidal waveform.
d)   convert between the average and maximum value for a sinusoidal waveform.
e)   calculate the instantaneous values of a sinusoidal waveform.
f)   convert between frequency and wavelength.

Frequency

The frequency; measured in hertz (*Hz*), of a waveform, is the number of complete cycles of the waveform occurring in one second.

Period

The period of a waveform is the time measured in seconds to complete one cycle of the waveform.

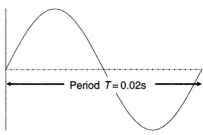

Fig.1. One complete cycle of sinusoidal waveform having a period of 0.02 seconds and a frequency of 50Hz.

It therefore follows, that if 50 complete cycles of a sinusoidal waveform occur in 1 second, then one cycle of the waveform must occur in $\frac{1}{50}$ of a second (0.02s).

Period and frequency are related by the formulae :-

$$T = \frac{1}{f}$$

$$f = \frac{1}{T}$$

Where:-
T = Periodic time of waveform in seconds.
f = Frequency of waveform in hertz.

Examples.

1. The sinewave shown in fig.2 has a frequency of 100Hz.
Calculate its periodic time T.

Use the formula $T = \frac{1}{f}$

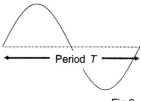

Period T

Fig.2

$$T = \frac{1}{f} = \frac{1}{100} = 0.01s = 10ms$$

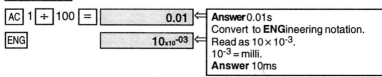

MODE NORM 2	
AC 1 ÷ 100 = 0.01	**Answer** 0.01s Convert to **ENG**ineering notation.
ENG $10_{x10}{}^{-03}$	Read as 10×10^{-3}. 10^{-3} = milli. **Answer** 10ms

2. The frequency of a waveform is 500kHz (500 $\times 10^3$Hz). What is the period?

$$T = \frac{1}{f} = \frac{1}{500 \times 10^3} = 2 \times 10^{-6}\, s = 2\ microseconds$$

Using the calculator for these examples I can either; carry on as in the previous example, or simply press the reciprocal key when the frequency has been entered.

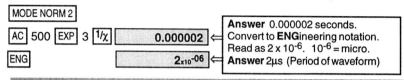

MODE NORM 2	
AC 500 EXP 3 $^{1}\!/\!\chi$	0.000002	Answer 0.000002 seconds. Convert to **ENG**ineering notation. Read as 2×10^{-6}. 10^{-6} = micro.
ENG	$2_{x10}{-06}$	Answer 2µs (Period of waveform)

3. A sinewave has a frequency of 400kHz (400 $\times 10^3$Hz). What is the period of the waveform?

$$T = \frac{1}{f} = \frac{1}{400 \times 10^3} = 2.5 \times 10^{-6}\, s = 2.5µs$$

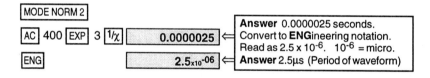

MODE NORM 2	
AC 400 EXP 3 $^{1}\!/\!\chi$	0.0000025	Answer 0.0000025 seconds. Convert to **ENG**ineering notation. Read as 2.5×10^{-6}. 10^{-6} = micro.
ENG	$2.5_{x10}{-06}$	Answer 2.5µs (Period of waveform)

4. An alternating current has a frequency of 160kHz (160 $\times 10^3$Hz). What is the periodic time of the waveform?

$$T = \frac{1}{f} = \frac{1}{160 \times 10^3} = 6.25 \times 10^{-6}\, s = 6.25µs$$

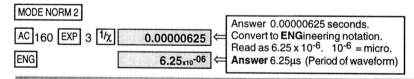

MODE NORM 2	
AC 160 EXP 3 $^{1}\!/\!\chi$	0.00000625	Answer 0.00000625 seconds. Convert to **ENG**ineering notation. Read as 6.25×10^{-6}. 10^{-6} = micro.
ENG	$6.25_{x10}{-06}$	Answer 6.25µs (Period of waveform)

5. The frequency of a sinusoidal waveform is 10Hz. What is the period of the waveform?

$$T = \frac{1}{f} = \frac{1}{10} = 0.1s$$

| MODE NORM 2 | |
| AC 10 $^{1}\!/\!\chi$ | 0.1 | **Answer** 0.1s (Period of waveform) |

**6. The r.f. carrier wave of a telegraphy transmitter is 50MHz (50×10^6Hz).
What is the periodic time of the carrier wave?**

$$T = \frac{1}{f} = \frac{1}{50 \times 10^6} = 20 \times 10^{-9} \, s = 20ns$$

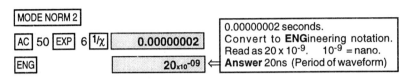

MODE NORM 2

| AC | 50 | EXP | 6 | 1/x | | 0.00000002 |

| ENG | | 20ₓ₁₀⁻⁰⁹ |

0.00000002 seconds.
Convert to **ENG**ineering notation.
Read as 20×10^{-9}. 10^{-9} = nano.
⟸ **Answer** 20ns (Period of waveform)

**7. A sinewave has a frequency of 800kHz (800×10^3Hz).
What is the period of the wave?**

$$T = \frac{1}{f} = \frac{1}{800 \times 10^3} = 1.25 \times 10^{-6} \, s = 1.25\mu s$$

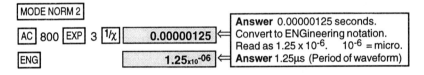

MODE NORM 2

| AC | 800 | EXP | 3 | 1/x | | 0.00000125 |

| ENG | | 1.25ₓ₁₀⁻⁰⁶ |

⟸ **Answer** 0.00000125 seconds.
Convert to ENGineering notation.
Read as 1.25×10^{-6}. 10^{-6} = micro.
⟸ **Answer** 1.25µs (Period of waveform)

**8. The output frequency of a signal generator is 1kHz (1×10^3Hz).
What is the period of the 1kHz signal?**

$$T = \frac{1}{f} = \frac{1}{1 \times 10^3} = 1 \times 10^{-3} \, s = 1ms$$

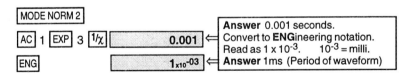

MODE NORM 2

| AC | 1 | EXP | 3 | 1/x | | 0.001 |

| ENG | | 1ₓ₁₀⁻⁰³ |

⟸ **Answer** 0.001 seconds.
Convert to **ENG**ineering notation.
Read as 1×10^{-3}. 10^{-3} = milli.
⟸ **Answer** 1ms (Period of waveform)

**9. A generator has an output frequency of 80MHz (80×10^6Hz).
How long does it take the generator to produce one complete cycle.**

$$T = \frac{1}{f} = \frac{1}{80 \times 10^6} = 12.5 \times 10^{-9} \, s = 12.5ns$$

MODE NORM 2

| AC | 80 | EXP | 6 | 1/x | | 0.000000012 |

| ENG | | 12.5ₓ₁₀⁻⁰⁹ |

⟸ **Answer** 0.000000012 seconds.
Convert to **ENG**ineering notation.
Read as 12.5×10^{-9}. 10^{-9} = nano.
⟸ **Answer** 12.5ns (Period of waveform)

10. The period of a waveform is 0.02s.
What is the frequency?

$$f = \frac{1}{T} = \frac{1}{0.02} = 50Hz$$

MODE NORM 2

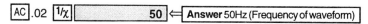

$\boxed{AC}$ .02 $\boxed{1/x}$ 50 ⟸ Answer 50Hz (Frequency of waveform)

---

11. The period of a waveform measured on an oscilloscope is 5µs (5×10^{-6}s).
What is the frequency of the waveform?

$$f = \frac{1}{T} = \frac{1}{5 \times 10^{-6}} = 200,000Hz = 200kHz$$

MODE NORM 2

$\boxed{AC}$ 5 $\boxed{EXP}$ 6 $\boxed{+/-}$ $\boxed{1/x}$ 200000 ⟸ Answer 200,000Hz
Convert to **ENG**ineering notation.
Read as 200×10^3. 10^3 = kilo.
$\boxed{ENG}$ $200_{x10}03$ ⟸ **Answer** 200kHz

---

12. The time of one cycle of a waveform is 1ms (1×10^{-3}s)
What is the frequency?

$$f = \frac{1}{T} = \frac{1}{1 \times 10^{-3}} = 1000Hz = 1kHz$$

MODE NORM 2

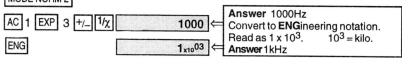

$\boxed{AC}$ 1 $\boxed{EXP}$ 3 $\boxed{+/-}$ $\boxed{1/x}$ 1000 ⟸ Answer 1000Hz
Convert to **ENG**ineering notation.
Read as 1×10^3. 10^3 = kilo.
$\boxed{ENG}$ $1_{x10}03$ ⟸ **Answer** 1kHz

---

13. A sinusoidal waveform has a period of 20µs (20×10^{-6}s).
What is the frequency?

$$f = \frac{1}{T} = \frac{1}{20 \times 10^{-6}} = 50,000Hz = 50kHz$$

MODE NORM 2

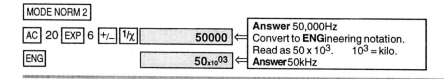

$\boxed{AC}$ 20 $\boxed{EXP}$ 6 $\boxed{+/-}$ $\boxed{1/x}$ 50000 ⟸ Answer 50,000Hz
Convert to **ENG**ineering notation.
Read as 50×10^3. 10^3 = kilo.
$\boxed{ENG}$ $50_{x10}03$ ⟸ **Answer** 50kHz

Peak and Peak-to-Peak Values

The peak, and peak-to-peak ampli-
tudes of a sinusoidal waveform are
shown in fig.3.

The peak value is the maximum
value of voltage or current. It is
measured either positive or negative
with respect to the zero reference.

The peak-to-peak value of a sinewave
is twice the peak value because a
sinewave is symmetrical about its x
axis. Other waveforms need not necessarily be symmetrical and would
need to be measured on an oscilloscope.

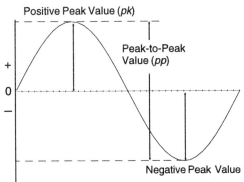

Fig.3. Showing Peak and Peak-to-Peak values
of a sinusoidal waveform.

Examples

**14. The peak voltage (V_{pk}) of a sinusoidal waveform is 125V.
What is the peak-to-peak value of the voltage (V_{pp})?**

$$V_{pp} = 2 \times V_{pk} = 2 \times 125 = 250V$$

| MODE NORM 2 |

| AC | 2 | ⊠ | 125 | = | 250 | ⇐ **Answer** 250 Volts (peak-to-peak) |

**15. The peak voltage (V_{pk}) of a sinusoidal waveform is 325V.
What is the peak-to-peak value of the voltage (V_{pp})?**

$$V_{pp} = 2 \times V_{pk} = 2 \times 325 = 650V$$

| AC | 2 | ⊠ | 325 | = | 650 | ⇐ **Answer** 650 Volts (peak-to-peak) |

**16. The peak-to-peak amplitude of a sinusoidal waveform is 12mV.
What is its peak value?**

$$V_{pk} = \frac{V_{pp}}{2} = \frac{12}{2} = 6mV$$

⇐ | Since our units are millivolts, the answer is in millivolts. |
⇓

| AC | 12 | ÷ | 2 | = | 6 | ⇐ **Answer** 6mV (peak) |

17. A radio frequency signal generator is adjusted to give an output signal of 600mV$_{pk}$.
What is the peak-to-peak value of the output signal?

$V_{pp} = 2 \times V_{pk} = 2 \times 600 = 1200mV = 1.2V$

MODE NORM 2

| AC | 2 | ☒ | 600 | = | | 1200 | ⇐ | Answer 1200mV (peak-to-peak) |

18. The peak-to-peak output of an a.c. generator is 880V.
What is the peak value of the voltage?

$V_{pk} = \dfrac{V_{pp}}{2} = \dfrac{880}{2} = 440V$

| AC | 880 | ÷ | 2 | = | | 440 | ⇐ | Answer 440 Volts (peak value) |

19. A sinusoidal current has a peak value of 235mA.
What is the peak-to-peak value of the current?

$I_{pp} = 2 \times I_{pk} = 2 \times 235 = 470mA$ ⇐ Since our units are milliamps, the answer is in milliamps.

| AC | 2 | ☒ | 235 | = | | 470 | ⇐ | Answer 470mA (peak-to-peak) |

20. Fig.4 shows an asymmetrical waveform generated by a function generator.
What is the peak-to-peak amplitude of the waveform?

The peak-to-peak amplitude of the waveform shown is the voltage measurement from the maximum positive peak to its maximum negative peak.

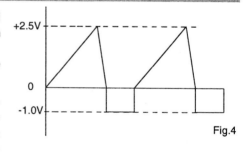

Fig.4

In this case Vpp is the sum of the voltage above the zero axis and the voltage below the zero axis; ignore the negative sign.

$V_{pp} = 2.5 + 1 = 3.5V$

| AC | 2.5 | + | 1 | = | | 3.5 | ⇐ | Answer 3.5 V (peak-to-peak) |

RMS Values

R.m.s. values are the most common method of expressing alternating voltages and currents.

The r.m.s. (root-mean-square), or effective value of a sinusoidal voltage or current; is that value of a direct voltage or current which causes the same amount of power dissipation (heat) in a given resistor.

The r.m.s. value of a sinusoidal voltage or current waveform is 70.7% or 0.707 of its maximum or peak value. See fig.5.

R.m.s. voltages and currents are denoted by E or V and I.

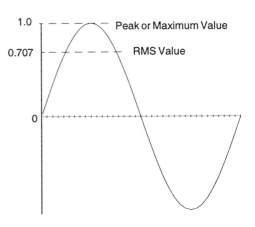

Fig.5. Maximum and r.m.s. values of a sinusoidal waveform.

Formulae to remember :-

$$V_{rms} = 0.707\ V_{pk} = 0.707 \times V_{pk}$$

$$I_{rms} = 0.707\ I_{pk} = 0.707 \times I_{pk}$$

$$V_{pk} = 1.414\ V_{rms} = 1.414 \times V_{rms}$$

$$I_{pk} = 1.414\ I_{rms} = 1.414 \times I_{rms}$$

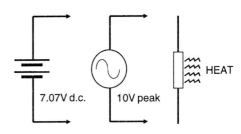

Fig.6. 7.07Vd.c. causes the same power dissipation in a given resistor as 10Vpk a.c.

Points to note.

1. The r.m.s. value is defined as the square *root* of the *mean* value of the *squares* of the instantaneous values taken over one complete cycle.
2. Alternating voltages and currents are normally expressed in r.m.s. values.
3. Normally, unless marked otherwise, the majority of a.c. measuring instruments will indicate the r.m.s. value of a sinusoidal alternating voltage or current.
4. An alternating current of 10A$_{rms}$ will produce the same amount of heat in a given resistor as will a direct current of 10A.
5. A steady direct current of 10A flowing in a given resistor will cause the resistor to get hotter than an alternating current with a peak value of 10A.
6. When an a.c. voltmeter, calibrated in r.m.s. reads 10 volts, there will be a maximum voltage of 14.14 volts across its terminals (assuming a sinusoidal waveform).
7. The r.m.s. value of a sinusoidal waveform is known as the effective value because it has the same heating effect as a direct current or voltage of that value.

Examples.

21. The r.m.s. value of a sinusoidal waveform is 100V.
What is the peak or maximum value of the waveform?

$$V_{pk} = 1.414 \, V_{rms} = 1.414 \times 100 = 141.4 \, V$$

| MODE NORM 2 |

| AC | 1.414 | × | 100 | = | | 141.4 | ⇐ | Answer 141.4V (Peak value) |

22. The maximum or peak value of a sinusoidal waveform is 1000V.
What is the r.m.s. value?

$$V_{rms} = 0.707 \, V_{pk} = 0.707 \times 1000 = 707 \, V$$

| AC | .707 | × | 1000 | = | | 707 | ⇐ | Answer 707 V (R.m.s. value) |

23. Calculate V_{rms} when V_{pk} is 250V.

$$V_{rms} = 0.707 \, V_{pk} = 0.707 \times 250 = 176.75 \, V$$

| AC | .707 | × | 250 | = | | 176.75 | ⇐ | Answer 176.75 V (R.m.s. value) |

24. The peak or maximum amplitude of a sine wave is 110 volts.
Calculate the r.m.s. or effective value.

$$V_{rms} = 0.707 \, V_{pk} = 0.707 \times 110 = 77.77 \, V$$

| AC | .707 | × | 110 | = | | 77.77 | ⇐ | Answer 77.77 V (R.m.s. value) |

25. The r.m.s. value of a sine wave is 440V. Calculate the peak or maximum value.

$$V_{pk} = 1.414 \, V_{rms} = 1.414 \times 440 = 622.16 \, V$$

| AC | 1.414 | × | 440 | = | | 622.16 | ⇐ | Answer 622.16 V (Peak value) |

26. The output level of an r.f. signal generator is 180mV$_{pk}$.
What is the r.m.s. value of the output signal?

$$V_{rms} = 0.707 \, V_{pk} = 0.707 \times 180 = 127.26 \, mV$$

| AC | .707 | × | 180 | = | | 127.26 | ⇐ | Answer 127.26mV (R.m.s.) |

27. A sinusoidal waveform has a peak or maximum amplitude of 325V. What is the r.m.s. value?

$V_{rms} = 0.707\ V_{pk} = 0.707 \times 325 = 229.775V$ _or by rounding_ $230V$

MODE NORM 2

| AC | .707 | ☒ | 325 | = | **229.775** | ⇐ Answer 229.775V (R.m.s. value) |

28. A generator supplies a sinusoidal current of 0.5Arms to a load. What is the peak or maximum current in the load?

$I_{pk} = 1.414\ I_{rms} = 1.414 \times 0.5 = .707A$

| AC | 1.414 | ☒ | .5 | = | **0.707** | ⇐ Answer 0.707A (Peak value) |

29. The r.m.s. current flowing in the antenna circuit of a high frequency radio transmitter is 90A. Calculate the peak or maximum value of the current.

$I_{pk} = 1.414\ I_{rms} = 1.414 \times 90 = 127.26A$

| AC | 1.414 | ☒ | 90 | = | **127.26** | ⇐ Answer 127.26A (Peak value) |

30. The r.m.s. voltage of an overhead power line is 11,000V. What is the peak or maximum value?

$V_{pk} = 1.414\ V_{rms} = 1.414 \times 11,000 = 15,554V = 15.554kV$

| AC | 1.414 | ☒ | 11000 | = | **15554** | ⇐ Answer 15,554V (Peak value) |

31. The peak current supplied by a radio frequency signal generator to a 50Ω load is 2mA. What is the r.m.s. current?

$I_{rms} = 0.707\ I_{pk} = 0.707 \times 2 = 1.414mA$

| AC | .707 | ☒ | 2 | = | **1.414** | ⇐ Answer 1.414mA (R.m.s. value) |

32. Calculate the peak or maximum voltage on a 500Vrms power line.

$V_{pk} = 1.414\ V_{rms} = 1.414 \times 500 = 707V$

| AC | 1.414 | ☒ | 500 | = | **707** | ⇐ Answer 707V (Peak value) |

Average Values

The average value of a sinusoidal waveform is the mean value taken over one half cycle.

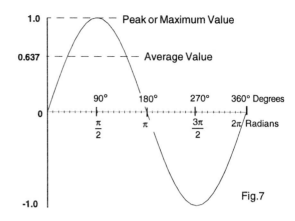

The average is taken over half a cycle because the average over a full cycle is zero. The average value for the sine wave is 0.637 or 63.7% of its peak or maximum value.

Fig.7

Average values are often considered in connection with rectifier and battery charging circuitry. Average values are denoted by the symbols E_{av} or V_{av} for voltage and I_{av} for current.

Formulae to remember :-

$$V_{av} = 0.637 \ V_{pk} = 0.637 \times V_{pk}$$

$$I_{av} = 0.637 \ I_{pk} = 0.637 \times I_{pk}$$

$$V_{pk} = 1.57 \ V_{av} = 1.57 \times V_{av}$$

$$I_{pk} = 1.57 \ I_{av} = 1.57 \times I_{av}$$

Examples.
33. The maximum or peak value of a sinusoidal waveform is 1000V. What is the average value?

$$V_{av} = 0.637 \ V_{pk} = 0.637 \times 1000 = 637 V$$

MODE NORM 2

| AC | .637 | ☒ | 1000 | = | 637 | ⇐ | Answer 637V (Average value) |

---

34. Calculate V_{pk} when V_{av} is 207V.

$$V_{pk} = 1.57 \ V_{av} = 1.57 \times 207 = 325 V$$

| AC | 1.57 | ☒ | 207 | = | 324.99 | ⇐ | Answer 325V (Peak value) |

3-11

Instantaneous Values

The instantaneous value of a sinusoidal waveform is the amplitude of the voltage or current at any particular instant into the cycle.

Fig.8 shows one cycle of a sinusoidal waveform. The X axis is time in seconds or angle in degrees or radians, and the Y axis the amplitude. Instantaneous values are denoted by v or e for voltage, and i for current.

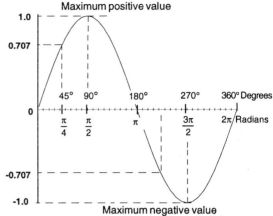

Fig.8

As seen from fig.8, there is only one instant in the cycle when the amplitude has a maximum positive value, and only one instant when the amplitude has a maximum negative value. All other values of amplitude will lie between these maxima.

Formulae to remember :-

$$i = I_{pk} \sin \theta$$

$$v = V_{pk} \sin \theta$$

Where:-
I_{pk} = Maximum or peak current (amps).
V_{pk} = Maximum or peak voltage (volts).
i = Instantaneous current (amps).
v = Instantaneous voltage (volts).
θ = (Theta) Angle in degrees, progressed by the wave from its start (zero).

Points to note.

1. Instantaneous values between 0° and 180° are positive.
2. Instantaneous values between 180° and 360° are negative.
3. From fig.8 it can be seen that the maximum positive value occurs when $\sin\theta = \sin 90° = 1$ and the maximum negative value when $\sin\theta = \sin 270° = -1$.
4. The instantaneous values are zero when $\sin\theta = 0$, i.e. $\theta = 0°$, 180° or 360°
5. π radians = 180°, 2π radians = 360°,   1 radian = 57.3°
6. To convert degrees to radians multiply the number of degrees by $\dfrac{\pi}{180}$
7. To convert radians to degrees multiply the number of radians by $\dfrac{180}{\pi}$

Examples

35. The sine wave shown in fig.9 has a maximum or peak value of 100 amps. Calculate the instantaneous values of the current at 30°, 45°, 60° and 90° into the cycle.

Reference to the sine curve of fig.9 shows that instantaneous values between 0° and 180° are positive.

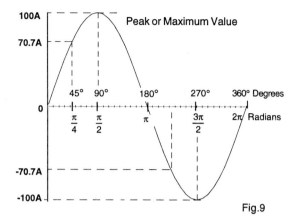

Fig.9

Calculate i at 30°.

$i = I_{pk} \sin \theta = 100 \sin 30° = 100 \times 0.5 = 50A$

For convenience FIX to 2 decimal places. Ensure that you are in DEGREE Mode

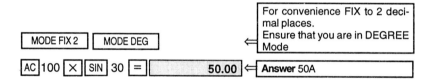

MODE FIX 2	MODE DEG	⇐

AC 100 ⨯ SIN 30 =	50.00	⇐ Answer 50A

Calculate i at 45°.

$i = I_{pk} \sin \theta = 100 \sin 45° = 100 \times 0.707 = 70.7A$

AC 100 ⨯ SIN 45 =	70.71	⇐ Answer 70.71A (Irms at 45°)

Calculate i at 60°.

$i = I_{pk} \sin \theta = 100 \sin 60° = 100 \times 0.8660 = 86.6A$

AC 100 ⨯ SIN 60 =	86.60	⇐ Answer 86.6A

Calculate i at 90°.

$i = I_{pk} \sin \theta = 100 \sin 90° = 100 \times 1 = 100A$

AC 100 ⨯ SIN 90 =	100.00	⇐ Answer 100A (Peak positive value at 90°)

36. Referring to fig.9. Calculate the instantaneous value of the current at 120°, 150°, 180°, 210°, 270° and 315° into the cycle. (I_{pk} = 100A.)

Reference to the sine curve of fig.9 shows that instantaneous values for angles between 0° and 180° are positive. If using a set of 0° to 90° sine tables, and the angle exceeds 90°, e.g. 120°, then its first quadrant equivalent angle must be found. For further information refer to a text book on basic trigonometry. However, the scientific calculator takes care of this little matter for us.

Calculate i at 120°.

$i = I_{pk} \sin \theta = 100 \sin 120° = 100 \times 0.8660 = 86.60A$

MODE FIX 2	MODE DEG

AC 100 × SIN 120 = | **86.60** ⇐ Answer 86.60A

Calculate i at 150°.

$i = I_{pk} \sin \theta = 100 \sin 150° = 100 \times 0.5 = 50A$

AC 100 × SIN 150 = | **50.00** ⇐ Answer 50A

Calculate i at 180°.

$i = I_{pk} \sin \theta = 100 \sin 180° = 100 \times 0 = 0A$

AC 100 × SIN 180 = | **0.00** ⇐ Answer 0A (Zero)

Calculate i at 210°.

Note. For angles between 180° and 360°, i.e. in the 3rd and 4th quadrants, instantaneous values are negative.

⇓

$i = I_{pk} \sin \theta = 100 \sin 210° = 100 \times (-0.5) = -50A$

AC 100 × SIN 210 = | **-50.00** ⇐ Answer -50A

Calculate i at 270°.

$i = I_{pk} \sin \theta = 100 \sin 270° = 100 \times (-1) = -100A$

AC 100 × SIN 270 = | **-100.00** ⇐ Answer -100A
(Peak negative value)

Calculate i at 315°.

$i = I_{pk} \sin \theta = 100 \sin 315° = 100 \times (-0.707) = -70.71A$

AC 100 × SIN 315 = | **-70.71** ⇐ Answer -70.71A

37. A sine wave has a peak or maximum value of 300V. Calculate the instantaneous amplitude of the wave 20°, 140°, 200° and 320° into the cycle.

Calculate v at 20°.
$v = V_{pk} \sin \theta = 300 \sin 20° = 300 \times 0.3420 = 102.61\ V$

MODE FIX 2	MODE DEG

| AC | 300 | × | SIN | 20 | = | 102.61 | ⇐ Answer 102.61V |

Calculate v at 140°.
$v = V_{pk} \sin \theta = 300 \sin 140° = 300 \times 0.6428 = 192.84\ V$

| AC | 300 | × | SIN | 140 | = | 192.84 | ⇐ Answer 192.84V |

Calculate v at 200°.
$v = V_{pk} \sin \theta = 300 \sin 200° = 300 \times (-0.3420) = -102.61\ V$

| AC | 300 | × | SIN | 200 | = | -102.61 | ⇐ Answer -102.61V |

Calculate v at 320°.
$v = V_{pk} \sin \theta = 300 \sin 320° = 300 \times (-0.6428) = -192.84\ V$

| AC | 300 | × | SIN | 320 | = | -192.84 | ⇐ Answer -192.84V |

38. A sinusoidal test tone has a maximum or peak amplitude of 5V. What is the instantaneous voltage of the wave 160° and 305° into the cycle?

Calculate v at 160°.
$v = V_{pk} \sin \theta = 5 \sin 160° = 5 \times 0.3420 = 1.71\ V$

MODE FIX 2	MODE DEG

| AC | 5 | × | SIN | 160 | = | 1.71 | ⇐ Answer 1.71V |

Calculate v at 305°.
$v = V_{pk} \sin \theta = 5 \sin 305° = 5 \times (-0.8192) = -4.1\ V$

| AC | 5 | × | SIN | 305 | = | -4.10 | ⇐ Answer - 4.10V |

In the previous examples the instantaneous values have been calculated in terms of the angle that developed from zero. However, the angle can also be measured in radians as shown on X axis, fig.10.

1 radian = 57.3°
π radians = 180°
2π radians = 360°

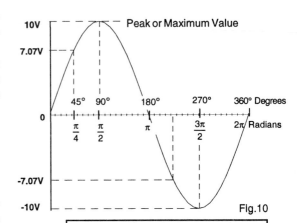

Using radian measure, the instantaneous values of voltage and current are given by the formulae:-

$i = I_{pk} \sin(\omega t) = I_{pk} \sin(2\pi f t)$

$v = V_{pk} \sin(\omega t) = V_{pk} \sin(2\pi f t)$

Where *i* and *v* are the instantaneous values of current and voltage at time *t*.
V_{pk} = peak or maximum voltage.
I_{pk} = peak or maximum current.
f = frequency (Hertz).
t = time in seconds.
ω (omega) = 2πf .(Angular velocity in radians per second)

Examples.
39. An a.c. waveform has a frequency of 50Hz and a peak value of 10V. Calculate its voltage 0.0125 seconds after its zero value.

$v = V_{pk} \sin(\omega t) = V_{pk} \sin(2\pi f t)$
$= 10 \times \sin(2 \times \pi \times 50 \times 0.0125) = 10 \times \sin 3.927$ ⇐ 3.927 Radians
$= 10 \times \sin(3.927 \times \frac{180}{\pi})$ degrees $= 10 \times \sin 225° = 10 \times -0.707 = -7.07V$

When using the formula it is convenient to convert the radians to degrees by multiplying by $\frac{180}{\pi}$ or 57.3

Using the calculator in the **RAD**ian mode saves converting to degrees.

MODE FIX2 | MODE RAD ⇐ Use **RAD**ian mode and **FIX** 2 decimal places. Full accuracy is maintained in the machine.

AC 10 × SIN [(--- 2 × π
× 50 × .0125 ---)] =   -7.07 ⇐ Answer -7.07 V

40. The output voltage of a small a.c. generator is expressed as :-
$v = 20 \sin (628.32t)$
Calculate :-
a) **The frequency of the generator.**
b) **The periodic time of the waveform.**
c) **The value of the voltage when $t = 0.00125$s.**

a) The frequency of the generator :-

Since $\omega = 2\pi f = 628.32$, $f = \dfrac{\omega}{2\pi} = \dfrac{628.32}{2\pi} = 100Hz$

> **Note.** Using either **RAD**ian or **DEG**ree mode will give the correct answer since we are not working with angles. **FIX** 2 decimal places.

MODE FIX 2	MODE RAD

[AC] 628.32 [÷] [[(---] 2 [×] [π] [---)]] [=]   **100.00** ⇐ Answer 100Hz

b) The periodic time of the waveform :-

$$T = \frac{1}{f} = \frac{1}{100} = 0.01 \ seconds$$

MODE FIX 2	MODE RAD

[AC] 100 [¹/ₓ]   **0.01** ⇐ Answer 0.01s (Period of waveform)

[ENG]   **10ₓ₁₀⁻⁰³** ⇐ Read as 10 x 10⁻³.
10⁻³ = milli.
Answer 10ms (Period of waveform)

c) The voltage when $t = 0.00125$s :-

$v = V_{pk} \sin (\omega t)$
$= 20 \times \sin (628.32 \times 0.00125) = 20 \times \sin 0.7854$
$= 20 \times \sin (0.7854 \times \dfrac{180}{\pi}) \ degrees = 20 \times \sin 45° = 20 \times 0.707 = 14.14V$
⇑

> Convert the radians to degrees by multiplying by $\dfrac{180}{\pi}$ or 57.3

> Use **RAD**ian mode and **FIX** 2 decimal places. Full accuracy is maintained in the machine.

MODE FIX 2	MODE RAD

[AC] 20 [×] [SIN] [[(---] 628.32 [×]
.00125 [---)]] [=]   **14.14** ⇐ Answer 14.14 V

41. A sine wave has a frequency of 50kHz (50×10^3Hz) and a peak voltage of 25V. Calculate the instantaneous value of the voltage 7.5µs (7.5×10^{-6}s) into the cycle.

$v = V_{pk} \sin(2 \pi f t)$

$\quad = 25 \times \sin(2 \times \pi \times 50 \times 10^3 \times 7.5 \times 10^{-6}) = 25 \times \sin 2.3562$

$\quad = 25 \times \sin(2.3562 \times \dfrac{180}{\pi})$ *degrees* $= 25 \times \sin 135° = 25 \times 0.707 = 17.68\,V$

MODE FIX 2	MODE RAD

⇐ Use **RAD**ian mode and **FIX** 2 decimal places.
Full accuracy is maintained in the machine.

[AC] 25 [×] [SIN] [((---]2 [×] [π] [×]

50 [EXP] 3 [×] 7.5 [EXP] 6 [+/_] [---)]] [=]   **17.68** ⇐ **Answer 17.68V**

---

42. The output current of an a.c. generator is given by the expression

$i = I_{pk}\sin(\omega t) = 5 \sin(5000\,t)$ **Calculate the :-**

a) frequency of the generator.

b) instantaneous amplitude of the current 0.00042s after the start of the cycle.

a) The frequency of the generator :-

Since $\omega = 2 \pi f = 5000$, $f = \dfrac{\omega}{2 \pi} = \dfrac{5000}{2 \pi} = 795.77 Hz$

Note. Using either **RAD**ian or **DEG**ree mode will give the correct answer since we are not working with angles. **FIX** 2 decimal places.

MODE FIX 2	MODE RAD

[AC] 5000 [÷] [((---] 2 [×] [π] [---)]] [=]   **795.77** ⇐ **Answer 795.77Hz**

b) The instantaneous value of the current when $t = 0.00042$s :-

$i = I_{pk} \sin(\omega t) = 5 \sin(5000\,t)$ Where $I_{pk} = 5A$ and $\omega = 5000$.

$\quad = 5 \times \sin(5000 \times 0.00042) = 5 \times \sin 2.1$

$\quad = 5 \times \sin(2.1 \times \dfrac{180}{\pi})$ *degrees* $= 5 \times \sin 120.32° = 5 \times 0.8632 = 4.32A$

⇐ Use **RAD**ian mode and **FIX** 2 decimal places.
Full accuracy is maintained in the machine.

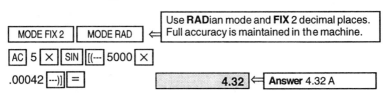

MODE FIX 2	MODE RAD

[AC] 5 [×] [SIN] [((--- 5000 [×]

.00042 [---)]] [=]   **4.32** ⇐ **Answer 4.32 A**

Frequency/Wavelength

Radiation from an antenna may be specified in terms of frequency f, or wavelength λ. If the radiated signal has a frequency, f hertz (Hz), then f complete cycles will leave the antenna every second. The radiated signal travels at 3×10^8m/s. Therefore, when the antenna has been radiating for one second, the surrounding electromagnetic field will extend to a distance of 3×10^8 metres.

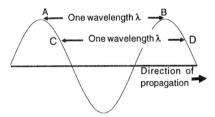

Fig. 11 The wavelength is the distance in metres between any two points of equal amplitude on successive cycles of the wave. E.g. A-B or C-D.

It follows that f complete cycles occupy a distance of 3×10^8 metres, with 1 cycle

occupying a distance of $\dfrac{3 \times 10^8}{f}$ metres. This distance is the wavelength (λ). See fig.11.

Frequency/wavelength conversion is essential when calculating the lengths of antennas and matching stubs. Also broadcast receivers, having dials calibrated in wavelength, can be read or recalibrated in frequency.

Formulae to remember:-

$$\lambda = \frac{v}{f} = \frac{3 \times 10^8}{f} \quad or \quad \frac{300 \times 10^6}{f}$$

Using 300×10^6 will make life easy when dealing with MHz.

$$f = \frac{v}{\lambda} = \frac{3 \times 10^8}{\lambda} \quad or \quad \frac{300 \times 10^6}{\lambda}$$

Where :-
λ (Lambda) = Wavelength in metres.
f = Frequency in hertz (Hz).
v = Velocity of radio waves in metres/second.
(Symbol c may be used in place of v for the velocity of the waves).

Examples.

43. A radio transmission has a frequency of 10MHz (10×10^6Hz). What is the wavelength?

Use the formula :- $\lambda = \dfrac{v}{f} = \dfrac{300 \times 10^6}{10 \times 10^6} = \dfrac{300}{10} = 30$ *metres*

I have **FIX**ed to 2 decimal places to avoid the display filling with unnecessary figures.

MODE FIX 2

AC | 300 | EXP | 6 | ÷ | 10 | EXP | 6 | = | **30.00**   ⇐ **Answer** 30 metres

**44. The frequency of a transmission is 500kHz (500 $\times$ 10³Hz).
What is the wavelength?**

$$\lambda = \frac{v}{f} = \frac{300 \times 10^6}{500 \times 10^3} = \frac{300 \times 10^3}{500} = \frac{3 \times 10^3}{5} = 600 \ \textit{metres}$$

MODE FIX 2

| AC | 300 | EXP | 6 | ÷ | 500 | EXP | 3 | = | 600.00 | ⇐ Answer 600 metres |

**45. You know that a radio transmission is being broadcast on a frequency of
200kHz (200 $\times$ 10³Hz). Your receiver however, has its dial marked in wavelength
(metres).
To what wavelength should you tune the receiver?**

$$\lambda = \frac{v}{f} = \frac{300 \times 10^6}{200 \times 10^3} = \frac{300 \times 10^3}{200} = \frac{3 \times 10^3}{2} = 1500 \ \textit{metres}$$

MODE FIX 2

| AC | 300 | EXP | 6 | ÷ | 200 | EXP | 3 | = | 1500.00 | ⇐ Answer 1500 metres |

**46. You are transmitting on a frequency of 145MHz (145 $\times$ 10⁶Hz).
What is the wavelength of your transmission?**

$$\lambda = \frac{v}{f} = \frac{300 \times 10^6}{145 \times 10^6} = \frac{300}{145} = 2.07 \ \textit{metres}$$

MODE FIX 2

| AC | 300 | EXP | 6 | ÷ | 145 | EXP | 6 | = | 2.07 | ⇐ Answer 2.07 metres |

**47. A received signal has a frequency of 14.5MHz (14.5 $\times$ 10⁶Hz). What is its
wavelength?**

$$\lambda = \frac{v}{f} = \frac{300 \times 10^6}{14.5 \times 10^6} = \frac{300}{14.5} = 20.69 \ \textit{metres}$$

MODE FIX 2

| AC | 300 | EXP | 6 | ÷ | 14.5 | EXP | 6 | = | 20.69 | ⇐ Answer 20.69 metres |

48. You intend to make an antenna suitable for operation at 500MHz (500 × 10⁶Hz) in the UHF frequency band.
The first step is to calculate the wavelength at this frequency.
What is the wavelength?

$$\lambda = \frac{v}{f} = \frac{300 \times 10^6}{500 \times 10^6} = \frac{300}{500} = 0.60 \text{ metres} \text{ or } 60cm$$

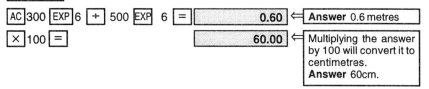

49. You are operating at a frequency of 1.2GHz (1.2 × 10⁹Hz).
What is your wavelength?

$$\lambda = \frac{v}{f} = \frac{300 \times 10^6}{1.2 \times 10^9} = \frac{300}{1.2 \times 10^3} = 0.25 \text{ metres} \text{ or } 25cm$$

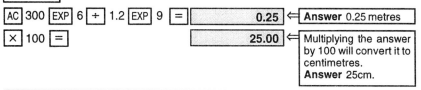

50. A receiver has its tuning dial calibrated in metres.
It is required to tune to a frequency of 900kHz (900 × 10³Hz).
To what wavelength on the dial should it be tuned?

$$\lambda = \frac{v}{f} = \frac{300 \times 10^6}{900 \times 10^3} = \frac{300 \times 10^3}{900} = 333.33 \text{ metres}$$

51. A transmission has a wavelength of 1500 metres. What is its frequency?

$$f = \frac{v}{\lambda} = \frac{300 \times 10^6}{\lambda} = \frac{300 \times 10^6}{1500} = 200 \times 10^3 = 200kHz$$

| MODE SCI 4 | ⇐ | **Note.** The change to **SCI**entific Mode and setting to 4 significant figures will make the result easier to read. |

| AC 300 EXP 6 ÷ 1500 = | $2.000_{x10}05$ | Read as 200×10^3 $10^3 =$ kilo |
| ENG | $200_{x10}03$ ⇐ | **Answer** 200kHz. |

---

52. The wavelength of a transmission is 40 metres. What is the frequency?

$$f = \frac{v}{\lambda} = \frac{300 \times 10^6}{\lambda} = \frac{300 \times 10^6}{40} = 7.5 \times 10^6 = 7.5MHz$$

| MODE SCI 4 | | Read as 7.5×10^6 $10^6 =$ Mega |
| AC 300 EXP 6 ÷ 40 = | $7.500_{x10}06$ ⇐ | **Answer** 7.5MHz. |

---

53. What frequency is related to a wavelength of 10.2 metres?

$$f = \frac{v}{\lambda} = \frac{300 \times 10^6}{\lambda} = \frac{300 \times 10^6}{10.2} = 29.41 \times 10^6 = 29.41MHz$$

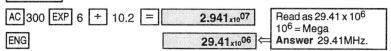

MODE SCI 4		
AC 300 EXP 6 ÷ 10.2 =	$2.941_{x10}07$	Read as 29.41×10^6 $10^6 =$ Mega
ENG	$29.41_{x10}06$ ⇐	**Answer** 29.41MHz.

---

54. A radiated signal has a wavelength of 3 metres. What is the frequency of this signal?

$$f = \frac{v}{\lambda} = \frac{300 \times 10^6}{\lambda} = \frac{300 \times 10^6}{3} = 100 \times 10^6 = 100MHz$$

MODE SCI 4		
AC 300 EXP 6 ÷ 3 =	$1.000_{x10}08$	Read as 100×10^6 $10^6 =$ Mega
ENG	$100_{x10}06$ ⇐	**Answer** 100MHz.

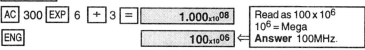

Capacitance

Chapter 4

Contents

In this section you will:-
a) calculate the charge and energy stored.
b) calculate the effective capacitance of capacitors connected in parallel.
c) calculate the effective capacitance of capacitors connected in series.
d) calculate the *'Time Constant'* of the series circuit containing C and R.

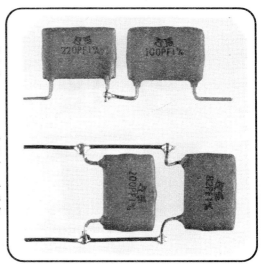

Top picture showing two capacitors 100pF and 220pF connected in series. The effective capacitance of this circuit is 68.75pF.

Lower picture showing two capacitors 200pF and 82pF connected in parallel. The effective capacitance is 282pF.
Due to the inductance of the connecting wires this combination is self resonant at approximately 100MHz.

Capacitance

Capacitance C is the measure of the ability of a conductor or a capacitor to store a charge of electricity.
A capacitor can be formed by two metal plates or conductors, separated by an insulator or 'dielectric'. Typical relative permittivities, 'K', of dielectric materials are :- Air 1, Paper 2, Mica 5, Glass 8, and ceramics 10 or higher.

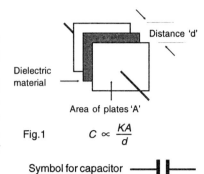

Distance 'd'

Dielectric material

Area of plates 'A'

Fig.1 $C \propto \dfrac{KA}{d}$

Symbol for capacitor —||—

Points to note.

1. Capacitance is the ability of a conductor to store a charge of electricity.
2. The unit of capacitance is the *FARAD*. However, the farad is too large a unit for most purposes. The more practical units are the microfarad μF ($10^{-6}F$), the nanofarad nF ($10^{-9}F$), and the picofarad pF ($10^{-12}F$).
3. A capacitor has a capacitance of 1 farad when a charge of 1 coulomb raises its potential by 1 volt.
4. Three factors affecting capacitance are shown in fig.1. Distance between the plates 'd', the area of the plates 'A', and the relative permittivity (dielectric constant) 'K' of the insulating material between the plates.
5. An increase in plate area 'A' increases the capacitance.
6. An increase in distance 'd' between the plates reduces the capacitance.
7. Electrical energy is stored in the electrostatic field between the plates.
8. The charge 'Q', developed on the plates of a capacitor is proportional to the applied voltage. Doubling the applied voltage V will double the charge Q.
9. The *relative permittivity,* or *dielectric constant* 'K' of a material, is the ratio of the capacitance of a capacitor employing that material as a dielectric to that of a similar capacitor employing air or a vacuum as a dielectric, 'K' = 1.
10. An air dielectric ($K = 1$) capacitor, having a capacitance of 100pF, will have a capacitance of 500pF if mica ($K = 5$) is substituted for the dielectric.
11. The *dielectric strength* of a dielectric material is a measure of the ability of that material to withstand electrical pressure (volts) across it.
12. Warning! Always discharge large value or high voltage capacitors through a suitable resistor. Avoid short-circuiting them when charged.
13. Capacitors are classified by their dielectric material.

Formulae to remember:-

Q = Charge in coulombs.
C = Capacitance in farads.
V = P.d. in volts.
W = Energy in joules.

Charge on a capacitor $Q = CV$ coulombs.

Energy stored in a capacitor $W = \dfrac{CV^2}{2} = \dfrac{1}{2}CV^2$ joules.

Examples.

**1. A 2μF capacitor is charged to a p.d. of 200 volts.
What is the charge 'Q' in coulombs?**

$C = 2\mu F = 2 \times 10^{-6} F.$

Use the formula $Q = CV = 2 \times 10^{-6} \times 200 = 0.0004C$ or $400\mu C$

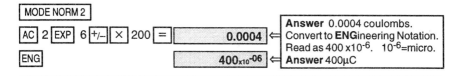

**2. A 5μF capacitor is charged to a potential difference of 100 volts.
Calculate the charge 'Q' and the energy stored in the capacitor.**

Charge $Q = CV = 5 \times 10^{-6} \times 100 = 500 \times 10^{-6} = 0.0005C$ or $500\mu C$

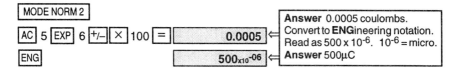

Now calculate the energy stored in the capacitor:-

Energy stored $= \dfrac{CV^2}{2} = \dfrac{5 \times 10^{-6} \times 100^2}{2} = \dfrac{5 \times 10^{-2}}{2} = 25 \times 10^{-3} J = 25mJ$

AC	5	EXP	6	+/–	×	100	χ²	=	**0.05** ⇐ = to display result of top line
+	2	=							**0.025** ⇐ Answer 0.0025J (joules)
ENG									**25ₓ₁₀⁻⁰³** ⇐ 25 x 10⁻³. 10⁻³ = milli Answer 25mJ

**3. A 0.2μF capacitor is connected to a 1000 volt d.c. source.
What is the charge on the capacitor?**

Use the formula $Q = CV = 0.2 \times 10^{-6} \times 1000 = 0.0002C$ or $200\mu C$

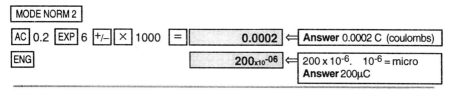

4. A variable air spaced high voltage transmitting capacitor is adjusted for a capacitance of 470pF (470 x 10^{-12}) and connected to a 1200 volt source. What is the charge and the energy stored?

Charge $Q = CV = 470 \times 10^{-12} \times 1200 = 564 \times 10^{-9}C$ or $564\,nC$

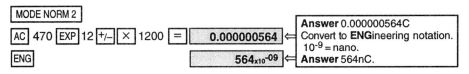

Energy stored:-

$$W = \frac{CV^2}{2} = \frac{470 \times 10^{-12} \times 1200^2}{2} = \frac{676.8 \times 10^{-6}}{2} = 338.4 \times 10^{-6}\,J \text{ or } 338.4\mu J$$

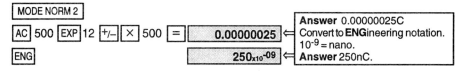

5. A high voltage, variable air spaced capacitor, has a maximum and minimum capacity of 500pF and 100pF respectively. It is adjusted to 500pF and connected to a 500 volt d.c. supply. The supply is then removed. What is the initial charge, and the potential difference across the plates when the capacitor is adjusted to 100pF?

The initial charge on the capacitor is:-

$Q = CV = 500 \times 10^{-12} \times 500 = 250 \times 10^{-9}C$ or $250nC$

MODE NORM 2		Answer 0.00000025C
AC 500 EXP 12 +/- × 500 = 0.00000025		Convert to **ENG**ineering notation. 10^{-9} = nano.
ENG 250ₓ₁₀⁻⁰⁹		Answer 250nC.

When the capacitor is adjusted to 100pF the charge remains the same, but as shown below, the p.d. across the plates increases.

From $Q = CV$ we get $V = \frac{Q}{C} = \frac{250 \times 10^{-9}}{100 \times 10^{-12}} = 2500V$

AC 250 EXP 9 +/- ÷ 100 EXP 12 +/- = **2500** ⇐ Answer 2500V

Capacitors in Parallel

When capacitors are connected in parallel, fig.2. The total capacitance C_T, (sometimes referred to as the effective capacitance), is equal to the sum of the individual capacitances.

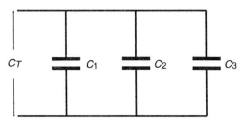

Fig.2. Capacitors connected in parallel.

For capacitors connected in parallel the effective capacitance, C_T, is given by:-

$$C_T = C_1 + C_2 + C_3 + \cdots C_N$$

C_T = Total capacitance of parallel circuit.
C_N = The Nth parallel connected capacitor.

Points to note.

1. Adding capacitors in parallel increases the total capacitance C_T because the combination acts as a single capacitor with a greater plate area.
2. The total capacitance of parallel connected capacitors is always greater than the largest value capacitor.
3. Capacitors are connected in parallel to achieve a higher capacitance.
4. The p.d. across each capacitor, fig.2 is the same for each.
5. The charge taken by each capacitor depends on its capacitance and applied voltage ($Q = C V$).

Examples

6. Two capacitors are connected in parallel. See fig.3. What is the total capacitance of the circuit?

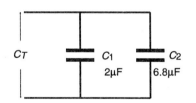

Fig.3

No real need to use the calculator for this example since both capacitors are expressed in the same unit, i.e. microfarads (μF).

$$C_T = C_1 + C_2 = 2 + 6.8 = 8.8 \; microfarads$$

Using the calculator :-

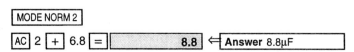

MODE NORM 2

AC   2   +   6.8   =   8.8   ⇐ Answer 8.8μF

7. What is the total, or effective capacitance of the circuit shown in fig.4?

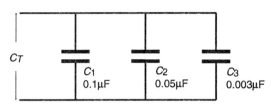

C_T

C_1 0.1μF C_2 0.05μF C_3 0.003μF

Fig.4

The total capacitance :-

$C_T = C_1 + C_2 + C_3 = 0.1 + 0.05 + 0.003 = 0.153$ *microfarads*

MODE NORM 2

AC .1 + .05 + .003 =   0.153 ⇐ **Answer** 0.153μF

---

8. A capacitance of 1.8μF is to be made-up from 2 separate capacitors. See Fig.5.
C_1 is 0.6μF.
What is the value of C_X?

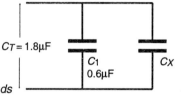

$C_T = 1.8$μF

C_1 0.6μF C_X

$C_T = C_1 + C_X$

∴ $C_X = C_T - C_1 = 1.8 - 0.6 = 1.2$ *microfarads*

Fig.5

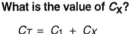

MODE NORM 2

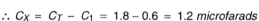

AC 1.8 − .6 =   1.2 ⇐ **Answer** 1.2μF

---

9. A variable capacitor, C_V, with a minimum capacitance of 100pF, and a maximum capacitance of 560pF, is connected in parallel with a 470pF fixed capacitor. What are the minimum and maximum values of capacitance that this combination can offer?

With C_V at minimum $C_T = 470 + 100 = 570$ *picofarads*

MODE NORM 2

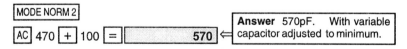

AC 470 + 100 =   570 ⇐ **Answer** 570pF. With variable capacitor adjusted to minimum.

With C_V at maximum $C_T = 470 + 560 = 1030$ *picofarads*

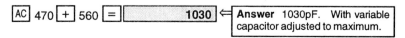

AC 470 + 560 =   1030 ⇐ **Answer** 1030pF. With variable capacitor adjusted to maximum.

Capacitors in Series

Fig.6 shows three capacitors connected in series.

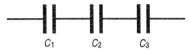

C_1 $\quad$ C_2 $\quad$ C_3

Fig.6

The formula for capacitors connected in series is given by :-

$$\frac{1}{C_T} = \frac{1}{C_1} + \frac{1}{C_2} + \frac{1}{C_3} + \cdots\cdots\cdots \frac{1}{C_N}$$

C_T = Total capacitance of series circuit.
C_N = The Nth series connected capacitor.

When there are only two capacitors connected in series the following formula may be used:-

$$C_T = \frac{C_1 \times C_2}{C_1 + C_2}$$

When N capacitors of equal value are connected in series, the combined or equivalent capacitance C_T is given by:-

$$C_T = \frac{\textit{Value of one capacitor}}{\textit{Number of capacitors}}$$

Points to note.

1. Connecting capacitors in series is equivalent to increasing the distance between the plates; hence the total, or effective capacitance decreases, and is less than the smallest individual value of capacitance.
2. Connecting capacitors in series increases the breakdown voltage rating.
3. The voltage across each capacitor in the series circuit is inversely proportional to its capacitance. The lowest value capacitor having the largest voltage across it.
4. The charging current is the same in all parts of a series circuit, therefore, each capacitor aquires the same charge, 'Q'.

Examples.

10. What is the total capacitance of the circuit shown in fig.7?

C_1 $\quad$ C_2
$4\mu F$ $\quad$ $4\mu F$

$$C_T = \frac{C_1 \times C_2}{C_1 + C_2} = \frac{4 \times 4}{(4 + 4)} = \frac{16}{8} = 2\mu F$$

Fig.7

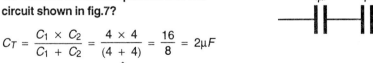

| MODE NORM 2 |
| AC | 4 | × | 4 | ÷ |

⇧ Using the calculator I've enclosed the bottom line in brackets.

| [(--- | 4 | + | 4 | ---)] | = | $\quad\quad\quad$ 2 | ⇐ | **Answer 2μF** |

---

11. Three capacitors, 100pF, 50pF and 40pF are connected in series as shown in fig.8. They are to be replaced by a single capacitor. What should be the value of the replacement?

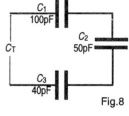

Fig.8

$$\frac{1}{C_T} = \frac{1}{C_1} + \frac{1}{C_2} + \frac{1}{C_3}$$

$$\frac{1}{C_T} = \frac{1}{100} + \frac{1}{50} + \frac{1}{40} = \frac{2+4+5}{200} = \frac{11}{200}$$ ⇐ Reciprocal of C_T (Not C_T)

Since $\frac{1}{C_T} = \frac{11}{200}$ ····· $C_T = \frac{200}{11} = 18.18\,pF$ Rounded to 2 decimal places.

Now using the calculator :-

MODE NORM 2

AC	100	1/x		0.01	⇐ Reciprocal of C_1
+	50	1/x		0.02	⇐ Reciprocal of C_2
+	40	1/x		0.025	⇐ Reciprocal of C_3
=				0.055	⇐ Sum of reciprocals
1/x				18.18181818	⇐ Reciprocal of sum of reciprocals. **Answer** 18.18pF (Rounded)

---

12. Four 0.5µF capacitors are connected in series. What is the total capacitance?

$$\frac{1}{C_T} = \frac{1}{C_1} + \frac{1}{C_2} + \frac{1}{C_3} + \frac{1}{C_4} = \frac{1}{0.5} + \frac{1}{0.5} + \frac{1}{0.5} + \frac{1}{0.5} = \frac{1+1+1+1}{0.5} = \frac{4}{0.5}$$

Since $\frac{1}{C_T} = \frac{4}{0.5}$ ····· $C_T = \frac{0.5}{4} = 0.125\mu F$

Note. Since there are 4 capacitors of equal value, we could divide the value of one capacitor by 4 to obtain the result, 0.5/4 = 0.125

MODE NORM 2

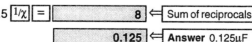

AC	.5	1/x	+	.5	1/x			
+	.5	1/x	+	.5	1/x	=	8	⇐ Sum of reciprocals
1/x							0.125	⇐ **Answer** 0.125µF

**13. Two capacitors in series have a total capacitance of 2μF.
One of the capacitors has a capacitance of 3μF.
What is the capacitance of the other?**

Let C_X be the unknown capacitance.

Transposing the formula $\quad \dfrac{1}{C_T} = \dfrac{1}{C_1} + \dfrac{1}{C_X}$; we obtain:- $\quad \dfrac{1}{C_X} = \dfrac{1}{C_T} - \dfrac{1}{C_1}$

$$\dfrac{1}{C_X} = \dfrac{1}{2} - \dfrac{1}{3} = \dfrac{3-2}{6} = \dfrac{1}{6}. \quad \text{Since } \dfrac{1}{C_X} = \dfrac{1}{6} \cdots\cdots C_X = 6\mu F$$

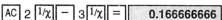

MODE NORM 2

$\boxed{\text{AC}}$ 2 $\boxed{1/\chi}$ $\boxed{-}$ 3 $\boxed{1/\chi}$ $\boxed{=}$ $\boxed{0.166666666}$

$\boxed{1/\chi}$ $\boxed{6}$ ⟸ $\boxed{\text{Answer } 6\mu F}$

---

14. Calculate the total capacitance of the circuit shown in fig.9.

First calculate the effective capacitance of the parallel combination.
The effective capacitance for C_1, C_2 = $C_1 + C_2 = 20 + 5 = 25$.
Now C_1, C_2 can be replaced in the circuit by a single capacitor C_P, of 25nF.
The equivalent circuit is as fig.10.

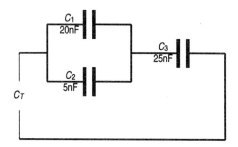

Fig.9

$$\dfrac{1}{C_T} = \dfrac{1}{C_P} + \dfrac{1}{C_3};$$

$$\dfrac{1}{C_T} = \dfrac{1}{25} + \dfrac{1}{25} = \dfrac{1+1}{25} = \dfrac{2}{25}$$

$$\text{Since } \dfrac{1}{C_T} = \dfrac{2}{25} \cdots\cdots C_T = \dfrac{25}{2} = 12.5nF$$

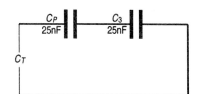

MODE NORM 2

$\boxed{\text{AC}}$ 25 $\boxed{1/\chi}$ $\boxed{+}$ 25 $\boxed{1/\chi}$ $\boxed{=}$ $\boxed{0.08}$

$\boxed{1/\chi}$ $\boxed{12.5}$ ⟸ $\boxed{\text{Answer } 12.5nF.}$

Fig.10

An alternative method is shown on the next page :- $\boxed{\text{Continued}} \Rightarrow$

4 - 9

14. continued. The above example could have been solved by modifying the following formula :-

$$C_T = \frac{C_1 \times C_2}{C_1 + C_2} \text{ to give } C_T = \frac{C_3 \times (C_1 + C_2)}{C_3 + (C_1 + C2)} = \frac{25 \times (20 + 5)}{25 + 20 + 5} = \frac{625}{50} = 12.5nF$$

MODE NORM 2		
AC 25 × [((--- 20 + 5 ---)] +	**625**	⇐ Result of top line.
[((--- 25 + 20 + 5 ---)] =	**12.5**	⇐ Answer 12.5nF

---

15. What is the total capacitance when a 0.0005μF (0.0005 × 10⁻⁶F) capacitor is connected in series with one of 1500pF (1500 × 10⁻¹²F)?

Using the formula $C_T = \dfrac{C_1 \times C_2}{C_1 + C_2}$

> **Note.** All capacitance values must be converted to a common unit. E.g. The farad. 0.0005μF must be entered as 0.0005 x 10⁻⁶F and 1500pF entered as 1500 x 10⁻¹²F.

we have $C_T = \dfrac{0.0005 \times 10^{-6} \times 1500 \times 10^{-12}}{0.0005 \times 10^{-6} + 1500 \times 10^{-12}} = 375 \times 10^{-12}F \text{ or } 375pF$

MODE NORM 2	
AC .0005 EXP 6 +/− × 1500 EXP 12 +/− ÷	**7.5ₓ₁₀⁻¹⁹**
[((--- .0005 EXP 6 +/− + 1500 EXP 12 +/− ---)] =	**3.75ₓ₁₀⁻¹⁰**
ENG	**375ₓ₁₀⁻¹²**

> Result converted to **ENG**ineering notation.
> $10^{-12} = $ pico.   **Answer** 375pF

To use an alternative method :-

> Reciprocal of C_T (Not C_T)

$$\frac{1}{C_T} = \frac{1}{C_1} + \frac{1}{C_2} = \frac{1}{0.0005 \times 10^{-6}} + \frac{1}{1500 \times 10^{-12}} = 2.667 \times 10^9$$

Since $\dfrac{1}{C_T} = 2.667 \times 10^9 \cdots C_T = \dfrac{1}{2.667 \times 10^9} = 375 \times 10^{-12}F \text{ or } 375 \ pF$

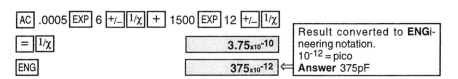

AC .0005 EXP 6 +/− 1/χ + 1500 EXP 12 +/− 1/χ		
= 1/χ	**3.75ₓ₁₀⁻¹⁰**	Result converted to **ENG**i-
ENG	**375ₓ₁₀⁻¹²**	neering notation. 10⁻¹² = pico ⇐ **Answer** 375pF

R & C in Series

It should not be assumed that a fully discharged capacitor becomes fully charged the instant a supply voltage is connected. Any resistance R in the circuit will slow the growth of the voltage V_C across the capacitor.

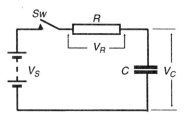

Fig.11 shows a capacitor connected in series with a resistor. The capacitor will take a definite time to charge. The charging time will depend on the values of C and R.

Fig.11

Consider the capacitor C initially uncharged. When the switch Sw is closed, there will be an initial flow of charging current, limited by the resistance R. The voltage across the capacitor V_C will begin to rise, rapidly at first, and then slow down more and more as V_C approaches V_S. The current flow will decrease as V_C increases, and when the voltage across the capacitor V_C is equal to the supply voltage V_S, no further current will flow, and the voltage V_R will be zero. As the voltage V_C opposes the supply voltage, it can be considered as a 'back e.m.f'.

Time Constant

Fig.12 shows the voltage across the capacitor increasing exponentially. After a certain time T, the voltage across the capacitor Vc, reaches 63% of its final value. This time, T, is called the *time constant* of the circuit, and is given by the formula $T = CR$.

A capacitor is, for most practical purposes, considered fully charged after a time equal to $5T$ or $5CR$ seconds, i.e. 'five time constants.' Where T = time in seconds, C = capacitance in farads, and R = resistance in ohms.

The charged capacitor can be discharged through a resistor, the discharge curve will be the opposite of the charge curve, provided that the same resistor is used. On discharge, the voltage across the capacitor will fall to 37% of its initial value in time T, 'one time constant'. For most practical purposes, the capacitor can be considered fully discharged in $5T$ seconds, 'five time constants'.

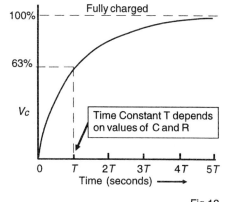

Fig.12

Points to note.

1. The initial charging current $I = \dfrac{V}{R}$
2. The final charging current is zero.
3. The voltage across the capacitor reaches 63% of its final voltage in a time equal to *CR* seconds.
4. An increase in *R* and/or *C* will increase the time constant.
5. A decrease in *R* and/or *C* will decrease the time constant.
6. The capacitor may be considered fully charged or discharged in 5*CR* seconds.

Examples.

16. What is the time constant of a 10μF (10×10^{-6}F) capacitor connected in series with a 100,000 (100×10^3) ohm resistor?

The time constant is given by the formula :-

$$T = CR = C \times R = 10 \times 10^{-6} \times 100 \times 10^3 = 1\ second$$

The voltage rises to 63% of its final value in 1 second.

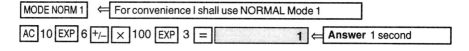

| MODE NORM 1 | ⇐ For convenience I shall use NORMAL Mode 1 |

AC 10 EXP 6 +/− × 100 EXP 3 = | 1 ⇐ **Answer** 1 second

17. A fully discharged 2μF (2×10^{-6}F) capacitor, connected in series with a 4MΩ (4×10^6Ω) resistor is charged from a 100 volt supply.
a) Calculate the time constant of the circuit.
b) The time taken for the capacitor voltage to rise to 63 volts.
c) The initial current in the circuit at switch-on.

a) The circuit time constant, $T = CR = 2 \times 10^{-6} \times 4 \times 10^6 = 8\ seconds$

AC 2 EXP 6 +/− × 4 EXP 6 = | 8 ⇐ **Answer** 8 seconds

b) The voltage across the capacitor will rise to 63% of its final charge in 8 seconds. As the supply voltage is 100 volts, the voltage across the capacitor will have risen to 63 volts in 8 seconds.

c) The initial charging current, $I = \dfrac{V}{R} = \dfrac{100}{4 \times 10^6} = 25 \times 10^{-6} = 25\ microamps$

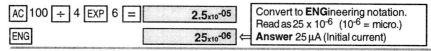

| AC 100 ÷ 4 EXP 6 = | 2.5x10⁻05 | Convert to **ENG**ineering notation. Read as 25 x 10⁻⁶ (10^{-6} = micro.) |
| ENG | 25x10⁻06 | ⇐ **Answer** 25 μA (Initial current) |

18. A 5000pF (5000 $\times$ 10^{-12}F) capacitor is connected in series with a 500kΩ (500 $\times$ 10$^{3}\Omega$) resistor.
What is the circuit time constant?

$$T = CR = C \times R = 5000 \times 10^{-12} \times 500 \times 10^{3} = 2.5 \times 10^{-3}s = 2.5 \text{ milliseconds}$$

| MODE NORM 1 |

AC 5000 EXP 12 +/− ×

500 EXP 3 =   **2.5**x10**-03** ⇐ Answer 2.5ms

---

19. The time constant T, of a circuit consisting of a capacitor and resistor in series is 5 seconds.
The value of the capacitor is known to be 2μF (2 $\times$ 10^{-6}F).
.What is the value of the resistor?

Transposing the formula $T = CR$ we get :-

$$R = \frac{T}{C} = \frac{5}{2 \times 10^{-6}} = 2.5 \times 10^{6} \text{ ohms or } 2.5 \text{ Megohms}$$

AC 5 ÷ 2 EXP 6 +/− =   **2500000** ⇐ Answer 2,500,000Ω

ENG   **2.5**x10**06** ⇐ Answer 2.5MΩ

---

20. A timer circuit consisting of R and C in series, is required to have a time constant of 100 milliseconds (100 $\times$ 10^{-3}s).
The resistance value is 200kΩ (200 $\times$ 10$^{3}\Omega$).
Calculate the value of the capacitor.

Transposing the formula $T = CR$ we get :-

$$C = \frac{T}{R} = \frac{100 \times 10^{-3}}{200 \times 10^{3}} = 0.5 \times 10^{-6}F = 0.5\mu F$$

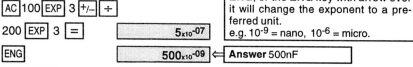

AC 100 EXP 3 +/− ÷

200 EXP 3 =   **5**x10**-07**

ENG   **500**x10**-09** ⇐ Answer 500nF

SHIFT ENG   **0.5**x10**-06** ⇐ Answer 0.5μF

> **Note.** Using the **ENG**, the Shifted **ENG**, or the **ENG** key with arrow over it will change the exponent to a preferred unit.
> e.g. 10^{-9} = nano, 10^{-6} = micro.

A ENG key may be available on some machines.

Notes

Inductance

Chapter 5

Contents

In this section you will:-
a) calculate the energy stored in the field of an inductor.
b) calculate the effective inductance of inductors connected in series.
c) calculate the effective inductance of inductors connected in parallel.
d) calculate the 'Time Constant' of the series circuit containing L and R.

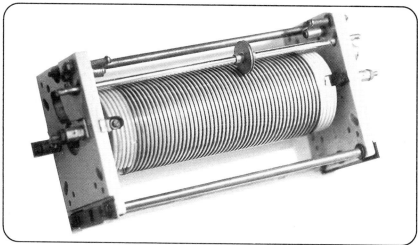

Photograph shows a variable inductor. Typically used for tuning medium to high power transmitters and antenna tuning units. The coil is wound with silver plated copper wire of approx. 14 SWG on a porcelain or ceramic former. Coil length approx. 23cm. Dia 7cm.

Inductance

Inductance

The inductance, or self-inductance of a circuit is that property of a circuit which opposes any change of current in that circuit. The symbol for inductance is *L*, and the unit is the henry (symbol *H*).

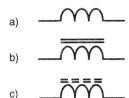

Fig.1 Inductor symbols.
a) Air-cored
b) Iron-cored
c) Dust-cored

Inductance is introduced into a circuit by means of a device called an inductor, or coil. Inductors may be used to oppose the flow of an alternting current whilst simutaneously passing direct, or steady current.

Points to note.

1. An inductor has a self-inductance of 1 henry when a current changing at the rateof 1A/s (1 amp per second) induces a back-e.m.f. of 1 volt across it.
2. The practical units are the henry (H) and the two smaller units, the milli-henry mH (10^{-3}H) and the microhenry μH (10^{-6}H)
3. Inductance is a property of an inductor.
4. Induction is the process of inducing voltage changes by changing magnetic flux.
5. Any conductor possesses inductance.
6. Winding a conductor into a coil increases inductance.
7. Inserting an iron core into an inductor increases the inductance.
8. Inductance is proportional to the square of the number of turns, i.e. $L \propto N^2$. (doubling the number of turns over the same length increases the inductance four times).
9. Generally, squeezing the turns of a coil closer together will increase the inductance, and stretching the coil will decrease the inductance.
10. Inductors resist, or react, to changing currents, but, apart from their winding resistance, have no effect on unchanging currents, i.e. steady d.c.
11. Energy is stored in the magnetic field of the inductor.
12. Low frequency inductors usually have laminated iron cores. Low power r.f. inductors usually employ dust-iron, ferrite or air cores, and may be self-supporting.
13. Due to the tendency of high frequency currents to concentrate near the surface, and less in the centre of a conductor, a phenomenon known as '*skin effect*', high power r.f. inductors are normally self-supporting, air cored, and con-structed from silver plated copper wire or tube. The coils may be of large diameter.

Formulae to remember:-

The inductance $L \propto \dfrac{N^2 A}{l}$

Energy stored $W = \dfrac{1}{2} L I^2$

L = Inductance in henrys.
I = Current in amperes.
W = Energy stored in magnetic field (joules).
N = Number of turns on inductor.
l = length of inductor.
A = Area of cross section.

Examples.
1. Calculate the energy stored in the magnetic field of a 2H inductor carrying a steady current of 5A.

Energy stored $\quad W = \dfrac{1}{2} L I^2 = \dfrac{2 \times 5^2}{2} = \dfrac{50}{2} = 25 \, joules$

MODE NORM 2

| AC | 2 ×| 5 $\boxed{\chi^2}$ ÷ | 2 | = | **25** | ⇐ **Answer** 25 J (Energy stored) |

---

2. Calculate the energy stored in the magnetic field of a 200mH inductor carrying a steady current of 1.5A.

Energy stored $\quad W = \dfrac{1}{2} L I^2 = \dfrac{200 \times 10^{-3} \times 1.5^2}{2} = \dfrac{0.45}{2} = 0.225 \, J \ or \ 225 \, mJ$

MODE NORM 2

$\boxed{AC}$ 200 $\boxed{EXP}$ 3 $\boxed{+/-}$ $\boxed{\times}$ 1.5 $\boxed{\chi^2}$

$\boxed{\div}$ 2 $\boxed{=}$ **0.225** ⇐ **Answer** 0.225 J (Energy stored)

$\boxed{ENG}$ **225**ₓ₁₀⁻⁰³ ⇐ **Answer** 225 mJ (Energy stored)

---

3. What is the energy stored in the magnetic field of a 400µH inductor when a steady d.c. current of 2.5A is flowing in the coil?

$$W = \frac{1}{2} L I^2 = \frac{400 \times 10^{-6} \times 2.5^2}{2} = \frac{2.5 \times 10^{-3}}{2} = 1.25 \times 10^{-3} \, J = 1.25 \, mJ$$

MODE NORM 2

$\boxed{AC}$ 400 $\boxed{EXP}$ 6 $\boxed{+/-}$ $\boxed{\times}$ 2.5 $\boxed{\chi^2}$ | Read as 1.25 x 10⁻³ |
$\boxed{\div}$ 2 $\boxed{=}$ **1.25**ₓ₁₀⁻⁰³ ⇐ | 10⁻³ milli
Answer 1.25 mJ (1.25 millijoules) |

---

4. A 0.5H inductor has a resistance of 2Ω. Calculate the energy stored in its magnetic field when connected to a 30V d.c. supply.

First calculate the steady current in the coil :- $I = \dfrac{V}{R} = \dfrac{30}{2} = 15 \, amps$

Energy stored $\quad W = \dfrac{1}{2} L I^2 = \dfrac{0.5 \times 15^2}{2} = \dfrac{112.5}{2} = 56.25 \, joules$

MODE NORM 2

| AC | .5 ×| 15 $\boxed{\chi^2}$ ÷ | 2 | = | **56.25** | ⇐ Answer 56.25 J (Energy stored) |

Inductors in Series

When inductors are connected in series, with no mutual coupling between them, i.e. the magnetic field of either inductor does not cut the other, the total or effective inductance L_T of the series connected inductors is:-

$$L_T = L_1 + L_2 + L_3 + \text{.......} + L_N$$

L_T = Total inductance of series circuit (in same units as L_1, L_2 etc.).
L_N = The Nth series connected inductor.

When two inductors are connected in series, and mutual inductance L_M exists between them, the direction of the coil windings, and the resulting magnetic fields due to the current in the coils will determine whether the mutual coupling increases or decreases the total, or effective inductance L_T. If the coils are connected series-aiding, fig.2, i.e. the magnetic fields are in the same direction, L_T increases. If the coils are series-opposing, fig.3, i.e. the magnetic fields are in opposite directions, L_T decreases.

For series-aiding :-

$$L_T = L_1 + L_2 + 2L_M$$

For series-opposing :-

$$L_T = L_1 + L_2 - 2L_M$$

It will be seen that in both cases the primary inductances, L_1 and L_2 add, and for series-aiding twice the value of L_M, ($2L_M$) is added, while for series-opposing, twice the value of L_M, ($2L_M$) is subtracted.

L_M = Mutual inductance in henrys.

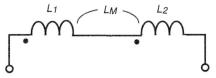

Fig.2 Series-aiding

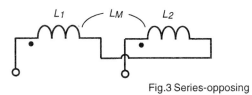

Fig.3 Series-opposing

Points to note.
1. Inductors in series are additive, providing no mutual inductance exists.
2. When mutual inductance exists, the effective inductance is modified by the direction of the magnetic fields.
3. If the fields are aiding, the effective inductance increases.
4. If the fields are opposing, the effective inductance decreases.
5. The spots on the coil symbols indicate the same direction of the windings.

Examples.

5. Two inductors are connected as shown in fig.4. No mutual coupling exists between them.
L_1 = 50mH and L_2 = 88mH.
Calculate L_T.

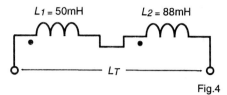

$L_1 = 50mH$ $L_2 = 88mH$

L_T

Fig.4

$L_T = L_1 + L_2 = 50 + 88 = 138$ *millihenrys*

MODE NORM 2

| AC | 50 | + | 88 | = | | 138 | ⇐ **Answer** 138mH (Total inductance) |

---

6. Two inductors of 100mH and 250mH respectively are connected in series. There is no mutual inductance between them. Calculate the resulting inductance.

Since all values are in millihenrys, there is no need to convert to a common unit.

$L_T = L_1 + L_2 = 100 + 250 = 350$ *millihenrys*

MODE NORM 2

| AC | 100 | + | 250 | = | | 350 | ⇐ **Answer** 350mH |

---

7. Two inductors of 500μH and 1.5mH respectively are connected in series. No mutual inductance exists between them. What is the total or effective inductance?

First convert the inductance values to a common unit (henrys).
500μH = 500×10^{-6}H and 1.5mH = 1.5×10^{-3}H.

$L_T = L_1 + L_2 = 500 \times 10^{-6} + 1.5 \times 10^{-3} = 2 \times 10^{-3}$ *henrys or* 2 *millihenrys*

MODE NORM 2

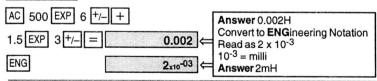

AC 500 EXP 6 +/- +

1.5 EXP 3 +/- = | 0.002 | ⇐

ENG | 2_{x10}-03 | ⇐

Answer 0.002H
Convert to **ENG**ineering Notation
Read as 2 x 10⁻³
10⁻³ = milli
Answer 2mH

8. Two inductors of 100mH and 250mH respectively are connected series-aiding. The mutual inductance between them is 50mH. Calculate the resulting inductance.

$$L_T = L_1 + L_2 + 2L_M = 100 + 250 + (2 \times 50) = 450mH$$

MODE NORM 2

| AC | 100 | + | 250 | + |

| [(--- | 2 | × | 50 | ---)] | = | | **450** | ⟸ | **Answer** 450mH |

9. Two inductors of 100mH and 250mH respectively, are connected in series-opposition. The mutual inductance between them is 50mH. Calculate the resulting inductance.

$$L_T = L_1 + L_2 - 2L_M = 100 + 250 - (2 \times 50) = 250mH$$

MODE NORM 2

| AC | 100 | + | 250 | − |

| [(--- | 2 | × | 50 | ---)] | = | | **250** | ⟸ | **Answer** 250mH |

Note. Examples 7, 8 and 9 show the same pair of inductors connected a) with no mutual inductance between them, b) series-aiding, and c) series-opposing. It will be seen that in the series-aiding case, an extra inductance, equal to the mutual inductance of 50mH is effectively added to each inductor, and in the series-opposing case, the inductance of each inductor is effectively reduced by the value of mutual inductance.

10. Two inductors of 120mH and 88mH respectively are connected series-aiding. The mutual inductance between them is 40mH. Calculate the resulting inductance.

$$L_T = L_1 + L_2 + 2L_M = 120 + 88 + (2 \times 40) = 288mH$$

MODE NORM 2

| AC | 120 | + | 88 | + |

| [(---2 | × | 40 | ---)] | = | | **288** | ⟸ | **Answer** 288mH |

11. The two inductors shown in fig.5 are connected series-aiding. The total inductance of the circuit L_T is 200mH. Calculate the value of mutual inductance L_M.

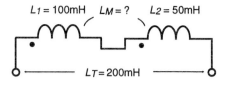

$L_1 = 100mH$ $L_M = ?$ $L_2 = 50mH$

$L_T = 200mH$

Fig.5

Transpose the formula for L_M :-

$$L_T = L_1 + L_2 + 2L_M$$

$$2L_M = L_T - L_1 - L_2$$

$$\therefore L_M = \frac{L_T - L_1 - L_2}{2} = \frac{200 - 100 - 50}{2} = \frac{50}{2} = 25mH$$

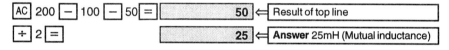

MODE NORM 2

| AC | 200 | − | 100 | − | 50 | = | | 50 | ⇐ Result of top line |

| ÷ | 2 | = | | 25 | ⇐ **Answer** 25mH (Mutual inductance) |

12. Two inductors, L_1 and L_2, of equal value, are connected series- aiding. The L_M between them is 250mH and the total inductance L_T is 1500mH. Calculate the value of L_1 and L_2.

$$L_T = L_1 + L_2 + 2L_M$$

$$L_1 + L_2 = L_T - 2L_M$$

Now since L_1 and L_2 are equal let $L_1 + L_2 = 2L$

$$\therefore 2L = L_T - 2L_M$$

$$\text{and} \quad L = \frac{L_T - 2L_M}{2} = \frac{1500 - (2 \times 250)}{2} = 500mH \quad or \quad 0.5H$$

MODE NORM 2

| AC | 1500 | − | [(⸱⸱⸱ | 2 | × | 250 | ⸱⸱⸱)] |

$L_1 + L_2 = 1000mH$
Since $L_1 = L_2$, both L_1 and L_2 are 500mH each.

| = | | 1000 |

| ÷ | 2 | = | | 500 | ⇐ **Answer** 500mH (Inductance of each inductor) |

This result can be tested by inserting the calculated values of L_1 and L_2 into the formula- $L_T = L_1 + L_2 + 2L_M$ and solving for L_T.

Inductors in Parallel

When inductors are connected in parallel, see fig.6, with no mutual coupling between them, i.e. the magnetic field of either inductor does not cut the other, the total or effective inductance L_T is :-

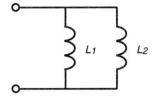

Fig.6

$$\frac{1}{L_T} = \frac{1}{L_1} + \frac{1}{L_2} + \frac{1}{L_3} + \dots\dots + \frac{1}{L_N}$$

For two inductors only, in parallel, with no mutual coupling :-

$$L_T = \frac{L_1 \times L_2}{L_1 + L_2}$$

Examples

13. Two inductors of 10H and 2H are connected in parallel. There is no mutual coupling between them. Calculate the effective inductance L_T.

Either of the above formula will be o.k.

$$\frac{1}{L_T} = \frac{1}{L_1} + \frac{1}{L_2} = \frac{1}{10} + \frac{1}{2} = \frac{1+5}{10} = \frac{6}{10} = 0.6 \quad \Leftarrow \boxed{\text{Reciprocal of } L_T \text{ (not } L_T\text{).}}$$

Now since $\dfrac{1}{L_T} = 0.6 \dots\dots L_T = \dfrac{1}{0.6} = 1.67H$

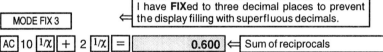

| | $\Leftarrow$ I have **FIX**ed to three decimal places to prevent the display filling with superfluous decimals. |

| $\boxed{\text{MODE FIX 3}}$ | |

| $\boxed{\text{AC}}$ 10 $\boxed{1/x}$ $\boxed{+}$ 2 $\boxed{1/x}$ $\boxed{=}$ | **0.600** $\Leftarrow$ Sum of reciprocals |
| $\boxed{1/x}$ | **1.667** $\Leftarrow$ **Answer** 1.667H |

Using the alternative formula :-

$$L_T = \frac{L_1 \times L_2}{L_1 + L_2} = \frac{10 \times 2}{10 + 2} = \frac{20}{12} = 1.67H$$

$\boxed{\text{AC}}$ 10 $\boxed{\times}$ 2 $\boxed{\div}$	**20.000** $\Leftarrow$ Result of multiplication. Division pending.
$\boxed{[(-}$ 10 $\boxed{+}$ 2 $\boxed{-)]}$	**12.000** $\Leftarrow$ Result of bottom line entered in brackets.
$\boxed{=}$	**1.667** $\Leftarrow$ **Answer** 1.667H

14. Two identical 120mH inductors are connected in parallel with no mutual coupling between them.
What is the total or effective inductance?

$$L_T = \frac{L_1 \times L_2}{L_1 + L_2} = \frac{120 \times 120}{120 + 120} = \frac{14400}{240} = 60mH$$

MODE FIX 3

AC	120	×	120	÷	**14400.000**	⇐ Result of multiplication. Division pending.
[(--	120	+	120	---)]	**240.000**	⇐ Result of bottom line entered in brackets.
=					**60.000**	⇐ Answer 60mH

15. A 150µH inductor is connected in parallel with one of 250µH.
Assuming no mutual inductance between them, calculate L_T.

$$L_T = \frac{L_1 \times L_2}{L_1 + L_2} = \frac{150 \times 250}{150 + 250} = \frac{37500}{400} = 93.75µH$$

MODE FIX 3

AC	150	×	250	÷	**37500.000**	⇐ Result of multiplication. Division pending.
[(---	150	+	250	---)]	**400.000**	⇐ Result of bottom line entered in brackets.
=					**93.750**	⇐ Answer 93.75µH

16. The L_T of two parallel connected inductors, L_1 and L_2 is 20mH. No mutual inductance exists. Find the value of L_2 when L_1 = 40mH.

Rearrange $\quad \dfrac{1}{L_T} = \dfrac{1}{L_1} + \dfrac{1}{L_2} \quad$ to give $\quad \dfrac{1}{L_2} = \dfrac{1}{L_T} - \dfrac{1}{L_1}$

$$\frac{1}{L_2} = \frac{1}{L_T} - \frac{1}{L_1} = \frac{1}{20} - \frac{1}{40} = \frac{2-1}{40} = \frac{1}{40} = 0.025$$

Now since $\dfrac{1}{L_2} = 0.025 \cdots\cdots L_2 = \dfrac{1}{0.025} = 40mH$

MODE FIX 3

| AC | 20 | 1/x | − | 40 | 1/x | = | **0.025** | |
| 1/x | | | | | | | **40.000** | ⇐ Answer 40mH |

Time Constant

Fig.7 shows L and R connected in series. When the switch Sw is closed, position 1, the current I_L will not reach its final steady value immediately, instead it increases exponentially as shown in fig.8.

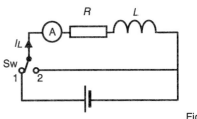

Fig.7

The slow increase in circuit current is due to the self-inductance of the inductor opposing any change in the circuit current.

Time Constant T, of the circuit fig.7 is the time taken for the current to reach 63% of its final steady $(I = \dfrac{V}{R})$ value.

The time constant in seconds:-

$$T = \frac{L}{R}.$$

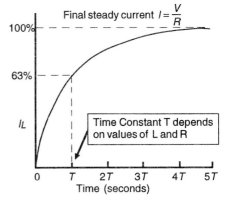

Fig.8

Points to note.

1. The initial current $I = 0$

2. Final steady current $I = \dfrac{V}{R}$ (Ohm's Law)

3. An increase in R reduces the final current (Ohm's Law).

4. The current in the inductor reaches 63% of its final value in one time constant:-
   $T = \dfrac{L}{R}$ seconds.

5. The larger the L the greater the time constant.

6. The larger the R the smaller the time constant.

7. For practical purposes, the current reaches its final steady value in approximately five time constants ($5T$ seconds).

8. When the switch Sw, fig.7, is moved to position 2, the collapsing magnetic field around the inductor causes a current to flow in the circuit that decays exponentially. This current will decay to 37% in one time constant.

Examples

17. Calculate the time constant of the circuit shown in fig.9.

$R = 5\Omega$ $L = 10H$

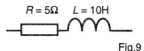

Fig.9

Use the formula $T = \dfrac{L}{R}$

$T = \dfrac{L}{R} = \dfrac{10}{5} = 2\ seconds$ ⇐ | **Note.** 2 seconds is the time taken for the current to reach 63% of its final steady value. i.e. One time constant.

| MODE NORM 2 |

| AC | 10 | ÷ | 5 | = | 2 | ⇐ | **Answer** 2s |

---

18. Increasing the value of *L*, fig.9, to 40H, *R* remaining 5Ω, will give a time constant of :-

$T = \dfrac{L}{R} = \dfrac{40}{5} = 8\ seconds$ ⇐ | **Note.** Increasing the inductance has increased the time constant.

| MODE NORM 2 |

| AC | 40 | ÷ | 5 | = | 8 | ⇐ | **Answer** 8s |

---

19. In the series circuit of fig.9, the value of *L* is 10H, and the value of *R* increased to 100Ω. Calculate the time constant of the circuit.

$T = \dfrac{L}{R} = \dfrac{10}{100} = 0.1\ seconds$ ⇐ | **Note.** Increasing the resistance has decreased the time constant.

| MODE NORM 2 |

| AC | 10 | ÷ | 100 | = | 0.1 | ⇐ | **Answer** 0.1s |

---

20. A 4mH (4×10^{-3}H) inductor has a resistance of 2Ω. Calculate the time constant.

$T = \dfrac{L}{R} = \dfrac{4 \times 10^{-3}}{2} = 2 \times 10^{-3}\ seconds\ or\ 2\ milliseconds$

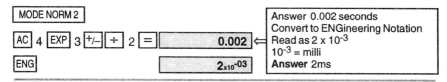

| MODE NORM 2 |

Answer 0.002 seconds
Convert to ENGineering Notation

| AC | 4 | EXP | 3 | +/– | ÷ | 2 | = | 0.002 | ⇐ Read as 2×10^{-3}
10^{-3} = milli

| ENG | 2_{x10}-03 | **Answer** 2ms

21. A relay coil has a resistance of 1000Ω, and an inductance of 20H when operated.
Calculate the time constant.

$$T = \frac{L}{R} = \frac{20}{1000} = 0.02 \, seconds \quad or \quad 20 \, milliseconds$$

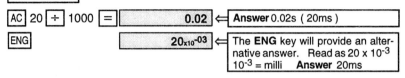

| MODE NORM 2 |

AC 20 ÷ 1000 = | 0.02 | ⇐ **Answer** 0.02s (20ms)

ENG | 20$_{x10}$-03 | ⇐ The **ENG** key will provide an alternative answer. Read as 20 x 10^{-3}
10^{-3} = milli   **Answer** 20ms

22. What value of inductor, in series with a 20Ω resistor will provide a time constant of 0.5s?

Transposing $T = \frac{L}{R}$ for L ..... $L = TR$

$L = TR = 0.5 \times 20 = 10 \, henrys$

| MODE NORM 2 |

AC .5 × 20 = | 10 | ⇐ **Answer** 10H

23. A 200mH (200 × 10^{-3}H) inductor is connected in series with a resistor. What is the value of the resistor if the time constant of the circuit is 0.1s ?

Transposing $T = \frac{L}{R}$ for R ..... $R = \frac{L}{T}$

$$R = \frac{L}{T} = \frac{200 \times 10^{-3}}{0.1} = \frac{0.2}{0.1} = 2 \, ohms$$

| MODE NORM 2 |

AC 200 EXP 3 +/- ÷ .1 = | 2 | ⇐ **Answer** 2Ω

Reactance

Chapter 6

Contents

In this section you will:-

a) calculate the reactance of circuits consisting pure capacitance.

b) calculate the reactance of circuits consisting pure inductance.

Capacitive Reactance X_C

Capacitive reactance Xc is the ability of a pure capacitor to resist the flow of alternating current. It can be considered analogous to resistance in a d.c. circuit; except that there is no energy or power dissipated in a pure capacitor. A pure capacitor has no loss associated with it. The unit of reactance, symbol X, is the ohm, symbol Ω.

Points to note.
1. No current flows in the dielectric between the plates of a pure capacitor.
2. The current I measured in the capacitive circuit is due to the alternate charge and discharge of the capacitor. See fig.1.
3. Xc is inversely proportional to frequency. See fig.2.
4. Xc is inversely proportional to the capacitance.
5. Xc is considered negative because the alternating voltage across the capacitor lags the current by 90°. See figs: 3 and 4.
6. In practice, most capacitors except electrolytic types can be regarded as pure.

Formulae to remember :-

$$X_C = \frac{1}{\omega C} = \frac{1}{2\pi f C}$$ Transposing formula for C and f:-

$$C = \frac{1}{2\pi f X_C} \quad \text{and} \quad f = \frac{1}{2\pi C X_C}$$

The current I in the circuit :-

$$I = \frac{V}{X_C} = \frac{V}{\frac{1}{\omega C}} = V\omega C$$

Where :-
X_C = Capacitive reactance in ohms Ω.
$\omega = 2\pi f$.
C = Capacitance in farads.
f = Frequency in hertz.
I = Current in amps.

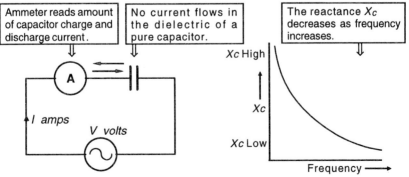

| Ammeter reads amount of capacitor charge and discharge current. | No current flows in the dielectric of a pure capacitor. | The reactance X_C decreases as frequency increases. |

I amps

V volts

Xc High

Xc

Xc Low

Frequency ⟶

Fig.1 Capacitor in an a.c. circuit.   Fig.2 Curve showing reactance / frequency.

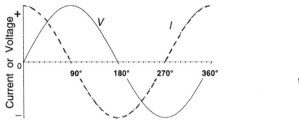

Fig.3 Showing voltage and current relationship in a circuit with pure capacitance. Current *I* leads voltage *V* by 90°.

Fig.4 Phasor diagram showing current *I* leading voltage *V* by 90°.

Examples.

1. Calculate the reactance of a 2μF (2 ×10^{-6}F) capacitor at a frequency of 3000Hz (3kHz or 3 × 10^{3}Hz).

$$X_C = \frac{1}{2\,\pi\,f\,C} = \frac{1}{2 \times \pi \times (3kHz) \times (2\mu F)} = \frac{1}{2 \times \pi \times 3 \times 10^3 \times 2 \times 10^{-6}}$$

$$= \frac{1 \times 10^3}{2 \times \pi \times 3 \times 2} = \frac{10^3}{37.7} = 26.53\Omega$$

Frequency in Hz. 3kHz = 3 × 10^{3}Hz	Capacitance in farads. 2μF = 2 × 10^{-6}F

There are two basic steps to working this example on the calculator :-
1) Calculate the bottom line.
2) Take the reciprocal of the bottom line.

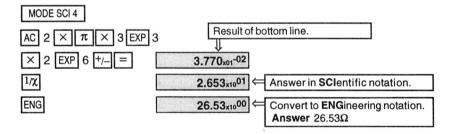

Note. When using the calculator we could have entered the top line of the equation first, in this case the 1, and then used brackets when entering the bottom line.

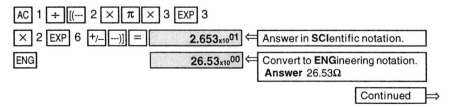

Continued ⟹

Example 1. Cont:

Example 1 may be worked on calculators that have the engineering symbol facility. Enter the value followed by a symbol :- i.e, if you are entering 2 microfarads, key in 2μ, if you are entering 3 kilohertz, key in 3k, and so on. The symbols are second functions on the Casio calculator. Therefore, the SHIFT key must be pressed first. Using this system saves time if you are confused by exponents and lots of noughts. Refer to the section on Operating Modes Table 1.

To enter Engineering Symbol Mode refer to chapter 1 Operating Modes or the calculator's manual. Keying [**MODE**][**MODE**][**MODE**][**MODE**][1] will enter and release Engineering Symbol Mode.

Now back to solving Example 1:-

$$X_C = \frac{1}{2\pi f C} = \frac{1}{2 \times \pi \times (3kHz) \times (2\mu F)} \quad enter\ calculator\ as \quad \frac{1}{2 \times \pi \times 3k \times 2\mu}$$

⇑ ⇑

Evaluating the bottom line first :-

> Engineering symbols take care of the EXPonent for us.
> Enter as 3 [SHIFT] k [×] 2 [SHIFT] μ
> The k will be key 6 on the numeric key pad and μ will be key 4

[MODE SCI 4][MODE ENG]

[AC] 2 [×][π][×] 3 [SHIFT][6k]

[×] 2 [SHIFT][4μ][=]   **37.7 m** ⇐ Result of bottom line.

[1/x]   **26.53** ⇐ Answer 26.53Ω

---

2. What is the X_C of a 6.8pF (6.8×10^{-12}F) capacitor at a frequency of 145MHz (145×10^6Hz)?

$$X_C = \frac{1}{2\pi f C} = \frac{1}{2 \times \pi \times 145 \times 10^6 \times 6.8 \times 10^{-12}} = \frac{1}{0.006195} = 161.4\ ohms$$

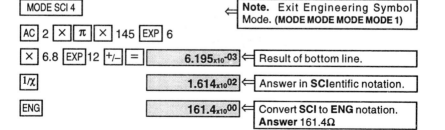

[MODE SCI 4]   ⇐ Note. Exit Engineering Symbol Mode. (**MODE MODE MODE MODE 1**)

[AC] 2 [×][π][×] 145 [EXP] 6

[×] 6.8 [EXP] 12 [+/−][=]   **6.195ₓ₁₀⁻⁰³** ⇐ Result of bottom line.

[1/x]   **1.614ₓ₁₀⁰²** ⇐ Answer in **SCI**entific notation.

[ENG]   **161.4ₓ₁₀⁰⁰** ⇐ Convert **SCI** to **ENG** notation. Answer 161.4Ω

3. An audio coupling capacitor has a capacitance of $4\mu F$ ($4 \times 10^{-6}F$). What is its reactance at a frequency of 2.5kHz ($2.5 \times 10^3 Hz$)?

$$X_C = \frac{1}{2\pi f C} = \frac{1}{2 \times \pi \times 2.5 \times 10^3 \times 4 \times 10^{-6}} = 15.92 \ ohms$$

 MODE SCI 4

 AC 2 × π × 2.5 EXP 3

× 4 EXP 6 +/– =	**6.283**ₓ₁₀⁻⁰²	⇐ Result of bottom line.

1/χ   **1.592**ₓ₁₀⁰¹ ⇐ Answer in **SCI**entific notation.

ENG   **15.92**ₓ₁₀⁰⁰ ⇐ Convert **SCI** to **ENG** notation.
                        Answer 15.92Ω

Now the same example using engineering symbol mode :-

$$X_C = \frac{1}{2\pi f C} = \frac{1}{2 \times \pi \times (3kHz) \times (2\mu F)} \quad enter \ calculator \ as \quad \frac{1}{2 \times \pi \times 3k \times 2\mu}$$

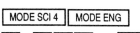 MODE SCI 4   MODE ENG   ⇐ **Note.** Enter Engineering Symbol
                                         Mode. (**MODE MODE MODE MODE 1**)

AC 2 × π × 2.5 SHIFT 6k

× 4 SHIFT 4μ =	**62.83 m**	⇐ Result of bottom line.

1/χ   **15.92** ⇐ **Answer** 15.92Ω

---

4. What is the value of a capacitor having a reactance of 50 ohms at a frequency of 21MHz ($21 \times 10^6 Hz$)?

$$C = \frac{1}{2\pi f X_C} = \frac{1}{2 \times \pi \times 21 \times 10^6 \times 50} = 151.6 \times 10^{-12} \ F \quad or \quad 151.6 pF$$

MODE SCI 4   ⇐ **Note.** Exit from Engineering Symbol
                                  Mode. (**MODE MODE MODE MODE 1**)

AC 2 × π × 21 EXP 6

× 50 =	**6.597**ₓ₁₀⁰⁹	⇐ Result of bottom line.

1/χ   **1.516**ₓ₁₀⁻¹⁰ ⇐ Answer in **SCI** notation.

ENG   **151.6**ₓ₁₀⁻¹² ⇐ Convert **SCI** to **ENG** notation.
                        Read as 151.6×10^{-12}.
                        10^{-12} = pico
                        Answer 151.6 pF

5. **What value capacitor has a reactance of 4kΩ (4 × 10³Ω) at a frequency of 50Hz?**

$$C = \frac{1}{2 \pi f X_C} = \frac{1}{2 \times \pi \times 50 \times 4 \times 10^3} = 795.8 \times 10^{-9} \quad or \quad 795.8 \; nF$$

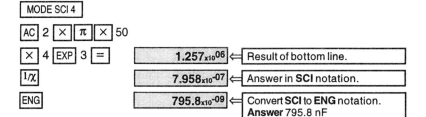

MODE SCI 4	
AC 2 × π × 50	
× 4 EXP 3 =	$1.257_{x10}06$ ⟸ Result of bottom line.
1/x	$7.958_{x10}{-07}$ ⟸ Answer in **SCI** notation.
ENG	$795.8_{x10}{-09}$ ⟸ Convert **SCI** to **ENG** notation. **Answer** 795.8 nF

6. **What value capacitor has a reactance of 5 ohms at a frequency of 796Hz? Round answer to nearest convenient value.**

$$C = \frac{1}{2 \pi f X_C} = \frac{1}{2 \times \pi \times 796 \times 5} = 39.99 \times 10^{-6} F \quad or \quad approx. \quad 40\mu F$$

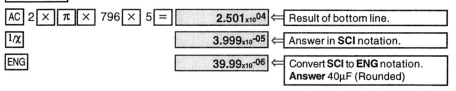

MODE SCI 4	
AC 2 × π × 796 × 5 =	$2.501_{x10}04$ ⟸ Result of bottom line.
1/x	$3.999_{x10}{-05}$ ⟸ Answer in **SCI** notation.
ENG	$39.99_{x10}{-06}$ ⟸ Convert **SCI** to **ENG** notation. **Answer** 40μF (Rounded)

7. **Calculate the frequency at which a 4μF (4 × 10⁻⁶F) capacitor has a reactance of 1kΩ (1 × 10³Ω). Answer to nearest Hz.**

$$f = \frac{1}{2 \pi C X_C} = \frac{1}{2 \times \pi \times 4 \times 10^{-6} \times 1 \times 10^3} = 39.79 \; Hz \quad or \; approx. \quad 40 \; Hz$$

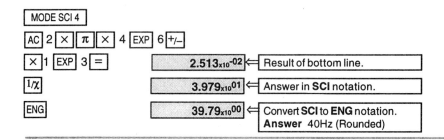

MODE SCI 4	
AC 2 × π × 4 EXP 6 +/−	
× 1 EXP 3 =	$2.513_{x10}{-02}$ ⟸ Result of bottom line.
1/x	$3.979_{x10}01$ ⟸ Answer in **SCI** notation.
ENG	$39.79_{x10}00$ ⟸ Convert **SCI** to **ENG** notation. **Answer** 40Hz (Rounded)

8. At what frequency has a 2000pF (2000 × 10⁻¹²F) capacitor a reactance of 5 ohms?

$$f = \frac{1}{2\pi C X_C} = \frac{1}{2 \times \pi \times 2000 \times 10^{-12} \times 5} = 15.92 \times 10^6 \ Hz \ (15.92 \ MHz)$$

MODE SCI 4

AC 2 × π × 2000 EXP 12 +/–

× 5 =	6.283ₓ₁₀⁻⁰⁸ ⟸ Result of bottom line.
1/χ	1.592ₓ₁₀⁰⁷ ⟸ Answer in **SCI** notation.
ENG	15.92ₓ₁₀⁰⁶ ⟸ 10⁶ = Mega **Answer** 15.92MHz

9. At what frequency has a 6.8pF (6.8 × 10⁻¹²F) capacitor a reactance of 160 ohms?

$$f = \frac{1}{2\pi C X_C} = \frac{1}{2 \times \pi \times 6.8 \times 10^{-12} \times 160} = 146.3 \times 10^6 \ Hz \ (146.3 \ MHz)$$

MODE SCI 4

AC 2 × π × 6.8 EXP 12 +/–

× 160 =	6.836ₓ₁₀⁻⁰⁹ ⟸ Result of bottom line.
1/χ	1.463ₓ₁₀⁰⁸ ⟸ Answer in **SCI** notation.
ENG	146.3ₓ₁₀⁰⁶ ⟸ 10⁶ = Mega **Answer** 146.3MHz

10. A capacitor has a reactance of 1,592Ω at a frequency of 50Hz. What will be the current in the circuit when it is connected to a 200V 50Hz supply?

$$I = \frac{V}{X_C} = \frac{200}{1,592} = 0.1256A \ or \ 125.6 \ mA$$ ⟸ **Note.** Formula similar to Ohm's Law $I = \frac{V}{R}$

MODE SCI 4

| AC 200 ÷ 1592 = | 1.256ₓ₁₀⁻⁰¹ ⟸ Answer in **SCI** notation. |
| ENG | 125.6ₓ₁₀⁻⁰³ ⟸ Convert **SCI** to **ENG** notation. 10⁻³ = milli **Answer** 125.6 mA |

**11. A pure capacitor is connected across a 250V, 100Hz supply.
The current flowing in the circuit is 1A. Calculate the :-
a) reactance of the capacitor X_C in ohms.
b) value of the capacitor.**

a) The reactance :-

$$X_C = \frac{V}{I} = \frac{250}{1} = 250 \; ohms$$

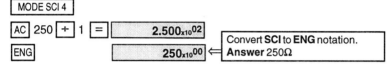

b) Capacitance :-

$$C = \frac{1}{2 \pi f X_C} = \frac{1}{2 \times \pi \times 100 \times 250} = \frac{1}{50000 \times \pi} = 6.366 \times 10^{-6}F = 6.366 \; \mu F$$

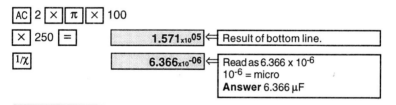

**12. A high power v.h.f. transmitter has a d.c. blocking capacitor in its antenna
circuit of 0.001µF, and rated at 5kV.
What is its reactance when the transmitter is operating at 50MHz?**

$$X_C = \frac{1}{2 \pi f C} = \frac{1}{2 \times \pi \times 50 \times 10^6 \times 0.001 \times 10^{-6}} = 3.183 \; ohms$$

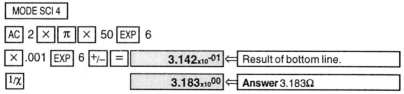

The d.c. blocking capacitor prevents potentially lethal d.c. voltages appearing at the
antenna whilst allowing the passage of r.f. currents.
Note that the voltage rating of the capacitor does not affect the reactance.

Inductive Reactance X_L

Inductive reactance X_L is the ability of a pure inductor to resist the flow of alternating or changing current. It can be considered analogous to resistance in a d.c. circuit; except that no energy or power is dissipated by a pure inductor since all energy used in building up the magnetic field is returned to the circuit when the field collapses.

In practice an inductor has some resistance, mainly due to the material with which it is constructed, and some power will be dissipated. However, when this resistance is very low its effects may be neglected.

The unit of reactance, symbol X, is the ohm, symbol Ω.

Points to note.

1. X_L depends on both inductance and frequency.
2. X_L increases as the frequency is increased.
3. X_L increases as the inductance is increased.
4. The graph fig.6 is a straight line.
5. X_L is considered positive because the alternating voltage across the inductor leads the current by 90°. See figs. 7 and 8.

Formulae to remember :-

$$X_L = \omega L = 2\pi f L$$

Where :-
X_L = Inductive reactance in ohms Ω.
$\omega = 2\pi f$.
L = Inductance in henrys.
f = Frequency in hertz.
I = Current in amps.

Transposing above formula for f and L :-

$$f = \frac{X_L}{2\pi L}$$

$$L = \frac{X_L}{2\pi f}$$

The current I in the circuit :-

$$I = \frac{V}{X_L} = \frac{V}{2\pi f L}$$

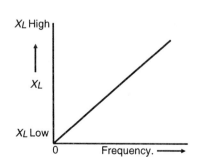

Fig.5 Pure Inductance in the a.c. circuit.   Fig.6 Inductive reactance / Frequency.

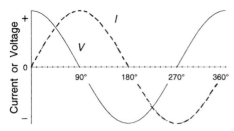

Fig.7 Showing voltage and current relationship in a circuit with pure inductance. Voltage *V* leads current *I* by 90°.

Fig.8 Phasor diagram showing voltage *V* leading current *I* by 90°.

Examples.

13. Calculate the reactance of a 2H inductor at a frequency of 50Hz.

$$X_L = 2 \pi f L = 2 \times \pi \times 50 \times 2 = 200 \times \pi = 628.32 \text{ ohms}$$

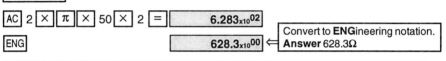

MODE SCI 4

AC 2 × π × 50 × 2 =   6.283_{x10}02

ENG   628.3_{x10}00 ← Convert to **ENG**ineering notation. **Answer** 628.3Ω

---

14. What is the reactance of a 0.5mH (0.5 × 10⁻³H) inductor at a frequency of 10kHz (10 × 10³Hz)?

$$X_L = 2 \pi f L = 2 \times \pi \times 10 \times 10^3 \times 0.5 \times 10^{-3} = 10 \times \pi = 31.42 \text{ ohms}$$

MODE SCI 4

AC 2 × π ×

Frequency in hertz
10kHz = 10 x 10³Hz

Inductance in henrys
0.5mH = 0.5 x 10⁻³H

10 EXP 3 × .5 EXP 3 +/– =   3.142_{x10}01

ENG   31.42_{x10}00 ← Convert to **ENG**ineering notation. **Answer** 31.42Ω

---

15. Calculate the reactance of a 25μH (25 × 10⁻⁶H) inductor at a frequency of 2MHz (2 × 10⁶Hz).

$$X_L = 2 \pi f L = 2 \times \pi \times 2 \times 10^6 \times 25 \times 10^{-6} = 100 \times \pi = 314.16 \text{ ohms}$$

MODE SCI 4

AC 2 × π × 2 EXP 6

× 25 EXP 6 +/– =   3.142_{x10}02

ENG   314.2_{x10}00 ← Convert to **ENG**ineering notation. **Answer** 314.2Ω

16. An 800mH (800 × 10⁻³H) inductor is connected across a 100V, 15.92Hz supply. Calculate :-
a) the inductive reactance X_L.
b) the current I flowing in the circuit.

a) Calculate the inductive reactance :-

$$X_L = 2 \pi f L = 2 \times \pi \times 15.92 \times 800 \times 10^{-3} = 80.02 \ ohms$$

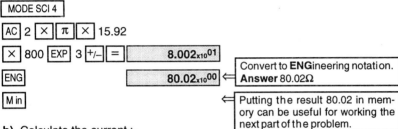

MODE SCI 4

$\boxed{AC}$ 2 $\boxed{\times}$ $\boxed{\pi}$ $\boxed{\times}$ 15.92

$\boxed{\times}$ 800 $\boxed{EXP}$ 3 $\boxed{+/-}$ $\boxed{=}$ $\quad$ 8.002ₓ₁₀⁰¹

$\boxed{ENG}$ $\quad$ 80.02ₓ₁₀⁰⁰ ⟸ Convert to **ENG**ineering notation. **Answer** 80.02Ω

$\boxed{M\ in}$ ⟸ Putting the result 80.02 in memory can be useful for working the next part of the problem.

b) Calculate the current :-

$$I = \frac{V}{X_L} = \frac{100}{80.02} = 1.25 \ amps$$

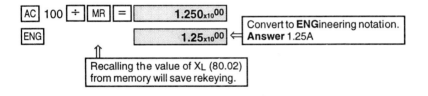

$\boxed{AC}$ 100 $\boxed{\div}$ $\boxed{MR}$ $\boxed{=}$ $\quad$ 1.250ₓ₁₀⁰⁰

$\boxed{ENG}$ $\quad$ 1.25ₓ₁₀⁰⁰ ⟸ Convert to **ENG**ineering notation. **Answer** 1.25A

⇑ Recalling the value of X_L (80.02) from memory will save rekeying.

---

17. What value of inductance has a reactance of 100Ω at a frequency of 796Hz?

Transposing $X_L = 2 \pi f L$ for L gives $L = \dfrac{X_L}{2 \pi f}$

$$L = \frac{X_L}{2 \pi f} = \frac{100}{2 \times \pi \times 796} = \frac{100}{5001} = 0.02H \ or \ 20mH \ (approx.)$$

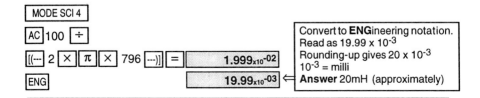

MODE SCI 4

$\boxed{AC}$ 100 $\boxed{\div}$

$\boxed{[(---}$ 2 $\boxed{\times}$ $\boxed{\pi}$ $\boxed{\times}$ 796 $\boxed{---)]}$ $\boxed{=}$ $\quad$ 1.999ₓ₁₀⁻⁰²

$\boxed{ENG}$ $\quad$ 19.99ₓ₁₀⁻⁰³ ⟸

Convert to **ENG**ineering notation. Read as 19.99 x 10⁻³ Rounding-up gives 20 x 10⁻³ 10⁻³ = milli **Answer** 20mH (approximately)

18. Calculate the value of inductance required to provide a reactance of 2kΩ (2 × 10^{3}Ω) at a frequency of 1kHz (1 × 10^{3}Hz).

$$L = \frac{X_L}{2\pi f} = \frac{2 \times 10^3}{2 \times \pi \times 1 \times 10^3} = \frac{1}{\pi} = 0.318H \ \ or \ \ 318mH$$

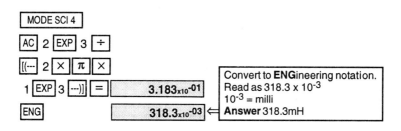

19. The choke used in a power supply unit has a reactance of 3142Ω at a frequency of 50Hz. What is its inductance?

$$L = \frac{X_L}{2\pi f} = \frac{3142}{2 \times \pi \times 50} = \frac{3142}{100 \times \pi} = 10H$$

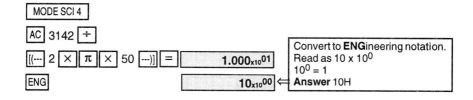

20. A radio frequency inductor has a reactance of 4000Ω at a frequency of 20MHz (20 × 10^{6}Hz). What is its inductance?

$$L = \frac{X_L}{2\pi f} = \frac{4000}{2 \times \pi \times 20 \times 10^6} = \frac{4000}{125.7 \times 10^6} = 31.83 \times 10^{-6}H \ \ or \ \ 31.83\mu H$$

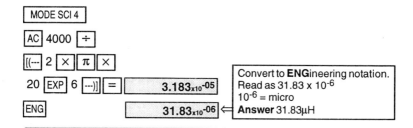

21. What is the frequency at which a 25H inductor has a reactance of 5000Ω?

$$f = \frac{X_L}{2\pi L} = \frac{5000}{2\times\pi\times 25} = \frac{5000}{50\times\pi} = \frac{100}{\pi} = 31.83Hz$$

[MODE SCI 4]

[AC] 5000 [÷]

[[(---] 2 [×] [π] [×] 25 [---)]] [=] **3.183x10^01**

[ENG] **31.83x10^00** ⇐

Convert to **ENG**ineering notation.
Read as 31.83 x 10^0
$10^0 = 1$
Answer 31.83Hz

---

22. At what frequency will a 126.7μH (126.7×10^{-6}H) inductor have a reactance of 1592Ω ?

$$f = \frac{X_L}{2\pi L} = \frac{1592}{2\times\pi\times 126.7\times 10^{-6}} = \frac{1592}{796\times 10^{-6}} = 2\times 10^6 Hz \text{ or } 2MHz$$

[MODE SCI 4]

[AC] 1592 [÷]

[[(---] 2 [×] [π] [×]

126.7 [EXP] 6 [+/−] [---)]] [=] **2.000x10^06** ⇐

Read as 2 x 10^6
10^6 = Mega
Answer 2MHz

---

23. Calculate the frequency at which a 5mH (5×10^{-3}H) inductor will have a reactance of 2000Ω.

$$f = \frac{X_L}{2\pi L} = \frac{2000}{2\times\pi\times 5\times 10^{-3}} = \frac{2000}{31.42\times 10^{-3}} = 63.66\times 10^3 Hz \text{ or } 63.66kHz$$

[MODE SCI 4]

[AC] 2000 [÷]

[[(---] 2 [×] [π] [×]

5 [EXP] 3 [+/−] [---)]] [=] **6.366x10^04**

[ENG] **63.66x10^03** ⇐

Convert to **ENG**ineering notation.
Read as 63.66 x 10^3
10^3 = kilo
Answer 63.66kHz

Notes

Impedance

Chapter 7

Contents

In this section you will calculate the impedance of a circuit with :-

a)   R and L in series.
b)   R and C in series.
c)   R, L and C in series.
d)   R and L in parallel.
e)   R and C in parallel.
f)   R, L and C in parallel.

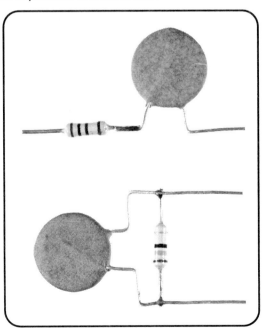

Top picture shows a resistor and
capacitor connected in series.
1.5 x Actual size.

Lower picture shows a resistor and
capacitor connected in parallel.
1.5 x Actual size.

Impedance

R and L in Series

Impedance Z

Impedance, symbol Z, measured in ohms, is the total opposition to current flow in a circuit where resistance R and reactance X are combined.
X may be inductive reactance X_L, or capacitive reactance X_C.

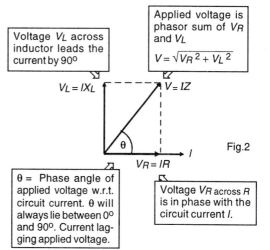

Fig.1

R and L in Series

Figs 1 and 2 show voltage and current relationships in the series R and L circuit.

Voltage V_L across inductor leads the current by 90°

Applied voltage is phasor sum of V_R and V_L

$V = \sqrt{V_R{}^2 + V_L{}^2}$

The Impedance Triangle

Fig 3 shows the impedance Z, with its two components, X_L and R represented by a right angle triangle (The impedance triangle).
The angle θ is the phase angle.
The sides of the triangle are obtained by dividing the voltages V, V_R and V_L in fig.2 by the current, which is common throughout the series circuit.

$V_L = IX_L$

$V = IZ$

θ

$V_R = IR$

I

Fig.2

θ = Phase angle of applied voltage w.r.t. circuit current. θ will always lie between 0° and 90°. Current lagging applied voltage.

Voltage V_R across R is in phase with the circuit current I.

Formulae to remember:-

$$Z^2 = R^2 + X_L{}^2 \quad \Leftarrow \boxed{\text{Applying Pythagoras to the impedance triangle.}}$$

$$\therefore \ Z = \sqrt{R^2 + X_L{}^2} \quad \Leftarrow \boxed{\text{Impedance.}}$$

$$V = \sqrt{V_R{}^2 + V_L{}^2} \quad \Leftarrow \boxed{\text{Applied voltage } V.}$$

$$I = \frac{V}{Z} \quad \Leftarrow \boxed{\text{Circuit current.}}$$

$$\theta = \tan^{-1}\frac{X_L}{R} = \tan^{-1}\frac{\omega L}{R} = \tan^{-1}\frac{2\pi f L}{R} \quad \Leftarrow \boxed{\text{Applied voltage } V \text{ leads the circuit current } I \text{ by the phase angle } \theta.}$$

Fig.3 Impedance triangle for figs.1 and 2.

Examples

1. In a series $R\,L$ circuit, X_L and R are known to be 40Ω and 30Ω respectively. Referring to impedance triangle fig 4, calculate the :-
a) impedance Z of the circuit.
b) phase angle θ.
c) circuit current when the supply voltage V is 100 volts.
d) voltage V_R across the resistor.
e) voltage V_L across the inductor.
f) Show that the supply voltage V is the phasor sum of V_R and V_L.

a) The impedance :-

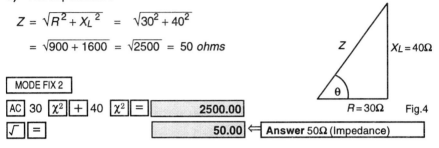

$$Z = \sqrt{R^2 + X_L{}^2} \;=\; \sqrt{30^2 + 40^2}$$

$$= \sqrt{900 + 1600} \;=\; \sqrt{2500} \;=\; 50 \; ohms$$

MODE FIX 2	
AC 30 $\boxed{\chi^2}$ $\boxed{+}$ 40 $\boxed{\chi^2}$ $\boxed{=}$	2500.00
$\boxed{\surd}$ $\boxed{=}$	50.00 ⟵ **Answer** 50Ω (Impedance)

b) The phase angle θ :-

$$\theta = \tan^{-1}\frac{X_L}{R} = \tan^{-1}\frac{40}{30} = \tan^{-1} 1.33 = 53.13 \; degrees$$

Read as "Theta (θ) is the angle whose tangent is X_L/R"

MODE FIX 2	
AC 40 $\boxed{\div}$ 30 $\boxed{=}$	1.33 ⟵ Tangent of angle θ
SHIFT $\boxed{\tan^{-1}}$ $\boxed{=}$	53.13 ⟵ Phase angle of circuit **Answer** 53.13 degrees

Note. *Since this is an inductive circuit, the voltage leads the current by 53.13°.*

c) Current in the series circuit :-

$$I = \frac{V}{Z} = \frac{100}{50} = 2 \; amps$$

AC 100 $\boxed{\div}$ 50 $\boxed{=}$	2.00 ⟵ Answer 2A (Circuit current)

Continued ⟹

d) The voltage across the resistor V_R :-

$V_R = IR = I \times R = 2 \times 30 = 60$ *volts*

MODE FIX 2

[AC] 2 [×] 30 [=]   **60.00** ⇐ **Answer** 60V (V_R)

---

e) The voltage across the inductor V_L :-

$V_L = IX_L = I \times X_L = 2 \times 40 = 80$ *volts*

[AC] 2 [×] 40 [=]   **80.00** ⇐ **Answer** 80V (V_L)

---

f) Show that the supply voltage V is the phasor sum of V_R and V_L.

Note. *Normal addition of the two voltages will not equal the supply voltage V. V is the phasor sum of V_R and V_L. I.e.* $V = \sqrt{V_R{}^2 + V_L{}^2}$

$V = \sqrt{V_R{}^2 + V_L{}^2} = \sqrt{60^2 + 80^2} = \sqrt{3600 + 6400} = \sqrt{10000} = 100$ *volts*

[AC] 60 [χ^2] [+] 80 [χ^2] [=]   **10000.00** ⇐ $V_R{}^2 + V_L{}^2$

[√] [=]   **100.00** ⇐ $\sqrt{V_R{}^2 + V_L{}^2}$
                     Answer 100V (Supply voltage)

---

2. A 90Ω resistor and an inductor of unknown value are connected in series to a 100Hz supply, the resulting impedance is 150Ω. Calculate the reactance of the inductor.

From Pythagoras' Theorem we know that :-

$$Z^2 = R^2 + X_L{}^2$$

so $X_L{}^2 = Z^2 - R^2$

∴ $X_L = \sqrt{Z^2 - R^2} = \sqrt{150^2 - 90^2} = \sqrt{22500 - 8100} = \sqrt{14400} = 120\ \Omega$

MODE FIX 2

[AC] 150 [χ^2] [−] 90 [χ^2] [=]   **14400.00** ⇐ Result of $Z^2 - R^2$

[√] [=]   **120.00** ⇐ **Answer** 120Ω (Reactance of L)

---

7 - 4

3. For the circuit shown in fig.5 calculate :-
a) the impedance **Z**.
b) the phase angle θ.
c) the current *I*.

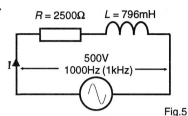

a) The impedance :-

$$Z = \sqrt{R^2 + X_L{}^2} = \sqrt{R^2 + (2\pi f L)^2}$$

$$= \sqrt{2500^2 + (2\times\pi\times 1000\times 796\times 10^{-3})^2} = 5591 \ ohms \ (approx.)$$

| MODE FIX 2 |

| AC | 2500 | χ^2 | + | **6250000.00** ⇐ R^2
| [(--- | 2 | × | π | × | 1000
| × | 796 | EXP | 3 | +/– | ---)] | **5001.42** ⇐ X_L (5000Ω approx. Use later)
| χ^2 | **25014157.05** ⇐ $X_L{}^2$
| = | **31264157.05** ⇐ $R^2 + X_L{}^2$
| √ | = | **5591.44** ⇐ $\sqrt{R^2 + X_L{}^2}$
                                        Answer 5591Ω (Rounded)

b) The phase angle θ :-

From above $X_L = 5000\Omega$ approx. This could have been stored in memory and recalled.

$$\theta = \tan^{-1}\frac{X_L}{R} = \tan^{-1}\frac{5000}{2500} = \tan^{-1} 2 = 63.4 \ degrees$$

| AC | 5000 | ÷ | 2500 | = | **2.00** ⇐ Tangent of angle θ
| SHIFT | tan⁻¹ | = | **63.43** ⇐ Phase angle of circuit
                                         Answer 63.43 degrees

c) Current in the series circuit :-

$$I = \frac{V}{Z} = \frac{500}{5591} = 0.089A \ \ or \ \ 89mA$$

| AC | 500 | ÷ | 5591 | = | **0.09** ⇐ **Answer** 0.09A (Circuit current)
| ENG | **90**ₓ₁₀**-03** ⇐ Read as 90 x 10⁻³ (10⁻³ = milli)
                                         Answer 90mA (The answer has been rounded in the calculator)

7 - 5

Impedance

R and C in series

R and C in series

Figs 6 and 7 show voltage and current relationships in the series RC circuit.
In this case the applied voltage V lags the circuit current by the phase angle θ.
For the RC circuit shown, the phase angle is always negative.

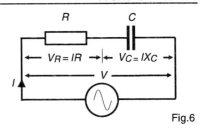

Fig.6

The Impedance Triangle

Fig 8 shows the impedance Z, with its two components, X_C and R represented by a right angle triangle (The impedance triangle). The angle θ is the phase angle.

The sides of the triangle are obtained by dividing the voltages V, V_R and V_C in fig.7 by the current, which is common throughout the series circuit.

θ = Phase angle of applied voltage w.r.t. circuit current. θ will always lie between 0° and -90°. Current leads applied voltage.

Voltage across R, V_R, is in phase with current I in circuit.

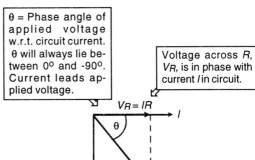

Fig.7

Voltage V_C across capacitor lags the current by 90°.

Applied voltage is phasor sum of V_R and V_C.

$V = \sqrt{V_R{}^2 + V_C{}^2}$

Formulae to remember:-

$$Z^2 = R^2 + X_C{}^2 \quad \Leftarrow \boxed{\text{Applying Pythagoras to the impedance triangle.}}$$

$$\therefore \; Z = \sqrt{R^2 + X_C{}^2} \quad \Leftarrow \boxed{\text{Impedance.}}$$

$$V = \sqrt{V_R{}^2 + V_C{}^2} \quad \Leftarrow \boxed{\text{Applied voltage } V.}$$

$$I = \frac{V}{Z} \quad \Leftarrow \boxed{\text{Circuit current.}}$$

$$\theta = \tan^{-1}\frac{X_C}{R} = \tan^{-1}\frac{1}{\omega C R} \quad \Leftarrow \boxed{\text{Applied voltage } V \text{ lags the circuit current } I \text{ by the phase angle } \theta.}$$

Fig.8 Impedance triangle for figs.6 and 7.

4. A 100Ω resistor and a capacitor having a reactance of 150Ω are connected in series. Calculate the impedance **Z**.

$$Z = \sqrt{R^2 + X_C{}^2} = \sqrt{100^2 + 150^2} = \sqrt{32500} = 180.28 \; ohms$$

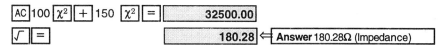

5. Fig.9 shows a series *RC* circuit.
The capacitor has a reactance X_C of
1000Ω at the supply frequency.
The impedance *Z* of the circuit is 2000Ω.
Calculate the :-
a) value of the series resistor *R*.
b) phase angle.

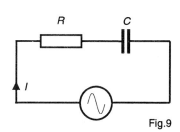

Fig.9

a) The value of resistor *R*.
From Pythagoras' Theorem we know that :-

$$Z^2 = R^2 + X_C{}^2 \quad \text{so that :-}$$

$$R^2 = Z^2 - X_C{}^2$$

$$\therefore \quad R = \sqrt{Z^2 - X_C{}^2} = \sqrt{2000^2 - 1000^2} = \sqrt{3,000,000} = 1732 \; ohms$$

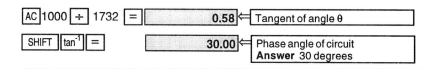

b) The phase angle θ :-

$$\theta = \tan^{-1}\frac{X_C}{R} = \tan^{-1}\frac{1000}{1732} = \tan^{-1} 0.58 = 30 \; degrees$$

AC 1000 ÷ 1732 =	0.58	Tangent of angle θ
SHIFT tan⁻¹ =	30.00	Phase angle of circuit **Answer** 30 degrees

6. A 3.183μF capacitor is connected in series with a 1500Ω resistor.
The combination is connected across a 230V, 50Hz supply.
Calculate the :-
a) impedance *Z* of the circuit.
b) phase angle.
c) current flowing in the circuit.
d) voltage across *R*, V_R.
e) voltage across *C*, V_C.
f) Show that the phasor sum of V_R and V_C equals the supply voltage.

a) Impedance *Z* of the circuit :-

$$Z = \sqrt{R^2 + X_C^2} = \sqrt{R^2 + \left(\frac{1}{2\pi f C}\right)^2} = \sqrt{1500^2 + 1000^2} = 1803\ ohms$$

One method of solving this problem is to first calculate the capacitive reactance X_C
and square it, then add R^2 and take the root of the sum of the squares.

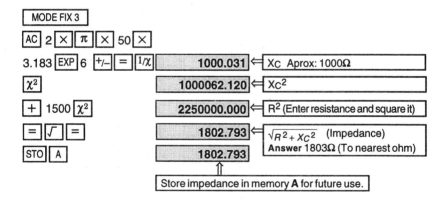

b) The phase angle θ :-

$$\theta = \tan^{-1}\frac{X_C}{R} = \tan^{-1}\frac{1000}{1500} = \tan^{-1}0.67 = 33.69\ degrees$$

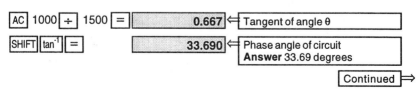

Continued ⇒

c) Current in the series circuit :-

$$I = \frac{V}{Z} = \frac{230}{1802.793} = 0.1276A \quad or \quad 128mA \,(Rounded)$$

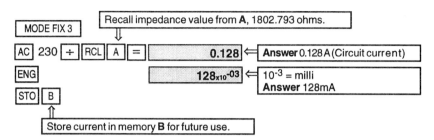

MODE FIX 3 | Recall impedance value from **A**, 1802.793 ohms.

AC 230 ÷ RCL A = | **0.128** ⇐ Answer 0.128 A (Circuit current)

ENG | **128ₓ₁₀-03** ⇐ 10⁻³ = milli / Answer 128mA

STO B

Store current in memory **B** for future use.

d) Voltage across *R*, V_R.

$$V_R = IR = I \times R = 0.1276 \times 1500 = 191.37 \, volts$$

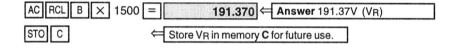

AC RCL B × 1500 = | **191.370** ⇐ Answer 191.37V (V_R)

STO C | ⇐ Store V_R in memory **C** for future use.

e) Voltage across *C*, V_C :-

$$V_C = IX_C = I \times X_C = 0.1276 \times 1000 = 127.6 \, volts$$

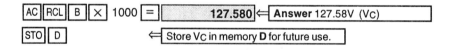

AC RCL B × 1000 = | **127.580** ⇐ Answer 127.58V (V_C)

STO D | ⇐ Store V_C in memory **D** for future use.

f) Show that the supply voltage *V*, is the phasor sum of V_R and V_C :-

Note. *Normal addition of the two voltages will not equal the supply voltage V.*
V is the phasor sum of V_R and V_C. I.e. $V = \sqrt{V_R{}^2 + V_C{}^2}$

$$V = \sqrt{V_R{}^2 + V_C{}^2} = \sqrt{191.37^2 + 127.6^2} = \sqrt{52899} = 229.998 \, volts$$

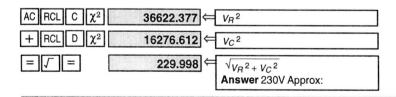

AC RCL C χ² | **36622.377** ⇐ $V_R{}^2$

+ RCL D χ² | **16276.612** ⇐ $V_C{}^2$

= √ = | **229.998** ⇐ $\sqrt{V_R{}^2 + V_C{}^2}$ / **Answer** 230V Approx:

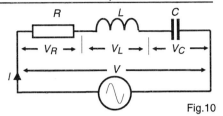

Fig.10

R, L and C in series

In the series circuit of fig.10, the current is the same throughout the circuit. Since V_L and V_C are 180° out of phase the voltage across the effective reactance is the difference between V_L and V_C, i.e. V_L-V_C.

Fig 11c shows V_L greater than V_C. The circuit is inductive.
Fig.12c shows V_C greater than V_L. The circuit is capacitive.

From the phasor diagrams it is possible to construct the impedance and voltage triangles of figs 11 and 12. Pythagoras may be used to solve the triangles as before.

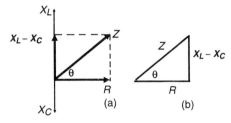

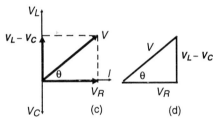

Fig.11 a,b,c,d. Showing phasor diagrams and impedance and voltage triangles when $X_L > X_C$

Formulae to remember :-

$$Z = \sqrt{R^2 + (X_L - X_C)^2}$$

$$V = \sqrt{V_R^2 + (V_L - V_C)^2}$$

$$\theta = \tan^{-1} \frac{(X_L - X_C)}{R}$$

$$Z = \frac{V}{I}$$

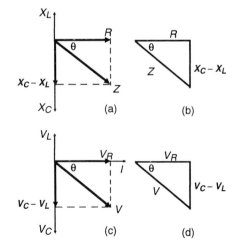

Fig.12 a,b,c,d. Showing phasor diagrams and impedance and voltage triangles when $X_C > X_L$

7. For the series circuit shown in fig.13 calculate :-
a) the impedance Z.
b) the circuit current I.
c) voltage across R, V_R.
d) voltage across L, V_L.
e) voltage across C, V_C.
f) circuit phase angle θ.
g) Test that the phasor sum of V_R, V_L, and V_C equals the applied voltage of 240V.
h) the inductance L.
i) the capacitance C.

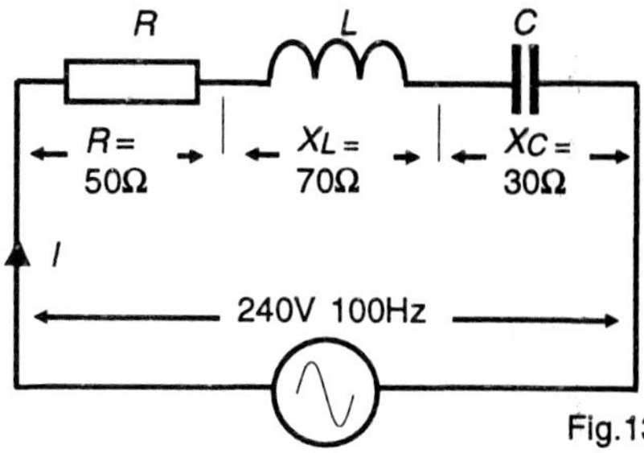

R   L   C

$R = 50\Omega$ $X_L = 70\Omega$ $X_C = 30\Omega$

I

240V 100Hz

Fig.13

a) Calculate Z:-

$$Z = \sqrt{R^2 + (X_L - X_C)^2} = \sqrt{50^2 + (70-30)^2} = \sqrt{50^2 + 40^2} = \sqrt{4100} = 64 \ \Omega \ approx.$$

MODE FIX 2

$\boxed{AC}$ 50 $\boxed{\chi^2}$ $\boxed{+}$

$\boxed{[(\cdots}$ 70 $\boxed{-}$ 30 $\boxed{\cdots)]}$ $\boxed{\chi^2}$

$\boxed{=}$ $\boxed{\sqrt{}}$ $\boxed{=}$ 64.03 ⇐ Answer 64.03Ω (Impedance)

b) Calculate the circuit current I.

$$I = \frac{V}{Z} = \frac{240}{64} = 3.75 \ amps.$$

$\boxed{AC}$ 240 $\boxed{\div}$ 64.03 $\boxed{=}$ 3.75 ⇐ Answer 3.75A

c) Calculate the voltage across R, V_R.

$$V_R = I R = 3.75 \times 50 = 187.5 \ volts$$

$\boxed{AC}$ 3.75 $\boxed{\times}$ 50 $\boxed{=}$ 187.50 ⇐ Answer 187.5V (V_R)

d) Calculate the voltage across L, V_L.

$$V_L = I X_L = 3.75 \times 70 = 262.5 \ volts$$

$\boxed{AC}$ 3.75 $\boxed{\times}$ 70 $\boxed{=}$ 262.50 ⇐ Answer 262.5V (V_L)

Continued ⇒

e) Calculate the voltage across C, V_C.

$V_C = I X_C = 3.75 \times 30 = 112.5 \ volts$

| AC | 3.75 | $\times$ | 30 | $=$ | 112.50 | $\Leftarrow$ **Answer** 112.5V (V_C) |

f) The circuit phase angle θ.

$\theta = \tan^{-1} \dfrac{X_L - X_C}{R} = \tan^{-1} \dfrac{70 - 30}{50} = \tan^{-1} 0.8 = 38.66 \ degrees$

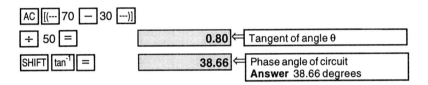

| AC | [(--- 70 | $-$ | 30 | ---)] |

| $\div$ | 50 | $=$ | 0.80 | $\Leftarrow$ Tangent of angle θ |

| SHIFT | $\tan^{-1}$ | $=$ | 38.66 | $\Leftarrow$ Phase angle of circuit **Answer** 38.66 degrees |

g) Test that the phasor sum of V_R, V_L, and V_C equals the 240 volts applied.

$V = \sqrt{V_R{}^2 + (V_L - V_C)^2} = \sqrt{187.5^2 + (262.5 - 112.5)^2}$

$= \sqrt{187.5^2 + 150^2} = \sqrt{57656.25} = 240.12 \ V$

| AC | 187.5 | χ^2 | $+$ |

| [(--- 262.5 | $-$ | 112.5 | ---)] | χ^2 |

| $=$ | $\sqrt{\ }$ | $=$ | 240.12 | $\Leftarrow$ **Answer** 240V (Approx:) |

> **Note.** Slight differences in the results are due to rounding errors.

h) Calculate the inductance L.

$X_L = 2 \pi f L$ Therefore by transposition :-

$L = \dfrac{X_L}{2 \pi f} = \dfrac{70}{2 \times \pi \times 100} = \dfrac{70}{628.3} = 0.1114 H \ or \ 111.4 \ mH$

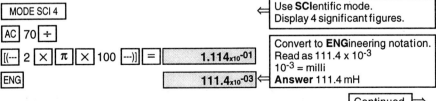

| MODE SCI 4 | $\Leftarrow$ Use **SCI**entific mode. Display 4 significant figures. |

| AC | 70 | $\div$ |

| [(--- 2 | $\times$ | π | $\times$ | 100 | ---)] | $=$ | $1.114_{x10^{-01}}$ | Convert to **ENG**ineering notation. Read as 111.4 x 10^{-3} 10^{-3} = milli |

| ENG | | $111.4_{x10^{-03}}$ | $\Leftarrow$ **Answer** 111.4 mH |

| Continued $\Rightarrow$ |

i) Calculate the capacitance C.

$X_C = \dfrac{1}{2\pi f C}$ Therefore by transposition :-

$C = \dfrac{1}{2\pi f X_C} = \dfrac{1}{2 \times \pi \times 100 \times 30} = \dfrac{1}{18849.56} = 53.05 \times 10^{-6} F = 53\ \mu F$ *approx.*

MODE SCI 4

$\boxed{\text{AC}}$ 1 $\boxed{\div}$ $\boxed{[(\cdots}$ 2 $\boxed{\times}$ $\boxed{\pi}$ $\boxed{\times}$

100 $\boxed{\times}$ 30 $\boxed{\cdots)]}$ $\boxed{=}$ **5.305**$_{x10}$**-05**

$\boxed{\text{ENG}}$ **53.05**$_{x10}$**-06**

⟸ Use **SCI**entific mode.
Display 4 significant figures.

Convert to **ENG**ineering notation.
Read as 53.05×10^{-6}
$10^{-6} =$ micro
Answer $53.05\ \mu F$

---

8. Referring to the series circuit shown in fig.14 calculate the:-
a) impedance Z.
b) current I.

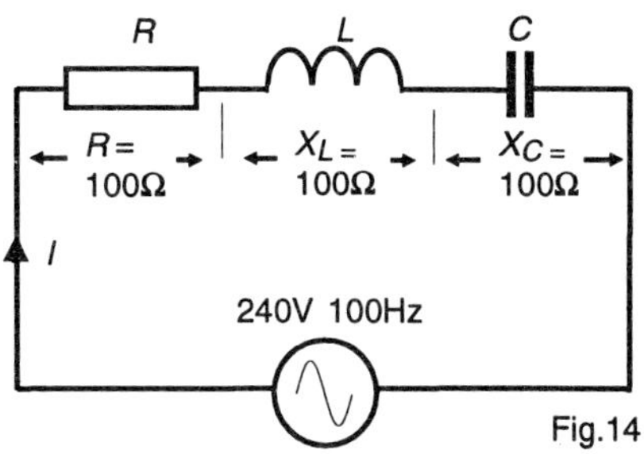

Fig.14

a) The impedance Z:-

$$Z = \sqrt{R^2 + (X_L - X_C)^2} = \sqrt{100^2 + (100 - 100)^2} = \sqrt{100^2} = 100\ \Omega$$

MODE FIX 2

$\boxed{\text{AC}}$ 100 $\boxed{x^2}$ $\boxed{+}$

$\boxed{[(\cdots}$ 100 $\boxed{-}$ 100 $\boxed{\cdots)]}$ $\boxed{x^2}$

$\boxed{=}$ $\boxed{\sqrt{}}$ $\boxed{=}$ **100.00** ⟸ **Answer** 100Ω (Resistive)

Note. Since X_L and X_C cancel; the net reactance is zero - this is the condition for resonance, see next section. The circuit phase angle is zero. The current and voltage are in phase and the circuit is resistive.

b) Calculate the circuit current I.

$$I = \frac{V}{Z} = \frac{240}{100} = 2.4\ amps.$$

$\boxed{\text{AC}}$ 240 $\boxed{\div}$ 100 $\boxed{=}$ **2.40** ⟸ **Answer** 2.4A

R and L in Parallel

In the parallel a.c. circuit the supply voltage, *V*, across each component is the same, and also in the same phase.

In the parallel *RL* circuit of fig.15, *I_R* is in phase with the circuit voltage, *V*, and the current in the inductor, *I_L*, lags the voltage by 90°.

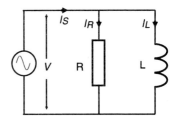

Fig.15

Fig 16 shows the voltage and current relationships in the parallel *RL* circuit.

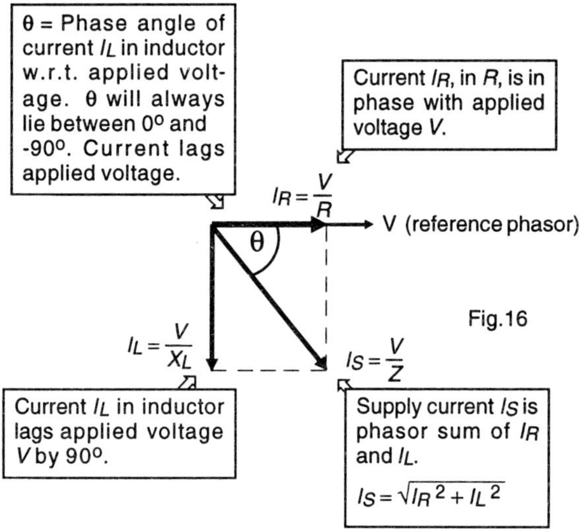

θ = Phase angle of current I_L in inductor w.r.t. applied voltage. θ will always lie between 0° and -90°. Current lags applied voltage.

Current I_R, in *R*, is in phase with applied voltage *V*.

Formulae to remember

$I_R = \dfrac{V}{R}$ (in phase with *V*)

$I_L = \dfrac{V}{X_L}$ (lags *V* by 90°)

Where $X_L = \omega L = 2\pi f L$

$I_S = \sqrt{I_R^2 + I_L^2}$

$Z = \dfrac{V}{I_S}$

$\theta = \tan^{-1} \dfrac{I_L}{I_R}$

$I_R = \dfrac{V}{R}$

V (reference phasor)

Fig.16

$I_L = \dfrac{V}{X_L}$

$I_S = \dfrac{V}{Z}$

Current I_L in inductor lags applied voltage *V* by 90°.

Supply current I_S is phasor sum of I_R and I_L.

$I_S = \sqrt{I_R^2 + I_L^2}$

Example.
9. Refer to fig.17. From the information given, calculate the :-

a) supply current *I_S*.
b) impedance Z.
c) phase angle.

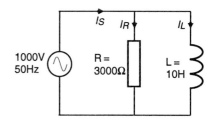

Fig.17

a) To calculate the supply current first calculate the current in each branch.

Current in resistor :- $I_R = \dfrac{V}{R} = \dfrac{1000}{3000} = 0.333 A$

Continued ⟹

7 - 14

MODE FIX 3

| AC | 1000 | ÷ | 3000 | = | **0.333** | ⇐ Answer 0.333A (current in resistor) |

| STO | A | | ⇐ Store I_R in memory **A** for future use. |

Current in inductor :- $I_L = \dfrac{V}{X_L} = \dfrac{V}{2\pi f L} = \dfrac{1000}{2 \times \pi \times 50 \times 10} = \dfrac{1000}{3142} = 0.318A$

| AC | 1000 | ÷ | [(⸱⸱⸱ | 2 | × | π | × |

| 50 | × | 10 | ⸱⸱⸱)] | = | **0.318** | ⇐ Answer 0.318A (current in inductor) |

| STO | B | | ⇐ Store I_L in memory **B** for future use. |

Total current :- $I_S = \sqrt{I_R^2 + I_L^2} = \sqrt{0.333^2 + 0.318^2} = \sqrt{0.212} = 0.46A$

| AC | RCL | A | x^2 | **0.111** | ⇐ I_R^2 |

| + | RCL | B | x^2 | **0.101** | ⇐ I_L^2 |

| = | √ | = | **0.461** | ⇐ $\sqrt{I_R^2 + I_L^2}$ **Answer** 0.46A (Supply current) |

| STO | C |

Store I_S in memory **C** for future use.

Differences due to rounding in one case, and the calculator working to its full accuracy in the other.

b) Impedance :-

$Z = \dfrac{V}{I_S} = \dfrac{V}{\sqrt{I_R^2 + I_L^2}} = \dfrac{1000}{0.46} = 2173.9\Omega$ *(rounded)*

| AC | 1000 | ÷ | RCL | C | = | **2169.650** | ⇐ Answer 2169.65 Ω |

c) Phase angle :-

$\theta = \tan^{-1}\dfrac{I_L}{I_R} = \tan^{-1}\dfrac{0.318}{0.333} = \tan^{-1} 0.955 = 43.68^o$

| AC | RCL | B | **0.318** | ⇐ I_L Current in inductor 0.318A |

| ÷ | RCL | A | **0.333** | ⇐ I_R Current in resistor 0.333A |

| = | SHIFT | tan⁻¹ | = | **43.679** | ⇐ **Answer** 43.68 degrees (rounded). The current, I_S, laging the applied voltage, V, by 43.68°, the phase angle of the circuit. |

R and C in Parallel

In the parallel a.c. circuit the supply voltage, V, across each component is the same, and also in the same phase.

In the parallel RC circuit of fig.18, I_R is in phase with the circuit voltage, V, and the current through the capacitor, I_C, leads the voltage by $90°$.

Fig 19 shows the voltage and current relationships in the parallel RC circuit.

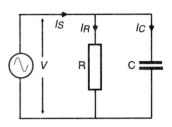

Fig.18

Formulae to remember

$$I_R = \frac{V}{R} \text{ (in phase with } V)$$

$$I_C = \frac{V}{X_C} \text{ (leads } V \text{ by } 90°)$$

Where $X_C = \dfrac{1}{\omega C} = \dfrac{1}{2\pi f C}$

$$I_S = \sqrt{I_R^2 + I_C^2}$$

$$Z = \frac{V}{I_S}$$

$$\theta = \tan^{-1} \frac{I_C}{I_R}$$

Current I_C through the capacitor leads the applied voltage V by $90°$.

Supply current I_S is phasor sum of I_R and I_C.

$$I_S = \sqrt{I_R^2 + I_C^2}$$

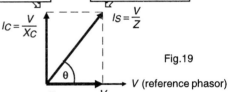

$$I_C = \frac{V}{X_C}$$

$$I_S = \frac{V}{Z}$$

Fig.19

V (reference phasor)

$$I_R = \frac{V}{R}$$

$\theta =$ Phase angle of circuit current w.r.t. applied voltage. θ will always lie between $0°$ and $90°$. Current leading applied voltage.

Current in R, I_R, is in phase with the applied voltage V.

Example.

10. Refer to fig.20. From the information given, calculate the :-

a) supply current I_S.
b) impedance Z.
c) phase angle.

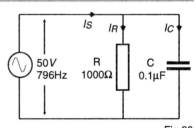

Fig.20

a) To calculate the supply current first calculate the current in each branch.

Current in resistor $I_R = \dfrac{V}{R} = \dfrac{50}{1000} = 0.05A \ (50mA)$

Continued ⟹

MODE FIX 3

| AC | 50 | ÷ | 1000 | = | 0.050 | ⇐ Answer 0.05A (current in resistor) |

Current in capacitor :-

$$I_C = \frac{V}{X_C} = \frac{V}{\frac{1}{2\pi f C}} = \frac{50}{\frac{1}{2 \times \pi \times 796 \times 0.1 \times 10^{-6}}} = \frac{50}{2000} = 0.025A \ (25mA)$$

AC | 50 | ÷

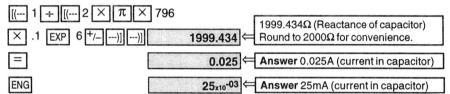

[(--- | 1 | ÷ | [(--- | 2 | × | π | × | 796

× | .1 | EXP | 6 | +/− | ---)] | ---)] | 1999.434 ⇐ 1999.434Ω (Reactance of capacitor) Round to 2000Ω for convenience.

= | 0.025 ⇐ Answer 0.025A (current in capacitor)

ENG | 25ₓ₁₀⁻⁰³ ⇐ Answer 25mA (current in capacitor)

Total current :- $I_S = \sqrt{I_R^2 + I_C^2} = \sqrt{0.05^2 + 0.025^2} = \sqrt{0.003} = 0.056A \ (56mA)$

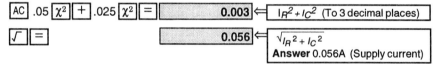

AC | .05 | χ^2 | + | .025 | χ^2 | = | 0.003 ⇐ $I_R^2 + I_C^2$ (To 3 decimal places)

√ | = | 0.056 ⇐ $\sqrt{I_R^2 + I_C^2}$
Answer 0.056A (Supply current)

b) Impedance :-

$$Z = \frac{V}{I_S} = \frac{50}{0.056} = 893\Omega \ (rounded)$$

AC | 50 | ÷ | .056 | = | 892.857 ⇐ Answer 893 Ω (rounded)

c) Phase angle :-

$$\theta = \tan^{-1}\frac{I_C}{I_R} = \tan^{-1}\frac{0.025}{0.05} = \tan^{-1} 0.5 = 26.57° \ (rounded\ )$$

AC | .025 | ÷ | .05 | = | 0.500 ⇐ Tangent of angle θ

SHIFT | tan⁻¹ | = | 26.565 ⇐ **Answer** 26.57 degrees (rounded)
The current, I_S, leading the applied voltage, V, by 26.57°, the phase angle of the circuit.

RL and C in Parallel

In the parallel a.c. circuit the supply voltage, *V*, across each component is the same, and also in the same phase.

In the parallel *RL & C* circuit of fig.21, I_R is in phase with the circuit voltage, *V*, the current through the capacitor, I_C, leads the voltage by 90°, and I_L lags the voltage by 90°.

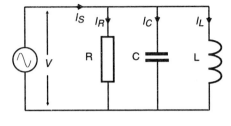

Fig.21

The voltage and current relationships are shown in fig.22.

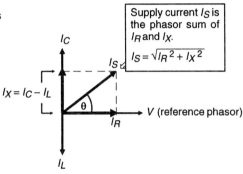

Supply current I_S is the phasor sum of I_R and I_X.

$$I_S = \sqrt{I_R^2 + I_X^2}$$

Formulae to remember

$I_R = \dfrac{V}{R}$ (in phase with V)

$I_C = \dfrac{V}{X_C}$ (leads V by 90°)

Where $X_C = \dfrac{1}{\omega C} = \dfrac{1}{2\pi f C}$

$I_L = \dfrac{V}{X_L}$ (lags V by 90°)

Fig.22. Phasor diagram showing current I_C greater than I_L.
Net reactive current $I_X = I_C - I_L$

Where $X_L = \omega L = 2\pi f L$

Total reactive current $I_X = I_C - I_L$

Total circuit current $I_S = \sqrt{I_R^2 + I_X^2}$

$Z = \dfrac{V}{I_S}$ $\theta = \tan^{-1}\dfrac{I_X}{I_R}$

Example.
11. From the information given in fig.23, calculate the :-

a) total supply current I_S.
b) impedance Z.

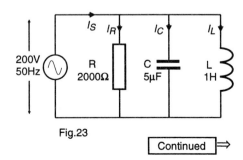

Fig.23

Continued ⇒

a) To calculate the supply current first calculate the current in each branch.

Current in resistor :- $I_R = \dfrac{V}{R} = \dfrac{200}{2000} = 0.1A$ $(100mA)$

| MODE FIX 3 |

| AC | 200 | $\div$ | 2000 | $=$ | | 0.100 | $\Leftarrow$ **Answer** 0.1A (current in resistor) |

Current in inductor :- $I_L = \dfrac{V}{X_L} = \dfrac{V}{2\,\pi\,f\,L} = \dfrac{200}{2 \times \pi \times 50 \times 1} = \dfrac{200}{314.16} = 0.637A$

| AC | 200 | $\div$ | [(--- | 2 | $\times$ | π | $\times$ |

| 50 | $\times$ | 1 | ---)] | $=$ | | 0.637 | $\Leftarrow$ Answer 0.637A (current in inductor) |

Current in capacitor :-

$$I_C = \frac{V}{X_C} = \frac{200}{\dfrac{1}{2\,\pi\,f\,C}} = \frac{200}{\dfrac{1}{2 \times \pi \times 50 \times 5 \times 10^{-6}}} = \frac{200}{636.62} = 0.314A$$

| AC | 200 | $\div$ |

| [(--- | 1 | $\div$ | [(--- | 2 | $\times$ | π | $\times$ | 50 |

| $\times$ | 5 | EXP | 6 | $^{+/-}$ | ---)] | ---)] | | 636.620 | $\Leftarrow$ 636.620Ω (Reactance of capacitor) |

| $=$ | | 0.314 | $\Leftarrow$ **Answer** 0.314A (current in capacitor) |

Total current :-

$$I_S = \sqrt{I_R{}^2 + (I_L - I_C)^2} = \sqrt{0.1^2 + (0.637 - 0.314)^2} = \sqrt{0.114} = 0.338A$$

| AC | .1 | χ^2 | $+$ | [(--- | .637 | $-$ | .314 | ---)] | χ^2 | $=$ | | 0.114 | $\Leftarrow$ $I_R{}^2 + I_X{}^2$ |

| $\sqrt{}$ | $=$ | | 0.338 | $\Leftarrow$ $\sqrt{I_R{}^2 + I_X{}^2}$ **Answer** 0.338A (Supply current) |

b) Circuit impedance Z :-

$$Z = \frac{V}{I_S} = \frac{200}{0.338} = 591.72\Omega$$

| AC | 200 | $\div$ | .338 | $=$ | | 591.716 | $\Leftarrow$ **Answer** 591.716Ω (Impedance) |

Notes

Resonance

Chapter 8

Contents

In this section you will:-

a) calculate the resonant frequency of the series $L \, C$ circuit.
b) calculate the resonant frequency of the parallel $L \, C$ circuit.
c) calculate the selectivity, bandwidth, and Q factor of tuned circuits.

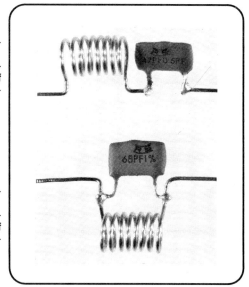

Top picture. A 47pF capacitor connected in series with an inductor. This circuit is resonant at approximately 44MHz. Changing the value of the components will change the resonant frequency. 1.5 x Actual size.

Lower picture. A 68pF capacitor connected in parallel with an inductor. This circuit is resonant at approximately 40MHz. Changing the value of the components will change the resonant frequency. 1.5 x Actual size.

Resonant Circuits

Circuits containing L and C connected in series or parallel, and tuned to resonance, are commonly used for tuning oscillators, radio receivers and transmitters, and in filters capable of selecting one particular frequency from a whole band of frequencies.

Resonance is a condition occurring in both series and parallel LC circuits. It occurs when the inductive reactance X_L is equal in magnitude and opposite in sign to the capacitive reactance X_C.

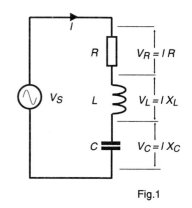

Fig.1

Resonance occurs when $X_L = X_C$

Therefore $2\pi f_r L = \dfrac{1}{2\pi f_r C}$

By transposition $f_r = \dfrac{1}{2\pi\sqrt{L\,C}}$

The Series Tuned Circuit

Fig.1 shows LC and R in series. Where R is the series resistance of the circuit, usually due to the ohmic resistance of the inductor.

Fig.2 shows reactance / frequency curves for X_L and X_C. It also shows that the resonant frequency occurs when $X_L = X_C$.

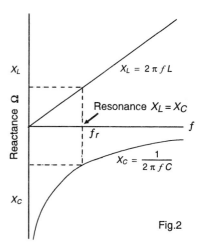

Fig.2

Fig.3 The response curve shows that the current in the series circuit is maximum at resonance and is limited by the series resistance R, fig.1.

Where :-
X_C = Capacitive reactance in ohms Ω.
X_L = Inductive reactance in ohms Ω.
C = Capacitance in farads.
L = Inductance in henrys.
f_r = Resonant frequency in hertz.
I = Current in amps.
$\omega = 2\pi f$

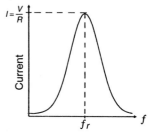

Fig.3

Points to note (Series circuit)

1. At resonance $X_L = X_C$. The reactances cancel. The net reactance is zero.
2. At resonance the series circuit is resistive. (R is low.)
3. At resonance the circuit current is limited only by the series resistance.
4. The lower the value of R, the sharper will be the response curve of fig.3.
5. The voltage developed across the reactive components can be higher than the supply voltage. This is Voltage magnification. Refer to Q Factor P8-19.
6. At resonance all the supply voltage is developed across R. $\therefore V_R = V_S$.
7. The voltage across the capacitor, $V_C = I\, X_C$.
8. The voltage across the inductor, $V_L = I\, X_L$.
9. The series circuit passes current easily at the resonant frequency.
10. A series resonant circuit is often referred to as an 'Acceptor Circuit'.
11. The value of R has no effect on the resonant frequency of the series circuit.
12. The series circuit is capacitive below resonance, inductive above resonance, and resistive at resonance.

Formulae to remember:-

$$f_r = \frac{1}{2\pi\sqrt{L\,C}}$$ The general formula for finding the resonant frequency.

$$C = \frac{1}{4\pi^2 f_r^2 L}$$ To calculate the capacitance when f_r and L are known.

$$L = \frac{1}{4\pi^2 f_r^2 C}$$ To calculate the inductance when f_r and C are known.

The current flowing in the circuit at resonance. $I = \dfrac{V}{R}$

The voltage developed across L. $V_L = I \times X_L = I\, X_L$

The voltage developed across C. $V_C = I \times X_C = I\, X_C = \dfrac{I}{\omega C}$

The magnification factor Q, of the series resonant circuit is given by:-

$$Q = \frac{X_L}{R} = \frac{\omega L}{R} = \frac{2\pi f L}{R}$$ if the inductive reactance is considered, or :-

$$Q = \frac{X_C}{R} = \frac{1}{\omega C R} = \frac{1}{2\pi f C R}$$ if the capacitive reactance is considered.

$$Q = \frac{V_L}{V_R}$$ if the voltage developed across the inductor is considered, or :-

$$Q = \frac{V_C}{V_R}$$ if the voltage developed across the capacitor is considered.

Resonance

The Series Tuned Circuit

Examples.

1. Calculate the resonant frequency of the series circuit shown in fig.4.
Where L = 10mH $(10 \times 10^{-3}H)$.
and C = 1μF $(1 \times 10^{-6}F)$.

Substitute the known values:-

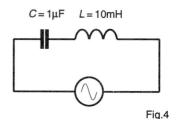

C = 1μF L = 10mH

Fig.4

$$f_r = \frac{1}{2\pi\sqrt{LC}} = \frac{1}{2\pi\sqrt{10mH \times 1\mu F}} = \frac{1}{2 \times \pi \times \sqrt{(10 \times 10^{-3}H) \times (1 \times 10^{-6}F)}}$$

$$= \frac{1}{6.283 \times 10^{-4}} = 1592Hz$$

Enter 10×10^{-3} as 10 [EXP] 3 [+/-]

Enter 1×10^{-6} as 1 [EXP] 6 [+/-]

Note. When using the calculator it is often convenient to evaluate the bottom line of the equation first, and finally use the $\boxed{1/x}$ key to obtain the reciprocal.

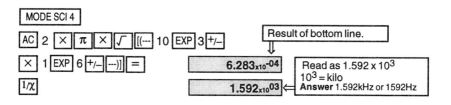

2. A series LC circuit has C = 40pF $(40 \times 10^{-12}F)$ and L = 10μH $(10 \times 10^{-6}H)$. What is the resonant frequency?

Substitute the known values :-

$$f_r = \frac{1}{2\pi\sqrt{LC}} = \frac{1}{2\pi\sqrt{10\mu H \times 40pF}} = \frac{1}{2 \times \pi \times \sqrt{(10 \times 10^{-6}H) \times (40 \times 10^{-12}F)}}$$

$$= \frac{1}{1.257 \times 10^{-7}} = 7.96 \times 10^{6}Hz = 7.96MHz$$

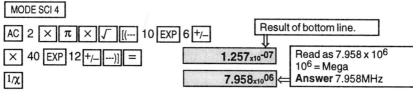

3. The circuit shown in fig.5 is operating at its resonant frequency :-
a) What is the current flowing in *R*?
b) What is the voltage V_L, across *L*?
c) What is the voltage V_C, across *C*?
d) What is the *Q* factor of the circuit?
e) Given that the resonant frequency is 7.960MHz. Calculate approximate values for *L* and *C*.

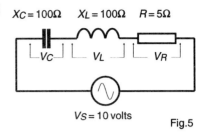

$X_C = 100\Omega$ $X_L = 100\Omega$ $R = 5\Omega$

$V_S = 10$ volts

Fig.5

a) At resonance the reactances X_L and X_C cancel, the net impedance of the circuit is *R*. In this case $R = 5\Omega$. Therefore :-

$$I = \frac{V_S}{R} = \frac{10}{5} = 2 \; amps$$

Note. At resonance, since X_L and X_C cancel, the supply voltage is developed across *R*. Therefore, at resonance, $V_S = V_R$.

MODE NORM 2

AC 10 ÷ 5 = | 2 ⟵ **Answer** 2 amps flow in *R*

b) The voltage across the inductor $V_L = I \, X_L = I \times X_L = 2 \times 100 = 200 \; volts.$

AC 2 × 100 = | 200 ⟵ **Answer** VL = 200 volts

c) The voltage across the capacitor $V_C = I \, X_C = I \times X_C = 2 \times 100 = 200 \; volts.$

AC 2 × 100 = | 200 ⟵ **Answer** VC = 200 volts

d) We have enough information about this circuit to use any of the formulae for *Q* given previously in this section.

$$Q = \frac{X_L}{R} = \frac{100}{5} = 20$$

AC 100 ÷ 5 = | 20 ⟵ **Answer** Q = 20

We can check the value of *Q* by using one of the alternative formulae:-

$$Q = \frac{V_L}{V_R} = \frac{200}{10} = 20$$

AC 200 ÷ 10 = | 20 ⟵ **Answer** Q = 20   Continued ⟹

8 - 5

e) You have been given the resonant frequency, 7.960MHz, and the values of X_L and X_C, now calculate the values of L and C.

Calculate L. By transposition make L the subject of the X_L formula:-

$$X_L = 2 \pi f L \quad \text{Therefore, by transposition} \quad L = \frac{X_L}{2 \pi f}$$

$$L = \frac{X_L}{2 \pi f} = \frac{100}{2 \times \pi \times 7.960 \times 10^6} = 1.999 \times 10^{-6} H \;\; or \; approx. \; 2\mu H$$

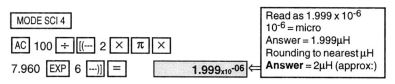

MODE SCI 4

AC 100 ÷ [(--- 2 × π ×

7.960 EXP 6 ---)] =   1.999ₓ₁₀⁻⁰⁶

Read as 1.999×10^{-6}
10^{-6} = micro
Answer = 1.999μH
Rounding to nearest μH
Answer = 2μH (approx:)

Calculate C. By transposition make C the subject of the X_C formula:-

$$X_C = \frac{1}{2 \pi f C} \quad \text{Therefore, by transposition} \quad C = \frac{1}{2 \pi f X_C}$$

$$C = \frac{1}{2 \pi f X_C} = \frac{1}{2 \times \pi \times 7.960 \times 10^6 \times 100} = 199.9 \times 10^{-12} F \;\; or \; approx. \; 200pF$$

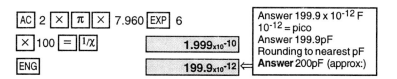

AC 2 × π × 7.960 EXP 6

× 100 = 1/χ   1.999ₓ₁₀⁻¹⁰

ENG   199.9ₓ₁₀⁻¹²

Answer 199.9×10^{-12} F
10^{-12} = pico
Answer 199.9pF
Rounding to nearest pF
Answer 200pF (approx:)

To check the calculated values of L and C, substitute them into the formula for resonance, and compare the result with the given resonant frequency.
The answer will be approximate due to rounding.

$$f_r = \frac{1}{2 \pi \sqrt{L C}} = \frac{1}{2 \times \pi \times \sqrt{2 \times 10^{-6} \times 200 \times 10^{-12}}} = 7.958 \times 10^6 Hz = 7.958 MHz$$

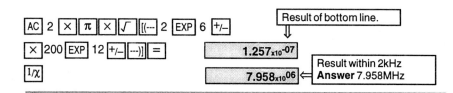

AC 2 × π × √ [(--- 2 EXP 6 +/–

× 200 EXP 12 +/– ---)] =   1.257ₓ₁₀⁻⁰⁷

1/χ   7.958ₓ₁₀⁰⁶

Result of bottom line.

Result within 2kHz
Answer 7.958MHz

4. A series *LC* circuit is required to resonate at a frequency of 8.388MHz (8.388×10^6Hz). The inductor chosen has an inductance of 18 µH (18×10^{-6}H). What value of capacitor is required to bring the circuit to resonance?

By transposition make *C* the subject of the f_r formula.

$$f_r = \frac{1}{2\pi\sqrt{LC}}$$ Therefore, by transposition $$C = \frac{1}{4\pi^2 f_r^2 L}$$

$$C = \frac{1}{4 \times \pi^2 \times (8.388 \times 10^6)^2 \times 18 \times 10^{-6}} = 20 \times 10^{-12}F = 20pF$$

> There is no need to use these brackets for the calculator.

MODE SCI 4

AC 4 ⌧ π χ² ⌧ 8.388 EXP 6 χ²

⌧ 18 EXP 6 +/– =   **5.000ₓ₁₀10** ← Result of bottom line.

1/χ   **2.000ₓ₁₀-11**   Read as 20×10^{-12}
10^{-12} = pico

ENG   **20ₓ₁₀-12** ← **Answer** 20pF

---

5. A series *LC* circuit has a resonant frequency of 79.6Hz. The inductor has a value of 2H. What is the value of the capacitor?

By transposition make *C* the subject of the f_r formula.

$$f_r = \frac{1}{2\pi\sqrt{LC}}$$ Therefore, by transposition $$C = \frac{1}{4\pi^2 f_r^2 L}$$

$$C = \frac{1}{4 \times \pi^2 \times 79.6^2 \times 2} = 1.999 \times 10^{-6}F \ or \ approx. \ 2\mu F$$

MODE SCI 4

AC 4 ⌧ π χ² ⌧ 79.6 χ²

⌧ 2 =   **5.003ₓ₁₀05** ← Result of bottom line.

1/χ   **1.999ₓ₁₀-06** ← Read as 1.999×10^{-6}
10^{-6} = micro. 1.999µF
Rounding to nearest µF.
Answer 2µF

6. **What value of series inductor is required to resonate a 500pF (500 x 10^{-12}F) capacitor at a frequency of 503.3kHz (503.3 x 10^3Hz.)?**

By transposition make L the subject of the f_r formula.

$f_r = \dfrac{1}{2\pi\sqrt{LC}}$ Therefore, by transposition $L = \dfrac{1}{4\pi^2 f_r^2 C}$

$L = \dfrac{1}{4 \times \pi^2 \times (503.3 \times 10^{\,3})^2 \times 500 \times 10^{-12}} = 200 \times 10^{-6} H = 200\mu H$

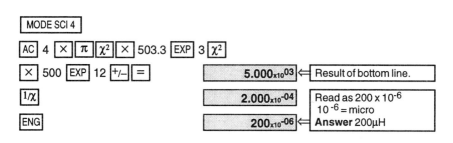

MODE SCI 4

| AC | 4 | × | π | χ^2 | × | 503.3 | EXP | 3 | χ^2 |

| × | 500 | EXP | 12 | +/− | = | **5.000**ₓ₁₀**03** ⟸ Result of bottom line.

| 1/χ | **2.000**ₓ₁₀**-04**   Read as 200 x 10⁻⁶ 10⁻⁶ = micro

| ENG | **200**ₓ₁₀**-06** ⟸ **Answer** 200µH

---

7. **A series *LC* circuit is required to offer minimum impedance to a signal of 15.92MHz (15.92 × 10^6Hz). The capacitor is 10pF (10 × 10^{-12}F).**
Assume the inductor has a resistance of 5 ohms at the resonant frequency, and is variable between 5µH and 50µH.
To what value will the inductor need to be adjusted for the circuit to offer a minimum impedance to the signal?

For the series circuit, the minimum impedance occurs at resonance, when the reactances, X_C and X_L cancel. The impedance of the circuit is then equal to the resistance R. Hence we need to calculate the value of L at resonance.

$f_r = \dfrac{1}{2\pi\sqrt{LC}}$ Therefore, by transposition $L = \dfrac{1}{4\pi^2 f_r^2 C}$

$L = \dfrac{1}{4 \times \pi^2 \times (15.92 \times 10^{\,6})^2 \times 10 \times 10^{-12}} = 9.994 \times 10^{-6} H \ \text{or approx. } 10\mu H$

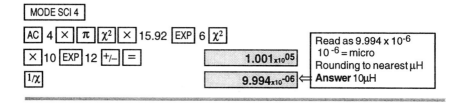

MODE SCI 4

| AC | 4 | × | π | χ^2 | × | 15.92 | EXP | 6 | χ^2 |

Read as 9.994 x 10⁻⁶
10⁻⁶ = micro
Rounding to nearest µH

| × | 10 | EXP | 12 | +/− | = | **1.001**ₓ₁₀**05**

| 1/χ | **9.994**ₓ₁₀**-06** ⟸ **Answer** 10µH

The Parallel Tuned Circuit

Fig.6 shows a circuit consisting L & C connected in parallel. R represents the resistance of the inductor and is usually very small compared with X_L.

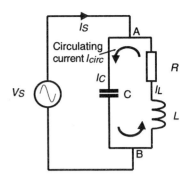

Fig.6

At the resonant frequency, with pure L and C connected in parallel, i.e. no resistance R present, the reactive branch currents I_C and I_L are equal in magnitude and opposite in sign, therefore they cancel, their vector sum is zero, and the supply current I_S is zero. Since there is an applied voltage and no supply current I_S flowing in the external circuit the impedance must be infinitely high.

There will, however, be a maximum circulating current within the closed LC circuit due to the initially established charge on the capacitor, or magnetic field of the inductor, causing a repeated interchange of energy between L and C.

In the practical circuit, fig.6, some power is dissipated by the resistance R, therefore, the supply current I_S, at resonance, will no longer be zero, but a finite minimum value to replace the power dissipated by R.

The circulating current, I_{circ}, is maximum at resonance and equal to $Q \times I_S$.

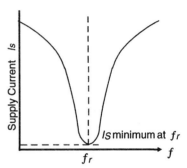

Fig.7 The response curve shows a dip in the supply line current at resonance, indicating a high impedance.

Fig.7 shows that the supply current is a minimum at resonance. An a.c. ammeter connected in the supply line will show a current dip at resonance. Similarly an a.c. ammeter in the closed LC circuit will peak at resonance.

Fig.8 shows the impedance curve of the parallel circuit between points A and B fig.6. The impedance is maximum at resonance and reduces either side of resonance. The impedance at resonance is referred to as the *dynamic resistance* R_D.

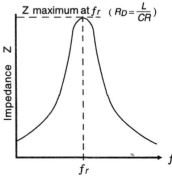

Fig.8 Response curve showing that impedance is maximum at resonance.

Points to note (Parallel circuit)

1. Resonance occurs when $X_L = X_C$
2. At resonance $I_L = I_C$. I_L lags V_S by 90° and I_C leads V_S by 90°. Therefore both I_L and I_C cancel to produce minimum current in the supply line.
3. At resonance the supply current I_S is minimum.
4. At resonance the circulating current I_{circ} is maximum.
5. At resonance the circulating current is greater than the supply current.
6. At resonance the circulating current $I_{circ} = Q \times I_S$.
7. At resonance the parallel tuned circuit has maximum impedance.
8. Reducing R, fig.6, sharpens the response curve (Q increases).
9. Increasing R, fig.6, broadens the response curve (Q Decreases).
10. When R is small compared with X_L, the resonant frequency, fr, is calculated using the same formula as the series circuit.
11. The parallel tuned circuit is sometimes to as a 'rejector' or 'tank' circuit'.
12. Increasing the L/C ratio increases the dynamic resistance R_D.
13. Use is made of the selective properties of parallel tuned circuits in filters, wavetraps, RF and IF amplifiers, radio receivers and transmitters, and the frequency determining elements of many types of oscillator.
14. The parallel circuit is inductive below resonance, capacitive above resonance and resistive at resonance.

Formulae to remember :-

Resonant frequency of parallel circuit when R (fig.6) is negligible:-

$$f_r = \frac{1}{2\pi\sqrt{LC}}$$ ⇐ | The most commonly used formula. |

Resonant frequency of parallel circuit when R is not negligible :-

$$f_r = \frac{1}{2\pi}\sqrt{\frac{1}{LC} - \frac{R^2}{L^2}}$$ ⇐ | This treatment of parallel resonance is beyond the scope of this book. |

Dynamic resistance $R_D = \dfrac{L}{CR}$

Supply current I_S at resonance $= \dfrac{V_S}{R_D}$

$$Q = \frac{Circulating\ current}{Supply\ current} = \frac{I_{circ}}{I_S}$$

$$Q = \frac{X_L}{R} = \frac{\omega L}{R} = \frac{2\pi f_r L}{R} \qquad Q = \frac{R_D}{X_L}$$

Examples.

8. Referring to fig.9 :-

$L = 100mH$ $(100 \times 10^{-3}H)$

$C = 1\mu F$ $(1 \times 10^{-6}F)$

$R = 5\Omega$

a) Calculate the resonant frequency.

b) Calculate the dynamic resistance R_D

c) Calculate I_s at resonance.

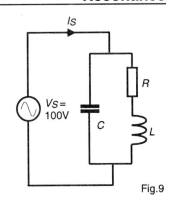

Fig.9

a) Calculate the resonant frequency of the circuit.

$$f_r = \frac{1}{2\pi\sqrt{LC}} = \frac{1}{2\pi\sqrt{(100mH)\times(1\mu F)}} = \frac{1}{2\pi\sqrt{(100\times10^{-3}H)\times(1\times10^{-6}F)}}$$

$$= \frac{1}{2\pi\sqrt{100\times10^{-3}\times1\times10^{-6}}} = 503.29Hz$$

> **Note.** For convenience I am evaluating the bottom line of the equation first, then taking the reciprocal $\boxed{1/x}$ to obtain the result. Finally the $\boxed{ENG}$ key will display the result in engineering units.

$\boxed{MODE\ SCI\ 4}$

$\boxed{\times}\ \boxed{1}\ \boxed{EXP}\ \boxed{6}\ \boxed{+/-}\ \boxed{\cdots)]}\ \boxed{=}$ $1.987_{x10}{}^{-03}$ $\Leftarrow$ $\boxed{\text{Result of bottom line.}}$

$\boxed{1/x}$ $5.033_{x10}{}^{02}$

$\boxed{ENG}$ $503.3_{x10}{}^{00}$ $\Leftarrow$ **Answer** 503.3Hz

b) Calculate the dynamic resistance. $R_D = \dfrac{L}{CR} = \dfrac{100\times.10^{-3}}{1\times10^{-6}\times5} = 20k\Omega$

$\boxed{AC}\ \boxed{100}\ \boxed{EXP}\ \boxed{3}\ \boxed{+/-}\ \boxed{\div}$

$\boxed{[(\cdots}\ \boxed{1}\ \boxed{EXP}\ \boxed{6}\ \boxed{+/-}\ \boxed{\times}\ \boxed{5}\ \boxed{\cdots)]}\ \boxed{=}$ $2.000_{x10}{}^{04}$

> Convert to **ENG**ineering notation. Read as 20×10^3
> $10^3 = $ kilo

$\boxed{ENG}$ $20_{x10}{}^{03}$ $\Leftarrow$ **Answer** 20 kilohms

c) Calculate the supply current at resonance.

I_s at resonance $= \dfrac{V_S}{R_D} = \dfrac{100}{20\times10^3} = 5\times10^{-3}A$ *or* $5mA$

> Read as 5×10^{-3}
> $10^{-3} = $ milli

$\boxed{AC}\ \boxed{100}\ \boxed{\div}\ \boxed{20}\ \boxed{EXP}\ \boxed{3}\ \boxed{=}$ $5.000_{x10}{}^{-03}$ $\Leftarrow$ **Answer** 5mA

9. A 200μH (200 × 10⁻⁶H) inductor having a resistance of 5Ω is connected
in parallel with a capacitor of 200pF (200 × 10⁻¹²F).
a) Calculate the resonant frequency f_r.
b) Calculate the dynamic resistance R_D.
c) Calculate the supply current at resonance if the voltage across the tuned
circuit is 400V.

a) The resonant frequency (Since the value of R, 5 ohms, is small compared with
X_L, 1000 ohms, it may be ignored in the resonant frequency calculation).

$$f_r = \frac{1}{2\pi\sqrt{LC}} = \frac{1}{2\pi\sqrt{(200\mu H)\times(200pF)}}$$

$$= \frac{1}{2\pi\sqrt{200\times10^{-6}\times200\times10^{-12}}} = 795.77\times10^3 Hz \ \text{or approx. } 796 kHz$$

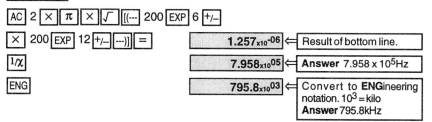

MODE SCI 4

| AC | 2 | × | π | × | √ | [(--- | 200 | EXP | 6 | +/- |

| × | 200 | EXP | 12 | +/- | ---)] | = | **1.257**ₓ₁₀-06 | ⇐ Result of bottom line. |

| 1/x | **7.958**ₓ₁₀05 | ⇐ **Answer** 7.958 x 10⁵Hz |

| ENG | **795.8**ₓ₁₀03 | ⇐ Convert to **ENG**ineering notation. 10³ = kilo **Answer** 795.8kHz |

b) The dynamic resistance :-

$$R_D = \frac{L}{CR} = \frac{200\times10^{-6}}{200\times10^{-12}\times5} = 200\times10^3 \Omega = 200k\Omega$$

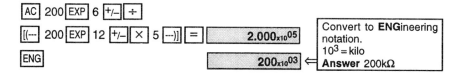

| AC | 200 | EXP | 6 | +/- | ÷ |

| [(--- | 200 | EXP | 12 | +/- | × | 5 | ---)] | = | **2.000**ₓ₁₀05 | Convert to **ENG**ineering notation. 10³ = kilo |

| ENG | **200**ₓ₁₀03 | ⇐ **Answer** 200kΩ |

c) Calculate the supply current at resonance (V = 400 volts and R_D = 200kΩ).

$$I_S \text{ at resonance} = \frac{V_S}{R_D} = \frac{400}{200\times10^3} = 2\times10^{-3}A \ \text{or } 2mA$$

| AC | 400 | ÷ | 200 | EXP | 3 | = | **2.000**ₓ₁₀-03 | Read as 2 x 10⁻³ 10⁻³ = milli ⇐ **Answer** 2mA |

10. The parallel circuit shown in fig.10 is required to tune the frequency band, 500kHz to 1500kHz - (500 × 10³Hz) to (1500 × 10³Hz).
The inductor has a value of 300μH (300 × 10⁻⁶H).
What is the capacitance range of *C*?

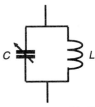

Fig.10

By transposition make *C* the subject of the f_r formula.

$$f_r = \frac{1}{2\pi\sqrt{LC}}$$ Therefore by transposition $$C = \frac{1}{4\pi^2 f_r^2 L}$$

Calculate *C* for the lowest frequency :-

$$C = \frac{1}{4\times\pi^2\times(500\times10^3)^2\times300\times10^{-6}} = 337.7\times10^{-12}F = \text{Approx. } 338pF$$

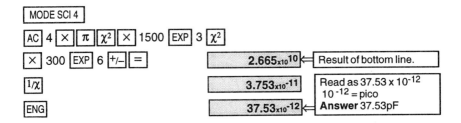

| MODE SCI 4 |
AC	4	×	π	χ^2	×	500	EXP	3	χ^2
×	300	EXP	6	+/−	=	2.961ₓ₁₀⁰⁹ ← Result of bottom line.
1/χ	3.377ₓ₁₀⁻¹⁰	Read as 337.7 x 10⁻¹² 10⁻¹² = pico
ENG	337.7ₓ₁₀⁻¹² ← Answer 337.7pF

Calculate *C* for the highest frequency :-

$$C = \frac{1}{4\times\pi^2\times(1500\times10^3)^2\times300\times10^{-6}} = 37.53\times10^{-12}F = \text{Approx. } 37.5pF$$

| MODE SCI 4 |
AC	4	×	π	χ^2	×	1500	EXP	3	χ^2
×	300	EXP	6	+/−	=	2.665ₓ₁₀¹⁰ ← Result of bottom line.
1/χ	3.753ₓ₁₀⁻¹¹	Read as 37.53 x 10⁻¹² 10⁻¹² = pico
ENG	37.53ₓ₁₀⁻¹² ← Answer 37.53pF

The capacitance range required to tune the *LC* circuit from 500kHz to 1500kHz is 337.7pF to 37.5pF.

11. The circuit shown in fig.11 is required to
resonate at a frequency of 4.502MHz.
a) To what value should the capacitor Cx be adjusted
to achieve resonance?
b) What is the dynamic resistance R_D of the circuit at
resonance?
c) What is the Q of the circuit at resonance?

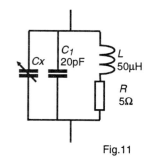

Fig.11

a) Calculate the capacitance required to resonate the
50μH inductor at 4.502MHz.

By transposition make C the subject of the f_r formula.

$$f_r = \frac{1}{2\pi\sqrt{LC}} \qquad \text{Therefore by transposition} \quad C = \frac{1}{4\pi^2 f_r^2 L}$$

$$C = \frac{1}{4\times\pi^2\times(4.502\times10^6)^2\times 50\times10^{-6}} = 25\times10^{-12}F = 25pF$$

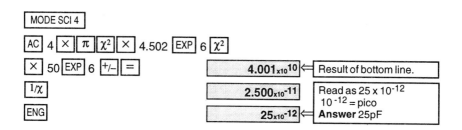

Since a total capacitance of 25pF is required to tune the 50μH inductor to resonance
at 4.502MHz, and C_1, 20pF already exists, a further 5pF is required. Therefore Cx
should be adjusted to make up the difference. I.e. Cx should be adjusted to 5pF.

b) The dynamic resistance :-

$$R_D = \frac{L}{CR} = \frac{50\times10^{-6}}{25\times10^{-12}\times 5} = 400\times10^3\Omega = 400k\Omega$$

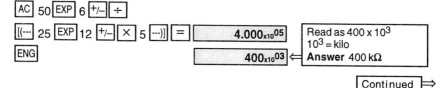

Continued ⇒

c) Calculate the Q of fig.11 at resonance:-

$$Q = \frac{X_L}{R} = \frac{\omega L}{R} = \frac{2 \pi f_r L}{R} = \frac{2 \times \pi \times 4.502 \times 10^6 \times 50 \times 10^{-6}}{5} = 282.9$$

| AC | 2 | × | π | × | 4.502 | EXP | 6 | × |

| 50 | EXP | 6 | +/- | = | = | ÷ | 5 | = |

| 2.829ₓ₁₀02 | Convert to **ENG**ineering notation. |

| ENG |

| 282.9ₓ₁₀00 | **Answer** $Q = 282.9$ |

---

12. The circuit shown in fig.12 resonates at a frequency of 10MHz (10×10^6Hz).
a) What is the value of L?
b) What is the R_D at resonance?

a) By transposition make L the subject of the fr formula.

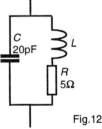

C 20pF
L
R 5Ω
Fig.12

$$f_r = \frac{1}{2 \pi \sqrt{L C}} \qquad \text{Therefore} \qquad L = \frac{1}{4 \pi^2 f_r^2 C}$$

$$L = \frac{1}{4 \times \pi^2 \times (10 \times 10^6)^2 \times 20 \times 10^{-12}} = 12.67 \times 10^{-6}H = 12.67\mu H$$

| MODE SCI 4 |

| AC | 4 | × | π | χ² | × | 10 | EXP | 6 | χ² |

| × | 20 | EXP | 12 | +/- | = |

| 7.896ₓ₁₀04 | Result of bottom line. |

| 1/χ |

| 1.267ₓ₁₀-05 | Read as 12.67 x 10⁻⁶ 10^{-6} = micro |

| ENG |

| 12.67ₓ₁₀-06 | **Answer** 12.67μH |

b) The dynamic resistance :-

$$R_D = \frac{L}{CR} = \frac{12.67 \times 10^{-6}}{20 \times 10^{-12} \times 5} = 126.7 \times 10^3 \Omega = 126.7k\Omega$$

| AC | 12.67 | EXP | 6 | +/- | ÷ |

| [(--- | 20 | EXP | 12 | +/- | × | 5 | ---)] | = |

| 1.267ₓ₁₀05 | Read as 126.7 x 10³ 10^3 = kilo |

| ENG |

| 126.7ₓ₁₀03 | **Answer** 126.7kΩ |

13. Fig.13 shows a simple absorption wavemeter. C **has a range of 5pF to 50pF. An induced 2.251MHz signal peaks the meter when the capacitor is set to 50pF.**
a) What is the value of the fixed inductor?
b) What frequency will peak the meter when the capacitor is set to its lowest capacitance (5pF)

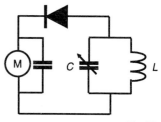

Fig.13

a) Calculate the inductance. Use the formula $L = \dfrac{1}{4\pi^2 f_r^2 C}$

$$L = \frac{1}{4 \times \pi^2 \times (2.251 \times 10^6)^2 \times 50 \times 10^{-12}} = 99.98 \times 10^{-6} H \text{ or approx. } 100\mu H$$

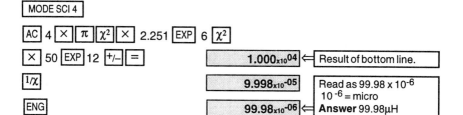

b) To calculate the resonant frequency when the tuning capacitor C is set to 5pF. (5pF is in parallel with the fixed 99.98μH inductor).

$$f_r = \frac{1}{2\pi \sqrt{LC}} = \frac{1}{2\pi \sqrt{(99.98\mu H) \times (5pF)}}$$

$$= \frac{1}{2\pi \sqrt{99.98 \times 10^{-6} \times 5 \times 10^{-12}}} = 7.118 \times 10^6 Hz = 7.118 MHz$$

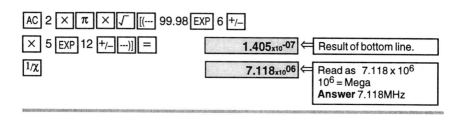

Note. *The following examples will be worked using Engineering Symbol Mode instead of entering the EXPonent. This mode is not available on all calculators.*

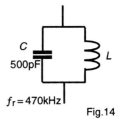

14. The parallel circuit shown in fig.14 is to be used as a rejector circuit to block an unwanted 470kHz i.f. (intermediate frequency) signal entering a receiver via the antenna.

C 500pF

L

$f_r = 470kHz$

Fig.14

The capacitor is 500pF.
a) What is the value of the inductor?
b) If the inductor has a resistance of 5Ω, what is the dynamic resistance R_D of the circuit at the intermediate frequency (470kHz)?

a) First calculate the inductance. Use the formula $L = \dfrac{1}{4\pi^2 f_r^2 C}$

$$L = \frac{1}{4 \times \pi^2 \times (470kHz)^2 \times (500pF)} = \frac{1}{4 \times \pi^2 \times (470 \times 10^3)^2 \times (500 \times 10^{-12})}$$

$$= \frac{1}{4360.4} = 229.3 \times 10^{-6}H = 229.3\mu H$$

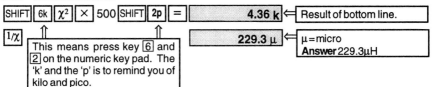

| MODE SCI 4 | MODE ENG |

⇐ Don't forget; to **Enter** Engineering Symbol Mode press - MODE MODE MODE MODE 1

AC 4 ✕ π 𝝌² ✕ 470

SHIFT 6k 𝝌² ✕ 500 SHIFT 2p =
4.36 k ⇐ Result of bottom line.

1/𝝌
229.3 μ ⇐ μ=micro **Answer 229.3μH**

This means press key 6 and 2 on the numeric key pad. The 'k' and the 'p' is to remind you of kilo and pico.

b) The dynamic resistance :-

$$R_D = \frac{L}{CR} = \frac{(229.3\mu H)}{(500pF) \times (5\Omega)} = \frac{229.3 \times 10^{-6}}{500 \times 10^{-12} \times 5} = 91.72 \times 10^3 \Omega = 91.72k\Omega$$

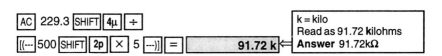

AC 229.3 SHIFT 4μ ÷

[(--- 500 SHIFT 2p ✕ 5 ---)] =
91.72 k ⇐ k = kilo
Read as 91.72 kilohms
Answer 91.72kΩ

Don't forget; to **Exit** Engineering Symbol Mode press - MODE MODE MODE MODE 1

15. The dynamic resistance R_D of the circuit shown in fig.15 is 500kΩ (500 $\times$ 10^3Ω).
L = 100μH (100 $\times$ 10^{-6}H) and R = 4Ω.
a) What is the value of the capacitor C?
b) What is the resonant frequency?

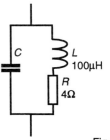

a) Calculate the value of C:-

Transpose the formula $R_D = \dfrac{L}{CR}$ for C Fig.15

$$C = \frac{L}{R_D R} = \frac{(100\mu H)}{(500k\Omega) \times (4\Omega)} = \frac{100 \times 10^{-6}}{500 \times 10^3 \times 4} = 50 \times 10^{-12}F = 50pF$$

		Don't forget; to **Enter** Engineering Symbol Mode $\Leftarrow$ press - MODE MODE MODE MODE 1

| MODE SCI 4 | MODE ENG |

| AC | 100 | SHIFT | 4μ | $\div$ |

| [(--- | 500 | SHIFT | 6k | $\times$ | 4 | ---)] | = | | **50 p** $\Leftarrow$ | p = pico
 Read as 50 picofarads.
 Answer = 50pF |

b) Now that the value of the capacitor has been found we can calculate the resonant frequency :-

$$f_r = \frac{1}{2\pi\sqrt{L\,C}} = \frac{1}{2\pi\sqrt{(100\mu H) \times (50pF)}}$$

$$= \frac{1}{2\pi\sqrt{100 \times 10^{-6} \times 50 \times 10^{-12}}} = 2.251 \times 10^6 Hz = 2.251 MHz$$

| AC | 2 | $\times$ | π | $\times$ | $\sqrt{}$ | [(--- | 100 | SHIFT | 4μ |

| $\times$ | 50 | SHIFT | 2p | ---)] | = | | **444.3 n** $\Leftarrow$ | Result of bottom line. |

| 1/x | | | | **2.251 M** $\Leftarrow$ | M = Mega
 Answer 2.251MHz |

| | | Don't forget; to **Exit** Engineering Symbol Mode press - MODE MODE MODE MODE 1 |

Selectivity, Bandwidth & Q.

The Q factor (magnification factor or quality factor) of a tuned circuit is a measure of its selectivity. A high Q indicates high selectivity and narrow bandwidth. A low Q indicates less selectivity and wide bandwidth.

Selectivity is the ability of a tuned circuit to respond to the frequency or band of frequencies to which it is tuned, whilst at the same time having poor response to frequencies either side of this frequency or band.

The bandwidth of a tuned circuit is the separation, either side of maximum response, by which the output has fallen to 0.707 (70.7%) of the maximum value (often referred to as the *half power bandwidth or -3dB bandwidth*). See fig.17.

Fig 16 shows typical response curves for high and low Q circuits.
For most practical purposes we can consider the current response curve for series circuits and the impedance curve for parallel circuits.

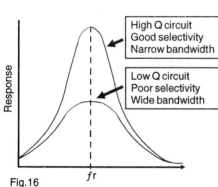

High Q circuit
Good selectivity
Narrow bandwidth

Low Q circuit
Poor selectivity
Wide bandwidth

Fig.16

The sharpness, hence selectivity, of a series or parallel resonant circuit is affected by the ratio of L to C and the circuit losses, usually attributable to the series resistance R of the inductor which increases with frequency.
In fig.16 the low Q response curve is due to increasing the series resistance (or loss) of the inductor.

From fig.17 it can be seen that the half power bandwidth (the *B/W* at the -3dB points) $= 2 \times \Delta f$. The relationship between Q and bandwidth is given by :-

$$Q = \frac{f_r}{B/W} = \frac{f_r}{2\Delta f} = \frac{f_r}{f_1 - f_2}$$

$$f_r = Q \times B/W \quad \text{and} \quad B/W = \frac{f_r}{Q}$$

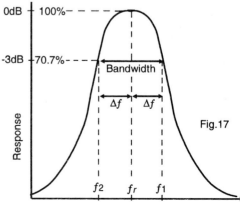

Fig.17

Points to note.
1. Q of a resonant circuit is a measure of its selectivity.
2. High Q circuits have good selectivity and narrow bandwidth.
3. Low Q circuits have poor selectivity and wide bandwidth.
4. Bandwidth and Q depend on R and the ratio of L to C.
5. The higher the circuit losses, due mainly to the resistance of L at the resonant frequency, the lower the Q and wider the bandwidth.
6. Bandwidth must be chosen to suit the application.
7. If bandwidth is too narrow (high Q), the sidebands of a wanted transmission may be attenuated.
8. If bandwidth is too wide (low Q), unwanted frequencies will be passed as well as the wanted.
9. The bandwidth of a parallel tuned circuit can be increased by damping the circuit with shunt resistance, however, this will lower the Q.
10. For parallel circuits a high resistance source is required for minimum damping, high Q and narrow bandwidth.
11. For series circuits a low resistance source is necessary for high Q and narrow bandwidth.

Formulae to remember :-

$$Q = \frac{f_r}{B/W} = \frac{f_r}{2\Delta f} = \frac{f_r}{f_1 - f_2}$$

$$f_r = Q \times B/W \quad \text{and} \quad B/W = \frac{f_r}{Q}$$

$$Q = \frac{\omega L}{R} \quad \text{also} \quad Q = \frac{1}{\omega CR}$$

$$Q = \frac{R_D}{X_L} = \frac{R_D}{\omega L} = \frac{R_D}{2\pi f L} \quad \text{(for parallel circuits)}.$$

$$R_D = Q\omega L = Q\, 2\pi f L \quad \text{(Dynamic resistance for parallel circuits)}.$$

16. The resonant frequency of a tuned circuit having a Q of 120 is
1.5MHz (1.5×10^6Hz).
What is the half power bandwidth of the circuit?

Use the formula $B/W = \dfrac{f_r}{Q}$

$$B/W = \frac{1.5 \times 10^6}{120} = 12.5 \times 10^3 \quad or \quad 12.5kHz$$

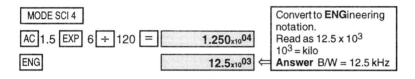

MODE SCI 4

[AC] 1.5 [EXP] 6 [÷] 120 [=]   **1.250**ₓ₁₀**04**   Convert to **ENG**ineering notation.
Read as 12.5 x 10^3
10^3 = kilo

[ENG]   **12.5**ₓ₁₀**03** ⇐ **Answer** B/W = 12.5 kHz

---

17. A parallel tuned circuit presents a maximum impedance to the supply at
a frequency of 465kHz (465×10^3 Hz). The Q of the circuit is 77.5.
What is the bandwidth?

Use the formula $B/W = \dfrac{f_r}{Q}$

$$B/W = \frac{465 \times 10^3}{77.5} = 6 \times 10^3 = 6000Hz \quad or \quad 6kHz$$

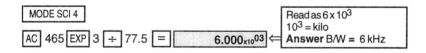

MODE SCI 4

[AC] 465 [EXP] 3 [÷] 77.5 [=]   **6.000**ₓ₁₀**03** ⇐ Read as 6 x 10^3
10^3 = kilo
Answer B/W = 6 kHz

---

18. A tuned circuit, resonant at a frequency of 1.6MHz (1.6×10^6 Hz) has a
Q factor of 200.
What is the bandwidth of the circuit?

Use the formula $B/W = \dfrac{f_r}{Q}$

$$B/W = \frac{1.6 \times 10^6}{200} = 8 \times 10^3 = 8000Hz \quad or \quad 8kHz$$

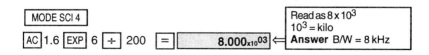

MODE SCI 4

[AC] 1.6 [EXP] 6 [÷] 200 [=]   **8.000**ₓ₁₀**03** ⇐ Read as 8 x 10^3
10^3 = kilo
Answer B/W = 8 kHz

19. A tuned circuit has a resonant frequency of 100MHz (100 $\times$ 10^{6}Hz). Measurements have enabled a response curve to be plotted which shows that the bandwidth of the circuit is 1.5MHz (1.5 $\times$ 10^{6}Hz). What is the Q of the circuit?

Use the formula $Q = \dfrac{f_r}{B/W}$

$$Q = \frac{100MHz}{1.5MHz} = \frac{100 \times 10^6}{1.5 \times 10^6} = 66.67$$

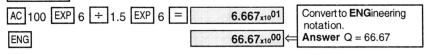

MODE SCI 4		
$\boxed{\text{AC}}$ 100 $\boxed{\text{EXP}}$ 6 $\boxed{\div}$ 1.5 $\boxed{\text{EXP}}$ 6 $\boxed{=}$ 6.667$_{x10}$01	Convert to **ENG**ineering notation.
$\boxed{\text{ENG}}$ 66.67$_{x10}$00	$\Longleftarrow$ **Answer** Q = 66.67

20. The tuned *LC* antenna circuit of a VHF receiver has a bandwidth of 1.2MHz (1.2 $\times$ 10^{6}Hz) centred on a frequency of 145MHz (145 $\times$ 10^{6}Hz). What is the Q of the tuned circuit?

Use the formula $Q = \dfrac{f_r}{B/W}$

$$Q = \frac{145MHz}{1.2MHz} = \frac{145 \times 10^6}{1.2 \times 10^6} = 120$$

MODE SCI 4		
$\boxed{\text{AC}}$ 145 $\boxed{\text{EXP}}$ 6 $\boxed{\div}$ 1.2 $\boxed{\text{EXP}}$ 6 $\boxed{=}$ 1.208$_{x10}$02	Convert to **ENG**ineering notation.
$\boxed{\text{ENG}}$ 120.8$_{x10}$00	$\Longleftarrow$ **Answer** Q = 120.8

21. Calculate the Q of a tuned circuit having a bandwidth of 5MHz (5 $\times$ 10^{6}Hz), and resonant at 450MHz (450 $\times$ 10^{6}Hz).

Use the formula $Q = \dfrac{f_r}{B/W}$

$$Q = \frac{450MHz}{5MHz} = \frac{450 \times 10^6}{5 \times 10^6} = 90$$

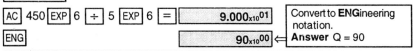

MODE SCI 4		
$\boxed{\text{AC}}$ 450 $\boxed{\text{EXP}}$ 6 $\boxed{\div}$ 5 $\boxed{\text{EXP}}$ 6 $\boxed{=}$ 9.000$_{x10}$01	Convert to **ENG**ineering notation.
$\boxed{\text{ENG}}$ 90$_{x10}$00	$\Longleftarrow$ **Answer** Q = 90

22. The resonant frequency of the circuit shown in fig.18 is approximately 503Hz.
Calculate the:-
a) *Q* **factor.**
b) **-3dB (half-power) bandwidth.**
c) **dynamic resistance** *R$_D$*, **using the**
formula *R$_D$ = Q ω L* **?**

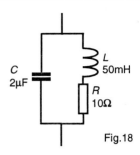

Fig.18

a) The *Q* factor can be calculated using the formula:-

$$Q = \frac{\omega L}{R} = \frac{2 \pi f L}{R}$$

$$= \frac{2 \times \pi \times 503 \times 50 \times 10^{-3}}{10} = \frac{158}{10} = 15.8$$

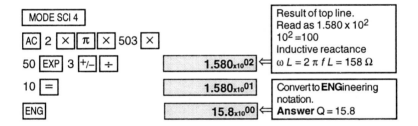

b) The half-power bandwidth is given by the formula :-

$$B/W = \frac{f_r}{Q} = \frac{503}{15.8} = 31.84 Hz$$

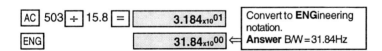

c) At resonance the dynamic resistance of the parallel tuned circuit is given by:-

$$R_D = Q \omega L = Q 2 \pi f L$$

$$\therefore R_D = 15.8 \times 2 \times \pi \times 503 \times 50 \times 10^{-3} = 2.497 \times 10^3 \ approx. \ 2.5k\Omega$$

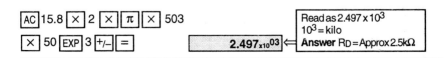

23. A parallel tuned circuit has the response curve shown in fig.19. The resonant frequency is 1000kHz (1000×10^3Hz). f_1 is 1005kHz and f_2 is 995kHz. What is :-

a) the half-power bandwidth of the circuit?

b) the Q factor?

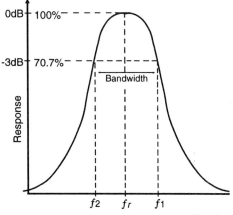

Fig.19

a) The bandwidth of the circuit is given by $B/W = f_1 - f_2$

$\therefore B/W = 1005kHz - 995kHz = 10kHz$

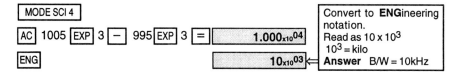

b) The Q factor can be calculated from the information given :-

Use the formula $Q = \dfrac{f_r}{B/W}$

$Q = \dfrac{1000kHz}{10kHz} = \dfrac{1000 \times 10^3}{10 \times 10^3} = 100$

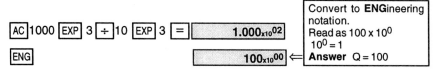

The Transformer

Chapter 9

Contents

In this section you will:-
a) calculate the voltage and turns ratio of a transformer.
b) calculate the primary and secondary current.
c) calculate the turns ratio for impedance matching.

Left. Small 50 Hz mains transformer.
Right. Tuned 465 kHz intermediate frequency transformer.

The Transformer

Transformer Basics

Transformers are used in radio and electronic equipment to increase or decrease a.c. mains supply voltages, couple and tune r.f. signals, and match source to load impedances. They *will not* operate on d.c. supplies.

In its basic form a transformer consists of two or more coils, electrically insulated from each other and coupled by mutual induction.

When an alternating current in one coil (the primary) changes, it creates a changing magnetic field that induces a voltage in the second coil (the secondary). To ensure that as much of the magnetic field (or flux) as possible cuts the secondary coil, the coils are wound on an iron core common to both. In the case of power and audio frequencies the cores are usually laminated iron, whilst at radio frequencies they are of iron dust or ferrite. Power transformers for radio frequency work are normally air cored.

Losses are mainly due to :-
a) resistance of windings (Copper Loss).
b) core not completely demagnetising after the current falls to zero. (Hysteresis).
c) eddy currents flowing in the core.

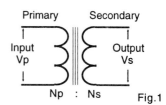

Fig.1

Turns Ratio and Voltage Ratio.

Assume a perfect transformer with no losses, i.e, all the lines of magnetic flux generated by the primary winding cut the secondary winding. When the turns on the primary and secondary (Np and Ns fig.1) are equal, i.e, the turns ratio is one to one 1:1, the voltage induced across the secondary (Vs) will be the same as that applied to the primary (Vp).

If there are twice as many turns on the secondary as on the primary, the secondary voltage will double (a *step-up* transformer). If the turns on the secondary are half of those on the primary, then the secondary voltage will be half of the primary voltage (a *step-down* transformer). It follows that :-

$$\frac{V_p}{V_s} = \frac{N_p}{N_s} \quad \therefore \quad V_s = V_p \times \frac{N_s}{N_p} \quad or \quad V_p = V_s \times \frac{N_p}{N_s}$$

With zero loss, the power in both the secondary and primary are equal :-

$$V_p I_p = V_s I_s \quad \therefore \quad \frac{V_p}{V_s} = \frac{I_s}{I_p} \quad and \quad I_p = I_s \times \frac{V_s}{V_p}$$

It can be seen from the above expression that stepping up the voltage steps down the current, and vice versa.

Impedance Matching

Since the load impedance connected across the secondary is reflected back to the primary, the transformer is also suitable for matching source and load impedances to ensure maximum power transfer.

Transformers can be used to match audio output stages to loudspeakers, r.f. power amplifier stages to antennas, antennas to small signal r.f. amplifiers, and microphones to audio amplifiers.

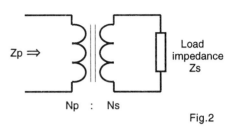

$Zp \Rightarrow$

Load impedance Zs

Np : Ns

Fig.2

When the load Zs is connected across the secondary terminals of the transformer, fig.2, the impedance looking into the primary terminals is :-

$$Z_p = \left(\frac{N_p}{N_s}\right)^2 \times Z_s$$

Where :-
Zp = Primary impedance.
Zs = Secondary load impedance.
Np = Number of turns on primary.
Ns = Number of turns on secondary.

The turns ratio, primary to secondary, required for transforming a given load impedance to that required by a source for optimum performance is given by:-

$$\frac{N_p}{N_s} = \sqrt{\frac{Z_p}{Z_s}}$$

Points to note.
1. Direct current will not pass across the windings of a transformer.
2. Operation on a.c. only.
3. Transformers can be step-down, step-up, or have a 1:1 ratio for isolation.
4. The voltage ratio is the same as the turns ratio.
5. The current ratio is the inverse of the voltage ratio.
6. A transformer does not generate power.
7. Primary and secondary windings are not physically connected to one another.
8. Power is transferred from primary to secondary by electromagnetic induction.
9. In a perfect transformer the output power equals the input power.
10. Transformers can be designed to operate from mains frequencies up to u.h.f. However, at the higher frequencies they may look completely different and be unrecognisable.

Examples.
1. Referring to fig.3. Calculate :-
a) the secondary voltage.
b) the primary current.
c) the impedance Zp with a 6Ω
load on the secondary.

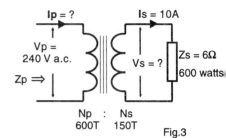

a) The secondary voltage :-

$$\frac{V_p}{V_s} = \frac{N_p}{N_s}$$

$$\therefore \ \ V_s = V_p \times \frac{N_s}{N_p} = 240 \times \frac{150}{600} = 240 \times 0.25 = 60 \ volts$$

MODE FIX 2	
AC 240 ✕ 150 ÷ 600 = **60.00**	The transformer is a step-down transformer with a of ratio 4:1, the secondary voltage is $\frac{1}{4} \times V_p$. **Answer** 60V

b) Current in primary.
First calculate the secondary current *Is*, this is already given in fig.3, 10A.

$$I_s = \frac{Power \ secondary}{Volts \ secondary} = \frac{600}{60} = 10 \ A$$

Now since in a perfect transformer, the power in both primary and secondary are equal, it follows that :-

$$V_p \, I_p = V_s \, I_s \qquad \Leftarrow \boxed{\text{Power in Watts} = V \, I}$$

$$\therefore \ \ I_p = I_s \times \frac{V_s}{V_p} = 10 \times \frac{60}{240} = 10 \times 0.25 = 2.5 \ A$$

AC 10 ✕ 60 ÷ 240 =   **2.50** $\Leftarrow$ **Answer** 2.5A (Primary current)

c) The primary impedance with a 6 ohm load connected on the secondary:-

$$Z_p = \left(\frac{N_p}{N_s}\right)^2 \times Z_s = \left(\frac{600}{150}\right)^2 \times 6 = 4^2 \times 6 = 16 \times 6 = 96 \ ohms$$

AC [(--- 600 ÷ 150 ---)]

χ^2 ✕ 6 =   **96.00** $\Leftarrow$ **Answer** 96Ω (Primary impedance)

2. Calculate the turns ratio 'T' of the transformer of fig.4.

$$T = \frac{V_p}{V_s} = \frac{240}{24} = 10$$

The ratio of turns on the primary to turns
on the secondary is 10:1.
Vp is stepped down by a factor of 10.

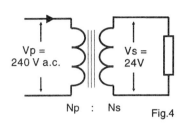

Vp =
240 V a.c.

Vs =
24V

Np : Ns

Fig.4

| MODE FIX 2 |

| AC | 240 | ÷ | 24 | = | 10.00 |⇐ **Answer** 10:1 Turns ratio (Step down) |

**3. A near perfect transformer, has 1000 turns on the primary and 4000 turns
on the secondary. A 250V a.c. supply is connected across the primary.
Calculate :-**
a) the secondary voltage.
b) the primary current with a 500Ω load connected to the secondary.

a) Secondary voltage. Since the transformer is a step-up transformer the secondary
voltage will be higher than the primary voltage.

$$\frac{V_p}{V_s} = \frac{N_p}{N_s}$$

$$\therefore \ V_s = V_p \times \frac{N_s}{N_p} = 250 \times \frac{4000}{1000} = 250 \times 4 = 1000 \ volts$$

| AC | 250 | × | 4 | = | 1000.00 |⇐ **Answer** 1000V (secondary voltage) |

b) Current in primary. First calculate the secondary current:-

$$I_s = \frac{V_s}{R_{Load}} = \frac{1000}{500} = 2 \ A$$

| AC | 1000 | ÷ | 500 | = | 2.00 |⇐ **Answer** 2A (Secondary current) |

Now since $V_p \, I_p = V_s \, I_s$ we can calculate the primary current I_P:-

$$\therefore \ I_p = I_s \times \frac{V_s}{V_p} = 2 \times \frac{1000}{250} = 2 \times 4 = 8 \ A$$

| AC | 2 | × | 1000 | ÷ | 250 | = | 8.00 |⇐ **Answer** 8A (Primary current) |

4. For optimum performance a transistor audio output stage requires a 200Ω load. It is to be connected to an 8Ω loudspeaker. Calculate the required turns ratio Np:Ns of the transformer fig.5.

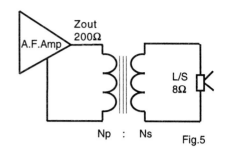

Fig.5

$$\frac{N_p}{N_s} = \sqrt{\frac{Z_p}{Z_s}} = \sqrt{\frac{200}{8}} = \sqrt{25} = 5$$

The turns ratio for optimum performance is therefore 5:1. The primary must have 5 times as many turns as the secondary.

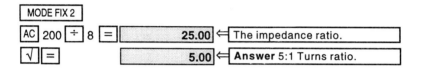

5. An ideal transformer having 1000 primary turns and 8000 secondary turns is connected to a 50Hz 200V supply.
Calculate :-
a) the secondary voltage Vs.
b) the frequency of the secondary voltage.

a) The transformer is a step-up transformer, therefore the secondary voltage will be higher than the primary voltage.

$$\frac{V_p}{V_s} = \frac{N_p}{N_s} \quad \therefore \quad V_s = V_p \times \frac{N_s}{N_p} = 200 \times \frac{8000}{1000} = 200 \times 8 = 1600 \ V$$

| AC | 200 | × | 8 | = | | 1600.00 | ⇐ Answer 1600V (secondary voltage) |

b) The frequency is 50Hz. There is no change of frequency between the primary and secondary windings of a transformer.

Decibels

Chapter 10

Contents

In this section you will:-
a) calculate power and voltage gain in an amplifier.
b) calculate attenuation and feeder loss.
c) convert dBµV to µV, and µV to dBµV.
d) convert power in dBW to watts, and watts to dBW.

The Decibel (dB)

The decibel (dB) is a unit based on common logarithms and is extensively used in radio and communication engineering to provide a measure of gain or loss in a system. The following system elements have their gain or loss measured in dB:- antennas, amplifiers (audio and r.f.), receivers, transmission lines, antenna feeders, attenuators and filters. Field strength is also measured in dB.

Basically the dB is a unit of power ratio, and not of absolute power, however, if some standard power level is used as a reference, then any absolute power can be expressed in dB above or below the reference power. Commonly used reference powers are 1 watt and 1 milliwatt. Similarly with voltage, 1 volt, 1 millivolt or 1 microvolt may be used as the reference. The power and voltage levels being expressed as dBW, dBmW, dBV, dBmV, and dBµV respectively. **Note.** dBW means decibels with respect to 1 watt, and dBV means decibels with respect to 1 volt.

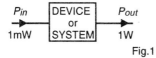

P_{in}	DEVICE	P_{out}
	or	
1mW	SYSTEM	1W

Fig.1

Note. This system has a gain. The output power is greater than the input power. If the output power is less than the input power the system has a loss.

When the ratio of two powers, see fig.1, is expressed in decibels, the number of decibels, N_{dB}, is given by :-

$$N_{dB} = 10\,Log_{10}\frac{P_{out}}{P_{in}}$$

Note. When the ratio $\frac{P_{out}}{P_{in}}$, $\frac{V_{out}}{V_{in}}$, $\frac{I_{out}}{I_{in}}$ is less than unity it is normal to invert the fraction and express the result as a dB loss. This avoids complicated negative logarithms. However, the scientific calculator has no problem in this respect.

When the ratio of two voltages or currents is expressed in decibels, the number of decibels, N_{dB}, is given by :-

$$N_{dB} = 20\,Log_{10}\frac{V_{out}}{V_{in}}$$

$$N_{dB} = 20\,Log_{10}\frac{I_{out}}{I_{in}}$$

Note. These two formulae hold good only when the values of input and output resistance (or impedance) are equal.

Absolute power (in dBW) referred to a standard reference power of 1W, is given by :-

$$Power\,level\,(dBW) = 10\,Log_{10}\frac{Actual\,power\,(watts)}{Reference\,power\,(1\,watt)}$$

Examples

1. Determine the gain in dB of the amplifier shown in fig.2.

Fig.2

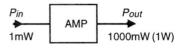

$$\text{Gain in } dB = 10\ Log_{10} \frac{Power\ out}{Power\ in}$$

$$= 10\ Log_{10} \frac{P_{out}}{P_{in}} = 10\ Log_{10} \frac{1000}{1} = 10\ Log_{10}\ 1000 = 10 \times 3 = 30\ dB$$

[MODE FIX 2]

[AC] 10 [×]

[LOG] [[(---] 1000 [÷] 1 [---)]] [=] [30.00] ⇐ [**Answer** 30 dB]

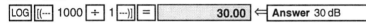

2. An amplifier produces an output power of 500mW for an input power of 20mW. What is the amplifier gain in dB?

$$\text{Gain } dB = 10\ Log_{10} \frac{Power\ out}{Power\ in}$$

$$= 10\ Log_{10} \frac{500}{20} = 10\ Log_{10}\ 25 = 10 \times 1.398 = 13.98\ dB$$

[MODE FIX 2]

[AC] 10 [×]

[LOG] [[(---] 500 [÷] 20 [---)]] [=] [13.98] ⇐ [**Answer** 13.98 dB]

---

3. A radio frequency power amplifier, having an input power of 2W delivers 200W to a 50 ohm load.
What is the gain of the amplifier in dB?

$$\text{Gain } dB = 10\ Log_{10} \frac{Power\ out}{Power\ in}$$

$$= 10\ Log_{10} \frac{200}{2} = 10\ Log_{10}\ 100 = 10 \times 2 = 20\ dB$$

[MODE FIX 2]

[AC] 10 [×]

[LOG] [[(---] 200 [÷] 2 [---)]] [=] [20.00] ⇐ [**Answer** 20 dB]

Decibels

4. An audio amplifier has a voltage gain of 40. What is the gain of the amplifier in dB?

$$\text{Gain } dB = 20 \, Log_{10} \frac{V_{out}}{V_{in}} = 20 \, Log_{10} 40 = 20 \times 1.602 = 32.04 \, dB$$

The voltage ratio $\frac{V_{out}}{V_{in}}$ is equal to 40

MODE FIX 2

AC 20 ×

LOG 40 = | 32.04 ⟸ **Answer** 32.04 dB (To 2 decimal places)

---

5. Express a power ratio of 10,000 in dB.

$$\text{Gain in } dB = 10 \, Log_{10} \frac{P_{out}}{P_{in}} = 10 \, Log_{10} 10{,}000 = 10 \times 4 = 40 \, dB$$

The power ratio $\frac{P_{out}}{P_{in}}$ is equal to 10,000

MODE FIX 2

AC 10 ×

LOG 10000 = | 40.00 ⟸ **Answer** 40 dB

---

6. The input power to a system is 1W, and the output power 0.25W. What is the system loss in dB?

Since P_{out} of the system is less than P_{in}, there must be loss or attenuation in the system. The equation is simplified by inverting the power ratio and either prefixing the result with a minus sign or expressing the result as a loss.

$$\text{Loss in } dB = 10 \, Log_{10} \frac{P_{in}}{P_{out}} = 10 \, Log_{10} \frac{1}{0.25} = 10 \, Log_{10} 4 = 6.02 \, dB \, Loss$$

The power ratio fraction of the gain formula has been inverted and the result expressed as 6.02 dB loss.

MODE FIX 2

AC 10 ×

LOG [(--- 1 ÷ .25 ---)] = | 6.02 ⟸ **Answer** 6.02 dB Loss or - 6.02 dB

7. An attenuator is correctly terminated with matching input and output imped-ances. The voltage across its input terminals is 50mV and the output voltage is 10mV. What is the attenuation?

The attenuation is expressed as :-

$$Atten. = 20 \, Log_{10} \frac{V_{in}}{V_{out}} = 20 \, Log_{10} \frac{50}{10} = 20 \, Log_{10} \, 5 = 20 \times 0.6990 = 13.98 \, dB$$

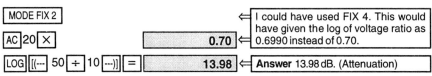

MODE FIX 2		⇐ I could have used FIX 4. This would have given the log of voltage ratio as 0.6990 instead of 0.70.
AC 20 ×	0.70 ⇐	
LOG [(--- 50 ÷ 10 ---)] =	13.98 ⇐	Answer 13.98 dB. (Attenuation)

---

8. A radio frequency attenuator has an attenuation of 40dB.
The input power is 10W.
Calculate the output power.

$$Attenuation \; dB \; = \; 10 \, Log_{10} \frac{P_{in}}{P_{out}}$$

$$40 \; = \; 10 \, Log_{10} \frac{10}{P_{out}}$$

$$\frac{40}{10} \; = \; Log_{10} \frac{10}{P_{out}}$$

$$Antilog \; 4 = \frac{10}{P_{out}}$$

$$\therefore \; P_{out} \; = \; \frac{10}{antilog \; 4} \; = \; \frac{10}{10,000} \; = \; 0.001W \; or \; 1mW$$

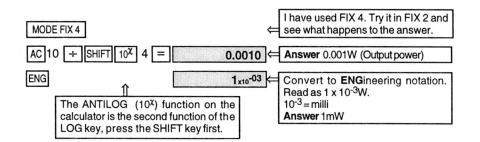

	I have used FIX 4. Try it in FIX 2 and ⇐ see what happens to the answer.
MODE FIX 4	
AC 10 ÷ SHIFT 10ˣ 4 =	0.0010 ⇐ **Answer** 0.001W (Output power)
ENG	1ₓ₁₀⁻⁰³ ⇐ Convert to **ENG**ineering notation. Read as 1 x 10⁻³W. 10⁻³ = milli **Answer** 1mW

⇑
The ANTILOG (10ˣ) function on the calculator is the second function of the LOG key, press the SHIFT key first.

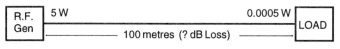

Fig.3

9. The radio frequency generator shown in fig.3, delivers a power of 5 watts to the system shown (A correctly matched load connected via 100 metres of feeder cable). Due to high feeder loss only 0.0005W is available at the load. Calculate :-
a) The feeder loss in dB.
b) The feeder loss in dB per metre (dB/metre).

a) The feeder loss :-

$$Loss = 10\ Log_{10}\frac{P_{in}}{P_{out}} = 10\ Log_{10}\frac{5}{0.0005} = 10\ Log_{10}\ 10,000 = 10 \times 4 = 40\ dB$$

MODE FIX 2

AC 10 ×

LOG [(--- 5 ÷ .0005 ---)] =   **40.00** ⇐ **Answer** 40 dB. (Feeder loss)

b) Feeder loss per metre :-

Since the loss in 100 metres of the feeder is 40dB, the loss in 1 metre will be $\frac{40}{100}$ = 0.4 *dB/metre*

AC 40 ÷ 100 =   **0.40** ⇐ **Answer** 0.4 dB/metre

---

10. Referring to fig.3. Extending the feeder length reduces the output power to 0.00025W.
What is the overall feeder loss?

$$Loss = 10\ Log_{10}\frac{P_{in}}{P_{out}} = 10\ Log_{10}\frac{5}{0.00025} = 10\ Log_{10}\ 20,000 = 10 \times 4.3 = 43\ dB$$

MODE FIX 2

AC 10 ×

LOG [(--- 5 ÷ .00025 ---)] =   **43.00** ⇐ **Answer** 43 dB. (Feeder loss)

10 - 6

11. An r.f. source is connected to a terminated feeder having a known loss of 16dB. The required power in the load is 0.5W. What power must the r.f. source deliver?

$$Loss\ dB = 10\ Log_{10}\frac{P_{in}}{P_{out}}$$

$$16 = 10\ Log_{10}\frac{P_{in}}{0.5}$$

$$\frac{16}{10} = Log_{10}\frac{P_{in}}{0.5}$$

$$Antilog\ 1.6 = \frac{P_{in}}{0.5}$$

$$\therefore\ P_{in} = antilog\ 1.6 \times 0.5 = 39.81 \times 0.5 = 19.9W$$

| MODE FIX 2 |

 AC SHIFT 10^x 1.6 × .5 =  **19.91** ⇐ **Answer** 19.91W (Source power).

---

12. A radio transmitter is connected to a matched feeder and antenna system. The output power measured at the transmitter is 100W, and the input power to the antenna is 63.1W. Calculate the feeder loss.

$$Loss = 10\ Log_{10}\frac{P_{in}}{P_{out}} = 10\ Log_{10}\frac{100}{63.1} = 10\ Log_{10}\ 1.58 = 10 \times 0.2 = 2\ dB$$

| MODE FIX 2 |

AC 10 ×

LOG [(--- 100 ÷ 63.1 ---)] = **2.00** ⇐ **Answer** 2 dB. (Feeder loss)

---

13. A transmitter and antenna are connected by a coaxial cable. The transmitter output power is 50W, the antenna input power is 12.5W. Calculate the feeder loss in dB.

$$Loss = 10\ Log_{10}\frac{P_{in}}{P_{out}} = 10\ Log_{10}\frac{50}{12.5} = 10\ Log_{10}\ 4 = 10 \times 0.6 = 6\ dB\ (approx)$$

| MODE FIX 2 |

AC 10 ×

LOG [(--- 50 ÷ 12.5 ---)] = **6.02** ⇐ **Answer** 6.02 dB. (Feeder loss)

Decibels

14. The output level of a radio frequency signal generator is 50 dB above 1μV (50 dBμV).
Calculate the output level in microvolts (μV).

1μV is the reference level. i.e. 1μV = 0dBμV.

$$dB = 20\, Log_{10} \frac{V}{V_{ref}}$$

$$50 = 20\, Log_{10} \frac{V}{1\mu V} \quad \Leftarrow \boxed{\text{Reference level} = 1\mu V.}$$

$$\frac{50}{20} = Log_{10}\, V$$

$$Antilog \frac{50}{20} = V$$

$$\therefore\ V = antilog\, 2.5 = 316.23\ \mu V \quad \Leftarrow \boxed{\begin{array}{l}\text{As the reference level is one}\\\text{microvolt the output voltage is}\\\text{in microvolts.}\end{array}}$$

$\boxed{\text{MODE FIX 2}}$

$\boxed{\text{AC}}\,50\,\boxed{\div}\,20\,\boxed{=}\,\boxed{\text{SHIFT}}\,\boxed{10^x}\,\boxed{=}\quad$ **316.23** $\Leftarrow \boxed{\textbf{Answer } 316.23\,\mu V}$

---

15. The output level of a radio frequency signal generator is -6 dBμV, i.e. 6 dB below a reference level of 1μV.
Calculate the output voltage in microvolts.

$$dB = 20\, Log_{10} \frac{V}{V_{ref}}$$

$$-6 = 20\, Log_{10} \frac{V}{1\mu V} \quad \Leftarrow \boxed{\text{Reference level} = 1\mu V.}$$

$$\frac{-6}{20} = Log_{10}\, V$$

$$Antilog \frac{-6}{20} = V$$

$$\therefore\ V = antilog\, -0.3 = 0.5\ \mu V \quad \Leftarrow \boxed{\begin{array}{l}\text{As the reference level is one}\\\text{microvolt the output voltage is}\\\text{in microvolts.}\end{array}}$$

$\boxed{\text{MODE FIX 2}}$

$\boxed{\text{AC}}\,\boxed{\text{SHIFT}}\,\boxed{10^x}\,\boxed{[(---}\,6\,\boxed{+/-}\,\boxed{\div}\,20\,\boxed{---)]}\,\boxed{=}\quad$ **0.50** $\Leftarrow \boxed{\textbf{Answer } 0.5\,\mu V}$

16. A signal level of 100μV is measured at the input to a radio receiver. Express this level in dB relative to 1 microvolt (dBμV).

1μV is the reference level. i.e. 1μV = 0dBμV.

$$dB = 20\,Log_{10}\frac{V}{V_{ref}} = 20\,Log_{10}\frac{100\mu V}{1\mu V}$$

⇐ Signal level = 100μV.

⇐ Reference level = 1μV.

$$= 20\,Log_{10}\,100 = 20 \times 2 = 40dB\mu V$$

| MODE FIX 2 |

AC 20 ×

LOG 100 =   **40.00** ⇐ Answer 40dBμV

---

17. A signal level of 3.162 millivolts (mV) is measured at the input to a television receiver.
Convert this signal level to dB relative to 1 microvolt (dBμV).

1μV is the reference level. i.e. 1μV = 0dBμV.

Note. Since the reference level is 1μV the signal level ⇐ must be converted to μV.

$$dB = 20\,Log_{10}\frac{V}{V_{ref}} = 20\,Log_{10}\frac{3162\mu V}{1\mu V}$$

⇐ Reference level = 1μV.

$$= 20\,Log_{10}\,3162 = 20 \times 3.5 = 70dB\mu V$$

| MODE FIX 2 |

AC 20 ×

LOG 3162 =   **70.00** ⇐ Answer 70 dBμV

---

18. The output voltage of a signal generator is 0.125μV.
Give this level in dB relative to 1μV (dBμV).

Note. The minus sign indicates that the level is less than (or below) 1μV.

$$dB = 20\,Log_{10}\frac{V}{V_{ref}} = 20\,Log_{10}\frac{0.125\mu V}{1\mu V}$$

$$= 20\,Log_{10}\,0.125 = 20 \times -0.903 = -18.06dB\mu V$$

| MODE FIX 2 |

AC 20 ×

LOG .125 =   **-18.06** ⇐ Answer -18.06 dBμV

10 - 9

Power (dBW)

The amateur radio licence currently specifies the maximum radio frequency power supplied to the antenna in dBW. It is often necessary to convert dBW to watts when taking measurements, and convert the measured watts to dBW when checking that the power level complies with the regulations.

The two useful formulae are :-

1) To convert *Actual Power in watts* to absolute power in *dBW* :-

$$dBW = 10 \, Log_{10} \frac{Actual \, power \, (watts)}{Reference \, power \, (1 \, watt)} = 10 \, Log_{10} \, Actual \, power \, (watts)$$

2) To convert *Power in dBW* to *Actual Power in watts*:-

$$Power \, (watts) = Antilog \frac{dBW}{10}$$

---

19. Convert 26dBW to actual power in watts.

$$Power \, (watts) = Antilog \frac{dBW}{10} = Antilog \frac{26}{10} = 398.11 \; W \; (approx \, 400 \, watts)$$

| MODE FIX 2 |

| AC | SHIFT | 10ˣ | [(--- | 26 | ÷ | 10 | ---)] | = | 398.11 | ⇐ Answer 398.11 W |

---

20. On a certain frequency band you are permitted a maximum power level at the input to your antenna of 22dBW. What is this power measured in watts at the input to the antenna?

$$Power \, (watts) = Antilog \frac{dBW}{10} = Antilog \frac{22}{10} = 158.49 \; W \; (approx \, 160 \, watts \,)$$

| MODE FIX 2 |

| AC | SHIFT | 10ˣ | [(--- | 22 | ÷ | 10 | ---)] | = | 158.49 | ⇐ Answer 158.49 W |

---

21. Regulations permit a maximum power level at the input to your antenna of 15dBW on a certain frequency band.
What is this power level, measured in watts, at the input to the antenna?

$$Power \, (watts) = Antilog \frac{dBW}{10} = Antilog \frac{15}{10} = 31.62 \; W \; (approx \, 32 \, watts \,)$$

| MODE FIX 2 |

| AC | SHIFT | 10ˣ | [(--- | 15 | ÷ | 10 | ---)] | = | 31.62 | ⇐ Answer 31.62 W |

---

22. The power measured at the input to an antenna is 100W.
Convert this power to dB relative to 1 watt (dBW).

$$dBW = 10\,Log_{10}\,\frac{Actual\,power\,(watts)}{1\,watt} = 10\,Log_{10}\,Actual\,power\,(watts)$$

$$= 10\,Log_{10}\,100 = 10 \times 2 = 20 dBW$$

| MODE FIX 2 |

$\boxed{AC}\,10\,\boxed{\times}$

$\boxed{LOG}\,100\,\boxed{=}$ **20.00** ⇐ Answer 20 dBW

---

23. The power permitted at the input to the antenna on a certain frequency band is 22dBW. You measure the power and find it to be 140W.
Are you operating within your permitted power level?

It is first necessary to convert the actual power of 140W to dBW, and then compare the result with the permitted power in dBW to ensure that you are not in excess of the permitted power.

$$dBW = 10\,Log_{10}\,\frac{Actual\,power\,(watts)}{1\,watt} = 10\,Log_{10}\,Actual\,power\,(watts)$$

$$= 10\,Log_{10}\,140 = 10 \times 2.15 = 21.46 dBW$$

| MODE FIX 2 |

$\boxed{AC}\,10\,\boxed{\times}$

$\boxed{LOG}\,140\,\boxed{=}$ **21.46** ⇐ Answer 21.46 dBW

Since 140W = 21.46dBW, and this is less than the maximum permitted power, you are operating in accordance with the regulations.

---

24. A radio frequency carrier wave has a measured power of 40W.
Convert this to decibels relative to one watt (dBW).

$$Power\,dBW = 10\,Log_{10}\,40 = 10 \times 1.6 = 16.02 dBW$$

| MODE FIX 2 |

$\boxed{AC}\,10\,\boxed{\times}$

$\boxed{LOG}\,40\,\boxed{=}$ **16.02** ⇐ Answer 16.02 dBW

Notes

VSWR

&

Antenna Basics

Chapter 11

Contents

In this section you will:-
a) calculate the *Voltage Standing Wave Ratio* of a system.
b) calculate the power reflected by a mismatched feeder.
c) calculate the *Effective Radiated Power* of an antenna system.
d) calculate the *Field Strength* at a distance from a transmitter.
e) calculate the length of a half-wave dipole.
f) calculate the length of a quarter-wave vertical antenna.
g) make approximate calculations for a trap dipole.
h) calculate the element length and spacing of a Yagi antenna.

Voltage Standing Wave Ratio (VSWR)

To obtain maximum power transfer from a transmission line to a load (or from a feeder to an antenna), the impedance of the load or antenna should match the characteristic impedance 'Z_o' of the feeder. A correct match will result in all the incident (forward) power being absorbed by the load and there will be no power reflected.

If there is a mismatch, i.e. the antenna impedance does not match the characteristic impedance of the feeder, some of the incident power will be reflected by the antenna. The reflected waves interact with the incident waves and set up *standing waves* on the feeder. Standing waves do not travel, they are stationary. In an antenna system, the *standing wave ratio* is an indication of the amount of mismatch between antenna and feeder. VSWR is often abbreviated to SWR.

The ratio of maximum voltage (or current) to the minimum voltage (or current) on a feeder defines the voltage or current standing wave ratio.

Hence:- $SWR = \dfrac{V_{max}}{V_{min}} = \dfrac{I_{max}}{I_{min}}$

Also:- $SWR = \dfrac{Z_o}{R_L} \text{ or } \dfrac{R_L}{Z_o}$ ⬅ For a feeder terminated by a resistive load R_L. Use whichever gives a quantity greater than 1.

Radio frequency SWR measurements may be made with a fairly simple reflectometer type instrument, employing a directional coupler and calibrated to read SWR directly. However, some reflectometer type instruments, usually referred to as directional RF wattmeters, are calibrated to measure forward and reflected power, which by means of a chart, or the formula below, can readily be converted to SWR. This type of measurement should be made as near to the load (or antenna) as possible or else feeder loss may need to be included in the calculations.

A low SWR, e.g. 1.2 : 1 is good, and a high SWR, e.g. 10 : 1 is bad.

$$SWR = \dfrac{1 + \sqrt{\dfrac{P_{Ref}}{P_{Fwd}}}}{1 - \sqrt{\dfrac{P_{Ref}}{P_{Fwd}}}}$$

Where:-
V_{max} = Maximum voltage on line.
V_{min} = Minimum voltage on line.
I_{max} = Maximum current on line.
I_{min} = Minimum current on line.
Z_o = Characteristic impedance of transmission line.
R_L = Load resistance.
P_{Fwd} = Forward power on line.
P_{Ref} = Reflected power on line.

% reflected power $= \dfrac{P_{Ref}}{P_{Fwd}} \times 100 \text{ or } \left(\dfrac{SWR - 1}{SWR + 1}\right)^2 \times 100$

Examples.

**1. Fig.1 shows the voltage stand-
ing wave amplitude measured on
a transmission line or feeder.
Calculate the:-**

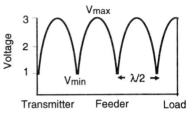

a) SWR on the feeder.
b) % incident power reflected by the load.
c) % incident power absorbed by the load.

Fig.1

a) From fig.1 we see that V_{max} equals 3V and V_{min} equals 1V.
Therefore:-

$$SWR = \frac{V_{max}}{V_{min}} = \frac{3}{1} \quad or \quad SWR = 3{:}1$$

MODE FIX 2

$\boxed{AC}$ 3 $\boxed{\div}$ 1 $\boxed{=}$ 〿 **3.00** ⇐ **Answer** 3 (SWR = 3:1)

b) % incident power reflected by the load:-

$$\left(\frac{SWR-1}{SWR+1}\right)^2 \times 100 = \left(\frac{3-1}{3+1}\right)^2 \times 100 = 0.5^2 \times 100 = 0.25 \times 100 = 25\%$$

Power reflected by the load is 25%.

$\boxed{AC}$ 3 $\boxed{-}$ 1 $\boxed{=}$ $\boxed{\div}$
$\boxed{[(--}$ 3 $\boxed{+}$ 1 $\boxed{--)]}$ $\boxed{=}$
$\boxed{x^2}$ $\boxed{\times}$ 100 $\boxed{=}$ 〿 **25.00** ⇐ **Answer** 25% (Power reflected)

c) % incident power absorbed or dissipated by the load is therefore:-

100% − 25% = 75%

$\boxed{AC}$ 100 $\boxed{-}$ 25 $\boxed{=}$ 〿 **75.00** ⇐ **Answer** 75% (% Power in load)

In practice this value of SWR might be unacceptable as it would result in 25% of the
incident power being reflected, leaving only 75% available for dissipation in the load,
or radiation by the antenna.

2. Fig.2 shows a 50Ω transmission line or feeder terminated in a 75Ω resistive load. Calculate the:-

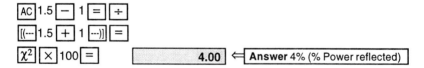

Fig.2

a) SWR on the feeder.
b) % incident power reflected by the load.
c) % incident power absorbed by the load.

a) SWR on the feeder:-

$$SWR = \frac{R_L}{Z_o} = \frac{75}{50} = 1.5 \ \ or \ \ SWR = 1.5{:}1$$

MODE FIX 2

| AC | 75 | ÷ | 50 | = | 1.50 | ⇐ | **Answer** 1.5 (SWR = 1.5:1) |

b) % incident power reflected by load:-

$$\left(\frac{SWR-1}{SWR+1}\right)^2 \times 100 = \left(\frac{1.5-1}{1.5+1}\right)^2 \times 100 = 0.2^2 \times 100 = 0.04 \times 100 = 4\%$$

Power reflected by the load is 4%.

AC	1.5	−	1	=	÷

[(---	1.5	+	1	---)]	=

| χ^2 | × | 100 | = | 4.00 | ⇐ | **Answer** 4% (% Power reflected) |

c) % incident power absorbed or dissipated by the load is therefore:-

$$100\% - 4\% = 96\%$$

| AC | 100 | − | 4 | = | 96.00 | ⇐ | **Answer** 96% (% Power in load) |

In practice this value of SWR (1.5:1) will usually be acceptable for the majority of amateur purposes as only 4% of the incident power is reflected, leaving 96% available for absorption or dissipation in the load, or radiation by an antenna.

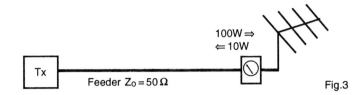

Fig.3

3. A reflectometer type power meter, connected near to the antenna as shown in fig.3, reads 100 watts in the forward direction and 10 watts in the reverse direction. What is the:-
a) SWR?
b) % reflected power?

a) The SWR:-

$$SWR = \frac{1 + \sqrt{\frac{P_{Ref}}{P_{Fwd}}}}{1 - \sqrt{\frac{P_{Ref}}{P_{Fwd}}}} = \frac{1 + \sqrt{\frac{10}{100}}}{1 - \sqrt{\frac{10}{100}}} = \frac{1 + 0.316}{1 - 0.316} = \frac{1.316}{0.684} = 1.92 \quad SWR = 1.92{:}1$$

It will save time if $\sqrt{\frac{P_{Ref}}{P_{Fwd}}}$ is calculated first and then stored in memory:-

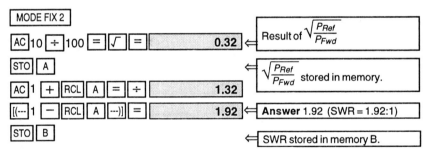

b) % power reflected by mismatch:-

$$\left(\frac{SWR-1}{SWR+1}\right)^2 \times 100 = \left(\frac{1.92-1}{1.92+1}\right)^2 \times 100 = 0.32^2 \times 100 = 0.1 \times 100 = 10\%$$

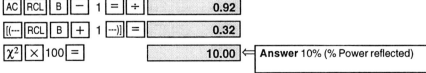

Effective Radiated Power (ERP)

ERP (watts) is the product of the input power to the antenna and the antenna gain in the direction of maximum radiation. The input power to the antenna should be measured as close to the antenna input terminals as possible. Reflected power may need to be considered if there is a significant mismatch.

When power measurements are taken at the transmitter, allowance must be made for feeder loss. ERP may be calculated from the derived formula:-

$$ERP = Antenna\ input\ power \times Antilog\left(\frac{Antenna\ Gain\ (dB)}{10}\right)$$

Antenna gain is the ratio (usually in the direction of maximum radiation) of the power required at the input of a reference antenna to the power supplied to the input of the antenna under test, to achieve the same field strength, at the same point. The reference antenna is usually a half-wave dipole for frequencies below 1GHz. The gain is then expressed in *dB* relative to a dipole (*dBd*). Antennas do not generate power, any power gain in one direction is at the expense of power radiated in another.

Examples.
4. The input power to a perfectly matched antenna is 100W.
The gain of the antenna is 3dB. What is the ERP?

$$Gain\ dB = 10\ Log_{10}\frac{P_{out}}{P_{in}}$$

$$3 = 10\ Log_{10}\frac{ERP}{100}$$

$$Antilog\frac{3}{10} = \frac{ERP}{100}$$

$$\therefore\ ERP = 100\ Antilog\frac{3}{10}$$

⟵ Note. I am going to use this transposition of the formula for the calculator.

$$= 100\ Antilog\ 0.3$$

$$= 100 \times 2 = 200W\ (ERP)$$

MODE FIX 2

| AC | SHIFT | 10ˣ | [(--- | 3 | ÷ | 10 | ---)] |

| × | 100 | = |

199.53 ⟸ **Answer** 200W ERP (Rounded)

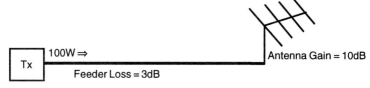

Fig.4

5. In fig.4 above, the transmitter delivers 100 watts to an antenna system having a 3dB feeder loss. The antenna has a gain of 10dB. Calculate the effective radiated power in watts.

It is first necessary to calculate the power available at the antenna input:-

$$Feeder\ Loss\ dB\ =\ 10\ Log_{10}\ \frac{P_{in}}{P_{out}}$$

$$3\ =\ 10\ Log_{10}\ \frac{100}{P_{out}}$$

$$\frac{3}{10}\ =\ Log_{10}\ \frac{100}{P_{out}}$$

$$Antilog\ \frac{3}{10}\ =\ \frac{100}{P_{out}}$$

$$\therefore\ P_{out}\ =\ \frac{100}{Antilog\ \dfrac{3}{10}}\ =\ \frac{100}{Antilog\ 0.3}\ =\ \frac{100}{2}\ =\ 50W\ (Antenna\ input\ power)$$

⇑

Note. I am going to use this transposition of the formula for the calculator.

MODE FIX 2

AC 100 ÷

SHIFT 10ˣ [(--- 3 ÷ 10 ---)] =   **50.12** ⇐ **Answer** 50W (Rounded) Antenna input power.

STO A   ⇐ Store in A for future use.

The effective radiated power:-

$$ERP\ =\ Antenna\ input\ power \times Antilog\left(\frac{Antenna\ Gain\ (dB)}{10}\right)$$

$$=\ 50 \times Antilog\left(\frac{10}{10}\right)\ =\ 50 \times Antilog\ 1\ =\ 50 \times 10\ =\ 500\,W\ (ERP)$$

AC RCL A ×   **50.12**

SHIFT 10ˣ [(---10 ÷ 10 ---)] =   **501.19** ⇐ **Answer** 500W (Rounded) Effective radiated power.

Field Strength

Field strength is the strength of an electromagnetic wave measured at a particular location. Field strength is measured in units of volts/metre (V/m), millivolts/metre (mV/m), or microvolts/metre (μV/m).

Practical field strength measurements are affected by any signal-reflecting, and/ or absorbing objects in, or near to the signal path between the transmitter and receiver. Antenna height, terrain and weather also affect measurement.

When dealing with interference and EMC problems it is often necessary to make an approximate calculation of field strength at a particular distance from a transmitter. The following formula can be used for approximation of field strength, it is derived from free-space propagation theory.

a) $$e = \frac{7.02 \sqrt{ERP}}{d}$$

b) $$d = \frac{7.02 \sqrt{ERP}}{e}$$

c) $$ERP = \left(\frac{e\,d}{7.02}\right)^2$$

Where:-
e = Field strength (volts/metre).
d = Distance from transmitter (metres).
ERP = Effective radiated power (watts).

Note:-
Formulas b) and c) are derived from the basic formula a) by transposition.

Examples.
6. A transmitter has an ERP of 400W.
Calculate the field strength at a distance of 30m.

Use formula (a). The field strength at 30 metres:-

$$e = \frac{7.02 \sqrt{ERP}}{d} = \frac{7.02 \sqrt{400}}{30} = \frac{140.4}{30} = 4.68 \; volts/metre$$

| MODE FIX 2 |

AC 7.02 × √ 400

÷ 30 =   4.68 ⇐ Answer 4.68V/m (Field strength)

Field strength at 30 metres is 4.68 V/m. This can only be an approximation due to signal reflection and absorption in or near the signal path.

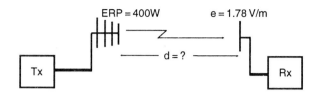

Fig.5

7. The radio transmitter shown in fig.5 has an ERP of 400W. Calculate the distance at which the field strength is 1.78 V/m.

Using formula (b) for distance in metres:-

$$d = \frac{7.02\sqrt{ERP}}{e} = \frac{7.02\sqrt{400}}{1.78} = \frac{140.4}{1.78} = 78.88 \text{ metres}$$

MODE FIX 2

$\boxed{AC}$ 7.02 $\boxed{\times}$ $\boxed{\sqrt{}}$ 400

$\boxed{\div}$ 1.78 $\boxed{=}$ 78.88 ⇐ Answer 78.88 metres

---

8. It has been calculated that in order to avoid interference problems with a sensitive receiving installation, at a point 100 metres from a transmitting antenna, the field strength should not exceed 0.5V/m at that point. What is the maximum ERP, in that direction, that should not be exceeded in this case?

Use formula (c) for ERP in watts:-

$$ERP = \left(\frac{e\,d}{7.02}\right)^2 = \left(\frac{0.5 \times 100}{7.02}\right)^2 = \left(\frac{50}{7.02}\right)^2 = 7.12^2 = 50.73 \text{ watts}$$

MODE FIX 2

$\boxed{AC}$ .5 $\boxed{\times}$ 100

$\boxed{\div}$ 7.02 $\boxed{=}$ $\boxed{x^2}$ 50.73 ⇐ Answer 50.73W (ERP)

In this practical situation rounding to 50 or 51 watts will be o.k.
Since the formula is derived from the free space formula it does not account for variables in the path. A variation of ±3dB or more may exist between the calculated field strength and the practical measured results due to terrain, signal reflections from nearby objects and ground effects.

The Half-Wave Dipole

The majority of antenna calculations in basic examinations require the length of λ/2, λ/4 and trapped antennas to be calculated. When the velocity factor and end-effects, which shorten the antenna length have to be considered, a multiplying factor is usually given, e. g. *VF* (or *'K'*) = 0.95.

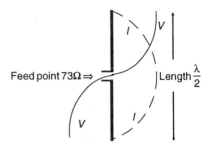

Feed point 73Ω ⇒   Length $\frac{\lambda}{2}$

Fig.6 shows the basic centre-fed half-wave dipole. At the tuned frequency the input impedance is approximately 73 ohms resistive. This resistance is due mainly to: a) the resistance of the antenna elements which is very low, and b), another resistance, referred to as the radiation resistance.

Fig.6 The half-wave, centre-fed antenna. Showing voltage and current standing waves. Current is maximum at centre and voltage maximum at ends.

The radiation resistance is not a physical resistance, it is a resistance, which when substituted in place of the antenna dissipates the same power as the antenna would radiate into space. For the half-wave centre-fed dipole the radiation resistance is considered to be about 73 ohms, the input resistance. The physical length of the antenna is about 4 - 5% less than the electrical length due to a) the velocity of the radio waves in the wire being less than in free space, b) the 'end effect' capacitance, and c) the wire diameter.

Points to note.
1. Calculations apply to half-wave dipoles at any frequency.
2. Radiation resistance is the same for all centre-fed half-wave antennas.
3. A wave is said to be vertically polarised when its *E* field (electric field) is vertical, this is produced by a vertical antenna.
4. A wave is said to be horizontally polarised when its *E* field (electric field) is horizontal, this is produced by a horizontal antenna.
5. The physical length of a dipole is slightly less than the electrical length.
6. If the transmitter frequency increases (wavelength decreases), the antenna becomes greater in length than the new half-wavelength, and the the antenna appears inductive to the transmitter.
7. If the transmitter frequency decreases (wavelength increases), the antenna becomes shorter in length than the new half-wavelength, and the antenna appears capacitive to the transmitter.
8. Adding parasitic elements, i.e. directors and reflectors increase the forward gain of the antenna, and hence the effective radiated power.
9. Adding parasitic elements reduces the input resistance, therefore matching is required, a folded dipole is usually employed to achieve this.

Formula to remember:-

Electrical length of half-wave dipole $= \dfrac{\lambda}{2} = \dfrac{300 \times 10^6 \times 0.5}{f}$

Where $\lambda = \dfrac{300 \times 10^6}{f}$ and f = frequency of signal in Hertz.

Physical or practical length of half-wave dipole $= \dfrac{\lambda}{2} \times VF$.

Where '*VF*'(or '*K*') is the factor by which the electrical (or free space) half wavelength must be multiplied to obtain resonance.

Examples.
9. Calculate the length of a half-wave dipole for operation on 3.6MHz. Ignore the velocity factor. Answer to 2 decimal places.

$\lambda = \dfrac{300 \times 10^6}{f} = \dfrac{300 \times 10^6}{3.6 \times 10^6} = 83.33$ *metres (full–wavelength)*

$\dfrac{\lambda}{2} = \dfrac{83.33}{2} = 41.67$ *metres (half–wavelength)*

——— 41.67 m ———

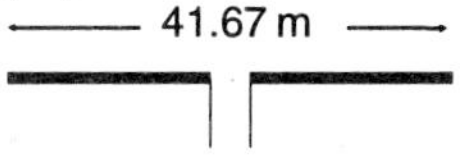

Fig.7 The half-wave dipole for 3.6MHz.

MODE FIX 2

AC 300 EXP 6 ÷
3.6 EXP 6 =   83.33
÷ 2 =   41.67

Answer 41.67 metres. Antenna length for half-wave dipole at 3.6MHz. In practice this antenna would be too long, and would need to be trimmed by about 5% to bring it to resonance.

10. A resonant half-wave antenna is required for 14.250MHz. Calculate the length. Ignore the velocity factor.

$\lambda = \dfrac{300 \times 10^6}{f} = \dfrac{300 \times 10^6}{14.250 \times 10^6} = 21.05$ *metres (full–wavelength)*

$\dfrac{\lambda}{2} = \dfrac{21.05}{2} = 10.53$ *metres (half–wavelength)*

——— 10.53 m ———

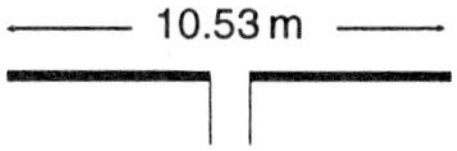

Fig.8 The half-wave dipole for 14.250MHz.

MODE FIX 2

AC 300 EXP 6 ÷
14.250 EXP 6 =   21.05
÷ 2 =   10.53

Answer 10.53 metres. In practice this antenna would be too long, and would need to be trimmed by about 5% to bring it to resonance.

11. A half-wave dipole is to be constructed to operate on a frequency of 70MHz.
Calculate the approximate length to which it should be cut.
Assume a *VF (or 'K')* of 0.96. Answer to 2 decimal places.

$$\lambda = \frac{300 \times 10^6}{f} = \frac{300 \times 10^6}{70 \times 10^6} = 4.29 \; metres$$

$$\frac{\lambda}{2} \times K = \frac{4.29}{2} \times 0.96 = 2.06 \; metres$$

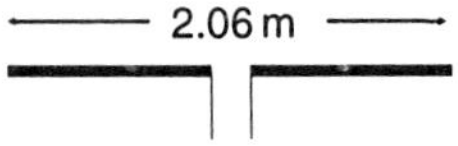

── 2.06 m ──

Fig.9 The practical half-wave
dipole for 70MHz.

MODE FIX 2

AC	300	EXP	6	÷

70 [EXP] 6 [=]   [4.29]

[÷] 2 [×] .96 [=]   [2.06] ←

Answer 2.06 metres.
Antenna length for a practical half-wave dipole at 70MHz.
In practice it should be cut slightly longer than calculated and trimmed to bring it to resonance.

---

12. To what length should a half-wave dipole be constructed if it is to operate
at a frequency of 432MHz?
Let *K* = 0.95. Answer to 2 decimal places.

$$\lambda = \frac{300 \times 10^6}{f} = \frac{300 \times 10^6}{432 \times 10^6} = 0.69m \;\; (69cm)$$

$$\frac{\lambda}{2} \times 0.95 = \frac{0.69}{2} \times 0.95 = 0.33m \;\; (33cm)$$

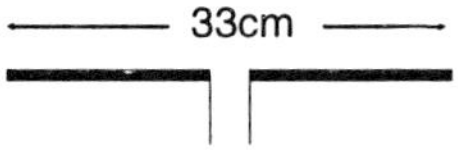

── 33cm ──

Fig.10 The practical half-wave
dipole for 432MHz.

MODE FIX 2

AC	300	EXP	6	÷

432 [EXP] 6 [=]   [0.69]

[÷] 2 [×] .95 [=]   [0.33] ←

Answer 0.33 metres (33cm).
Antenna length for a practical half-wave dipole at 432MHz.
In practice it should be cut slightly longer than calculated and trimmed to bring it to resonance.

13. A centre-fed half-wave dipole has a length of 5 metres. At which approximate frequency, from the list below, would you expect it to operate most efficiently?
a) 2.5MHz.   **b) 4MHz.**   **c) 20MHz.**   **d) 30MHz.**

Since half a wavelength in this example is 5 metres, a full wavelength is therefore 10 metres. The normal wavelength to frequency conversion formula can be used:-

$$f = \frac{300 \times 10^6}{\lambda} = \frac{300 \times 10^6}{10} = 30 \times 10^6 Hz \quad or \quad 30MHz$$

──────── 5 m ────────

MODE FIX 2

AC	300	EXP	6

Fig.11 The 5m dipole will operate best on 30MHz (10m Band)

| ÷ | 10 | = | 30000000.00 |

← **Answer** 30,000,000Hz. The antenna is tuned to approximately 30MHz.

| ENG | 30ₓ₁₀06 |

Convert display to **ENG**ineering notation. Read as 30 x 10⁶Hz. 10⁶ = Mega
Answer 30MHz

───────────────────────────────

14. You are given three, second-hand, centre-fed dipoles, the overall lengths of which are 0.9m, 1.1m and 2.2m. Which one is likely to require the least modification if it is to be used on the 145MHz band?
Assume *VF* (or *K*) = 0.96.

First calculate the length of a half-wave dipole for the required frequency, and then select the dipole which is that length or longer.

$$\lambda = \frac{300 \times 10^6}{f} = \frac{300 \times 10^6}{145 \times 10^6} = 2.07 \; metres$$

$$\frac{\lambda}{2} \times K = \frac{2.07}{2} \times 0.96 = 0.99 \; metres$$

──────── 0.99 m ────────

Fig.12 This dipole has been cut to operate at 145MHz.

MODE FIX 2

AC	300	EXP	6	÷

| 145 | EXP | 6 | = | 2.07 |

Answer 0.99 metres (99cm). Antenna length for a practical half-wave dipole at 145MHz.

| ÷ | 2 | × | .96 | = | 0.99 |

From the three available dipoles the 1.1m dipole will require the least modification. The 0.9m dipole is too short for this frequency. The 2.2m antenna could possibly be used later for the 70MHz (4m) band.

15. A quarter-wave ground-plane antenna is required for mobile operation on 145MHz. Assume $K = 0.96$.
Calculate the height of the antenna to 2 decimal places.

This is a typical mobile antenna. Ideally, to achieve a good horizontal omnidirectional radiation pattern it should be mounted in the centre of a metal car roof; this will provide the ground-plane. The input impedance of this antenna is about 36.5 ohms.

$$\lambda = \frac{300 \times 10^6}{f} = \frac{300 \times 10^6}{145 \times 10^6} = 2.07 \text{ metres}$$

$$\frac{\lambda}{4} \times K = \frac{2.07}{4} \times 0.96 = 0.5 \text{ metres}$$

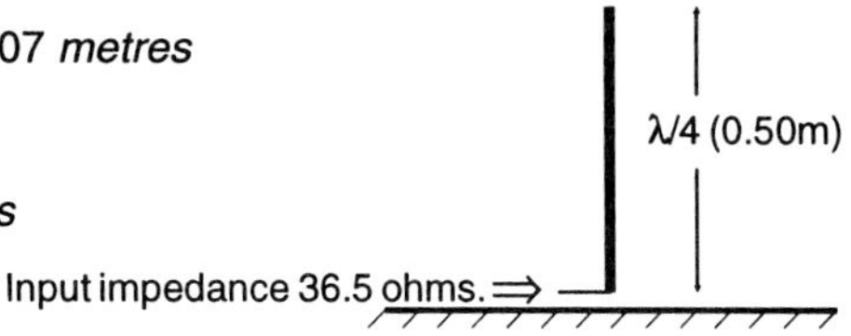

Input impedance 36.5 ohms. $\Rightarrow$

$\lambda/4$ (0.50m)

Fig.13 $\lambda/4$ 145MHz Ground-plane antenna mounted on car roof.

MODE FIX 2

AC 300 EXP 6

÷ 145 EXP 6 =   **2.07**

÷ 4 × .96 =   **0.50** ⇐ Answer 0.50 metres. Antenna height for a practical $\lambda/4$ antenna at 145MHz.

---

16. A vertical $\lambda/4$ ground-plane antenna is to be constructed to operate at 14MHz. Assume $K = 0.95$.
Calculate the height of the antenna.

A ground-plane antenna should be operated over a perfectly conducting ground. The metal car roof in example 15 provided the ground-plane for the 145MHz antenna, but in the case of the 14MHz vertical antenna, the conductivity of the ground may need to be improved by employing a number of radial wires, about $\lambda/4$ long, and buried just below the surface of the ground.

$$\lambda = \frac{300 \times 10^6}{f} = \frac{300 \times 10^6}{14 \times 10^6} = 21.43 \text{ metres}$$

$$\frac{\lambda}{4} \times K = \frac{21.43}{4} \times 0.95 = 5.09 \text{ metres}$$

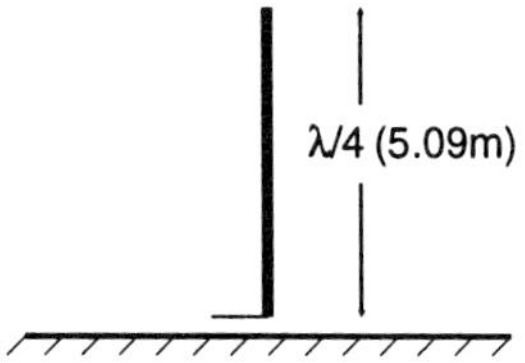

$\lambda/4$ (5.09m)

Fig.14   A practical $\lambda/4$ 14MHz Ground-plane antenna.

MODE FIX 2

AC 300 EXP 6 ÷

14 EXP 6 =   **21.43**

÷ 4 × .95 =   **5.09** ⇐ Answer 5.09 metres. Antenna height for a practical $\lambda/4$ antenna at 14MHz.

The Trap Dipole

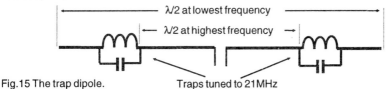

Fig.15 The trap dipole.   Traps tuned to 21MHz

The *trap dipole* is a multiband antenna. The antenna shown in fig.15 will operate on two bands, e.g. 14MHz and 21MHz. When operating on the highest frequency, the traps (due to their high impedance at resonance) isolate the section between the traps, from the section beyond the traps. When operating at the lower frequency, the traps are no longer resonant and the full length of the antenna is used. The full length of the antenna may be shorter than normal due to the loading effect of the traps.

17. For the dual band, half-wave, trap dipole shown in fig.15, calculate:-
a) the length between the traps for operation at 21.25MHz.
b) the approximate overall length for operation on 14.2MHz.
Assume a 'K' factor of 0.95.

a) The length between the traps for $\lambda/2$ at 21.25MHz:-

$$\lambda = \frac{300 \times 10^6}{f} = \frac{300 \times 10^6}{21.25 \times 10^6} = 14.12 \ \textit{metres}$$

$$\frac{\lambda}{2} \times K = \frac{14.12}{2} \times 0.95 = 6.71 = 6.71 \ \textit{metres}$$

MODE FIX 2

AC	300	EXP	6	÷

21.25 EXP 6 =	**14.12**	**Answer** 6.71 metres. Slight adjustment of this length may be necessary for
÷ 2 × .95 =	**6.71** ⇐	resonance due to the traps.

b) The approximate length of the dipole for $\lambda/2$ operation at 14.2MHz:-

$$\lambda = \frac{300 \times 10^6}{f} = \frac{300 \times 10^6}{14.2 \times 10^6} = 21.13 \ \textit{metres}$$

$$\frac{\lambda}{2} \times K = \frac{21.13}{2} \times 0.95 = 10.04 \ \textit{metres}$$

AC 300 EXP 6 ÷		**Answer** 10.04 metres.
14.2 EXP 6 =	**21.13**	**Note.** This assumes a K of 0.95. In practice, due to the effect of the traps, the antenna will be too long and the ends will
÷ 2 × .95 =	**10.04** ⇐	need to be trimmed for resonance.

The Yagi Antenna

The Yagi antenna shown in fig.16, consists of a driven element, a reflector and a number of directors. Its gain, in the direction of maximum radiation is usually specified relative to a half-wave dipole. The reflector is slightly longer than the driven element, while the directors are progressively shorter toward the front. The driven element is normally a folded λ/2 dipole, having an input impedance of 300Ω when operated on its own,

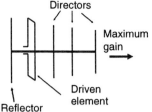

Fig.16

but, when operated close to the parasitic elements its impedance falls to about 75Ω to provide a reasonable match to low impedance feeder cable. Since this is a balanced antenna, and the feeder is normally an unbalanced 50Ω coaxial cable, a *balun* (**bal**ance to **un**balance) transformer should be used, this can also provide an impedance match, i.e. 50/75Ω. The gain and directional characteristics are determined by the spacing and number of the elements. Typical gain figures relative to a dipole may be 3 to 14dB.

---

18. Using the information given in fig.17 calculate the lengths and spacing of the elements when the Yagi antenna is to be constructed for operation at 145MHz.

The dimensions given are approximate and will vary from one design to another.
Use can be made of the calculator's Constant Multiplication ability.

First calculate the wavelength :-

$$\lambda = \frac{300 \times 10^6}{f} = \frac{300 \times 10^6}{145 \times 10^6} = 2.07 \ metres$$

MODE FIX 2

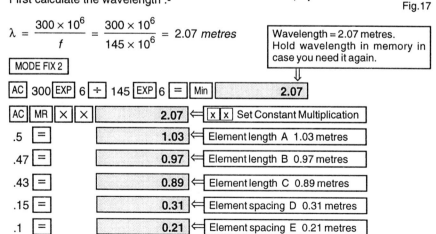

Fig.17

Wavelength = 2.07 metres.
Hold wavelength in memory in case you need it again.

| AC | 300 EXP 6 ÷ 145 EXP 6 = Min | **2.07** |

| AC MR × × | **2.07** | ⟸ x x Set Constant Multiplication |

| .5 = | **1.03** | ⟸ Element length A 1.03 metres |

| .47 = | **0.97** | ⟸ Element length B 0.97 metres |

| .43 = | **0.89** | ⟸ Element length C 0.89 metres |

| .15 = | **0.31** | ⟸ Element spacing D 0.31 metres |

| .1 = | **0.21** | ⟸ Element spacing E 0.21 metres |

Appendix A1 - Decibel Table

Power ratio	Voltage ratio	dB	Voltage ratio	Power ratio
Gain			Loss	
1.000	1.000	0.0	1.000	1.000
1.023	1.012	0.1	0.989	0.977
1.047	1.023	0.2	0.977	0.955
1.072	1.035	0.3	0.966	0.933
1.096	1.047	0.4	0.955	0.912
1.122	1.059	0.5	0.944	0.891
1.148	1.072	0.6	0.933	0.871
1.175	1.084	0.7	0.923	0.851
1.202	1.096	0.8	0.912	0.832
1.230	1.109	0.9	0.902	0.813
1.259	1.122	1.0	0.891	0.794
1.585	1.259	2.0	0.794	0.631
1.995	1.413	3.0	0.708	0.501
2.512	1.585	4.0	0.631	0.398
3.162	1.778	5.0	0.562	0.316
3.981	1.995	6.0	0.501	0.251
5.012	2.239	7.0	0.447	0.200
6.310	2.512	8.0	0.398	0.158
7.943	2.818	9.0	0.355	0.126
10.000	3.162	10	0.316	0.100
12.589	3.548	11	0.282	0.079
15.849	3.981	12	0.251	0.063
19.953	4.467	13	0.224	0.050
25.119	5.012	14	0.200	0.040
31.623	5.623	15	0.178	0.032
39.811	6.310	16	0.158	0.025
50.119	7.079	17	0.141	0.020
63.096	7.943	18	0.126	0.016
79.433	8.913	19	0.112	0.013
100.000	10.000	20	0.100	0.010
1.00E+3	31.623	30	0.032	1.00E-3
1.00E+4	1.00E+2	40	0.010	1.00E-4
1.00E+5	3.16E+2	50	3.16E-3	1.00E-5
1.00E+6	1.00E+3	60	1.00E-3	1.00E-6
1.00E+7	3.16E+3	70	3.16E-4	1.00E-7
1.00E+8	1.00E+4	80	1.00E-4	1.00E-8
1.00E+9	3.16E+4	90	3.16E-5	1.00E-9
1.00E+10	1.00E+5	100	1.00E-5	1.00E-10

The gain or loss of a system in decibels is given by:-

$$N_{dB} = 10 \times Log_{10} \frac{P_{out}}{P_{in}}$$

A system *gain* will result in a positive dB value. A system *loss* will result in a negative dB value.

Provided that the resistances through which the input and output current flow (or across which the input and output voltages are measured) are equal, the following formulae may be applied:-

$$N_{dB} = 20 \times Log_{10} \frac{V_{out}}{V_{in}}$$

$$N_{dB} = 20 \times Log_{10} \frac{I_{out}}{I_{in}}$$

Where:-
N_{dB} = Number of decibels. P_{out}, P_{in}, V_{out}, V_{in}, I_{out} and I_{in} are the output and input power, voltage and current levels.

Note 1. Adding decibels is the same as multiplying the ratios of voltage or power.

E.g. 6dB + 3dB = 9dB.

This is the same as multiplying the equivalent voltage ratios:-

1.995 x 1.413 = 2.818 = 9dB

Note 2. In the table, very small and very large numbers are shown in scientific notation.

E.g:-

$1.00E+3 = 1 \times 10^3 = 10^3 = 1000$

$1.00E-3 = 1 \times 10^{-3} = 10^{-3} = 0.001$

$3.16E+4 = 3.16 \times 10^4 = 31,600$

Appendix A2 - Frequency / Wavelength

Freq MHz	W/L Metres	Freq MHz	W/L Metres	Freq MHz	W/L Metres	Freq MHz	W/L Metres
0.1	3000.00	26	11.538	60	5.000	360	0.833
0.2	1500.00	27	11.111	65	4.615	380	0.789
0.3	1000.00	28	10.714	70	4.286	400	0.750
0.4	750.00	29	10.345	75	4.000	420	0.714
0.5	600.00	30	10.000	80	3.750	440	0.682
0.6	500.00	31	9.677	85	3.529	460	0.652
0.7	428.57	32	9.375	90	3.333	480	0.625
0.8	375.00	33	9.091	95	3.158	500	0.600
0.9	333.33	34	8.824	100	3.000	520	0.577
1	300.00	35	8.571	110	2.727	540	0.556
2	150.00	36	8.333	120	2.500	560	0.536
3	100.00	37	8.108	130	2.308	580	0.517
4	75.00	38	7.895	140	2.143	600	0.500
5	60.00	39	7.692	150	2.000	620	0.484
6	50.00	40	7.500	160	1.875	640	0.469
7	42.86	41	7.317	170	1.765	660	0.455
8	37.50	42	7.143	180	1.667	680	0.441
9	33.33	43	6.977	190	1.579	700	0.429
10	30.00	44	6.818	200	1.500	720	0.417
11	27.27	45	6.667	210	1.429	740	0.405
12	25.00	46	6.522	220	1.364	760	0.395
13	23.08	47	6.383	230	1.304	780	0.385
14	21.43	48	6.250	240	1.250	800	0.375
15	20.00	49	6.122	250	1.200	820	0.366
16	18.75	50	6.000	260	1.154	840	0.357
17	17.65	51	5.882	270	1.111	860	0.349
18	16.67	52	5.769	280	1.071	880	0.341
19	15.79	53	5.660	290	1.034	900	0.333
20	15.00	54	5.556	300	1.000	920	0.326
21	14.29	55	5.455	310	0.968	940	0.319
22	13.64	56	5.357	320	0.938	960	0.313
23	13.04	57	5.263	330	0.909	980	0.306
24	12.50	58	5.172	340	0.882	1000	0.300
25	12.00	59	5.085	350	0.857		

For Frequency to Wavelength conversion use the formula given.

$$f = \frac{3 \times 10^8}{\lambda} \qquad \lambda = \frac{3 \times 10^8}{f}$$

A - 2

Appendix A3 - Power (watts) / dBW

Power Watts	Power dBW	Power Watts	Power dBW	Power Watts	Power dBW	Power Watts	Power dBW
1	0.00	50	16.99	175	22.43	300	24.77
2	3.01	55	17.40	180	22.55	320	25.05
4	6.02	60	17.78	185	22.67	340	25.31
6	7.78	65	18.13	190	22.79	360	25.56
8	9.03	70	18.45	195	22.90	380	25.80
10	10.00	75	18.75	200	23.01	400	26.02
12	10.79	80	19.03	205	23.12	420	26.23
14	11.46	85	19.29	210	23.22	440	26.43
16	12.04	90	19.54	215	23.32	460	26.63
18	12.55	95	19.78	220	23.42	480	26.81
20	13.01	100	20.00	225	23.52	500	26.99
22	13.42	105	20.21	230	23.62	520	27.16
24	13.80	110	20.41	235	23.71	540	27.32
26	14.15	115	20.61	240	23.80	560	27.48
28	14.47	120	20.79	245	23.89	580	27.63
30	14.77	125	20.97	250	23.98	600	27.78
32	15.05	130	21.14	255	24.07	620	27.92
34	15.31	135	21.30	260	24.15	640	28.06
36	15.56	140	21.46	265	24.23	660	28.20
38	15.80	145	21.61	270	24.31	680	28.33
40	16.02	150	21.76	275	24.39	700	28.45
42	16.23	155	21.90	280	24.47	720	28.57
44	16.43	160	22.04	285	24.55	740	28.69
46	16.63	165	22.17	290	24.62	760	28.81
48	16.81	170	22.30	295	24.70	780	28.92
50	16.99	175	22.43	300	24.77	800	29.03

$$Power\,(dBW) = 10 \times Log_{10}\,(Actual\;Power\;in\;watts)$$

$$Power\,(watts) = Antilog\frac{dBW}{10}$$

Appendix A4 - VSWR Chart

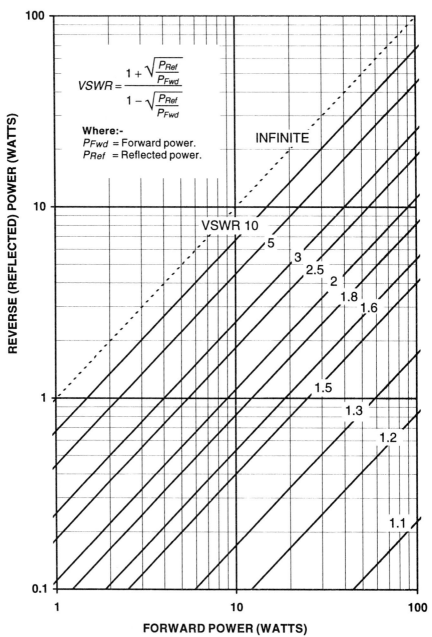

$$VSWR = \frac{1 + \sqrt{\frac{P_{Ref}}{P_{Fwd}}}}{1 - \sqrt{\frac{P_{Ref}}{P_{Fwd}}}}$$

Where:-
P_{Fwd} = Forward power.
P_{Ref} = Reflected power.

FORWARD POWER (WATTS)

Nomograph for use with a through-line power meter. The VSWR on a transmission line or feeder may be ascertained when forward and reverse power are known.

Appendix B - Note to Users of Earlier Calculators

Some previous calculators, such as the fx82, fx250D, fx115D, fx570D, 991D and other earlier models use a different keying sequence for some of the functions. The functions mainly concerned - for this book - are the square root, root, cube root, trigonometric and log function keys. With the latest models the above listed function keys are pressed before the value is entered, but in earlier models the value is entered before the function key is pressed. If in doubt about using a different calculator in conjunction with this book, please read the manufacturers instruction manual. Below are some examples to demonstrate the main keying differences.

Keying new VPAM models ⇒   Keying earlier calculators

Press the function key before entering the value.

Enter the value before pressing the function key.

Example. Calculate the square root of 100.

| AC | √ | 100 | = | **10** |

| AC | 100 | √ | **10** |

With the VPAM system the formula is entered as it is written or spoken. E.g. 'The square root of 100 equals 10.'

With these calculators the result appears immediately the function key is pressed.

Example. Calculate the cube root of 27.

| AC | SHIFT | ³√ | 27 | = | **3** |

| AC | 27 | SHIFT | ³√ | **3** |

Example. Find the sine and cosine of 30 degrees.

| AC | sin | 30 | = | **0.5** |

| AC | 30 | sin | **0.5** |

| AC | cos | 30 | = | **0.8660** |

| AC | 30 | cos | **0.8660** |

Example. Find the angle whose tangent is 0.4 (tan^{-1} 0.4).

| AC | SHIFT | tan⁻¹ | .4 | = | **21.80** |

| AC | .4 | SHIFT | tan⁻¹ | **21.80** |

Example. Find the logarithm of 5.

| AC | Log | 5 | = | **0.6990** |

| AC | 5 | Log | **0.6990** |

Example. Find the antilogarithm of 2.6.

| AC | SHIFT | 10ˣ | 2.6 | = | **398.11** |

| AC | 2.6 | SHIFT | 10ˣ | **398.11** |